Experimental Superfluidity

CHICAGO LECTURES IN PHYSICS

Experimental Superfluidity

R. J. DONNELLY

Notes compiled by W. I. Glaberson and P. E. Parks from a course given at the University of Chicago

Chicago and London
THE UNIVERSITY OF CHICAGO PRESS

Library of Congress Catalog Card Number: 66-23686

THE UNIVERSITY OF CHICAGO PRESS, CHICAGO & LONDON
The University of Toronto Press, Toronto 5, Canada

Published 1967. Printed in the United States of America

PREFACE

These notes stem from material presented in a graduate course at the University of Chicago in the winter quarter of 1966. The problem of superfluidity has many aspects that could not be treated in a single course. Subjects were chosen that would give the student an elementary introduction to some of the important problems, particularly those related to current research in our laboratories. Emphasis was placed on those aspects of the problems that are of interest to experimental physicists. To this end, a number of useful tables and magnitudes are included in the appendices.

I appreciate the efforts of Peter E. Parks and William I. Glaberson who compiled these notes. Far from being a transcription of my lectures, their present form reflects a great deal of thought in understanding and organizing the subject matter. I am also indebted to Mrs. Audrey Kisel and Robert W. Koster for their careful preparation of the manuscript and illustrations.

My research is supported by the National Science Foundation under Grant GP-5302 and by the Air Force Office of Scientific Research under Grant AF-AFOSR 785-65. P. E. Parks is indebted to the Advanced Research Projects Agency for a research assistantship under the Grant for Materials Research. W. I. Glaberson is indebted to the Fannie and John Hertz Foundation for a fellowship.

R. J. D.

CONTENTS

1. INTRODUCTORY CONCEPTS 1

1. Some Properties of Helium 1

2. Production of Low Temperatures 3

3. Measurement of Temperature 7

References 9

2. TWO-FLUID MODEL AND MACROSCOPIC QUANTIZATION 10

4. Isothermal Flow Effects 10

5. Thermal Effects 22

6. Internal Convection and the Equations of Motion in the Two-Fluid Model 28

7. The Propagation of Sound in Helium II 39

8. Breakdown of the Simple Two-fluid Model: Macroscopic Quantum Effects 50

9. Critical Velocities Owing to Vortex Generation 58

References 63

3. Quasi Particle Model For Helium 65

10. Excitation Spectrum of He II 65

11. Thermodynamic Properties of He II 75

12. Calculation of ρ_n and ρ_s 82

13. Condition for Superfluidity 87

14. Mobility of Ions 90

15. Viscosity Coefficient 96

References 99

4. GENERALIZED HYDRODYNAMIC EQUATIONS 101

16. Landau's Hydrodynamic Equations 101

17. The Bekaravich-Khalatnikov Hydrodynamic Equations 115

18. Second Sound in Rotating Helium. Determination of the B-coefficients 130

19. Hydrodynamic Stability of He II 144

References 146

5. MICROSCOPIC THEORY OF HELIUM II 148

20. Ideal Bose-Einstein Gas 148

21. Bogoliubov's Theory—The Weakly Interacting Bose Gas 151

22. Hartree Self-consistent Field Approach 163

References 170

6. IONS IN HELIUM II 172

23. Structure of Ions 172

24. Interaction Between Ions and Quantized Vortices 177

25. Escape of Ions from Vortex Lines and Rings 183

26. Capture of Ions by Vortex Lines 196

27. Further Aspects of Ion Motion 207

References 208

APPENDIX A 211

APPENDIX B 213

APPENDIX C 214

Publishers' Acknowledgments 250

Index 255

CHAPTER 1

INTRODUCTORY CONCEPTS

§1. Some Properties of Helium

Helium exists in two stable isotopic forms, He^3 and He^4. These notes deal specifically with the latter, and where no confusion arises, its mass number is not indicated. The phase diagram for He^4 is shown in Figure 1.1. The figure is exaggerated for clarity.

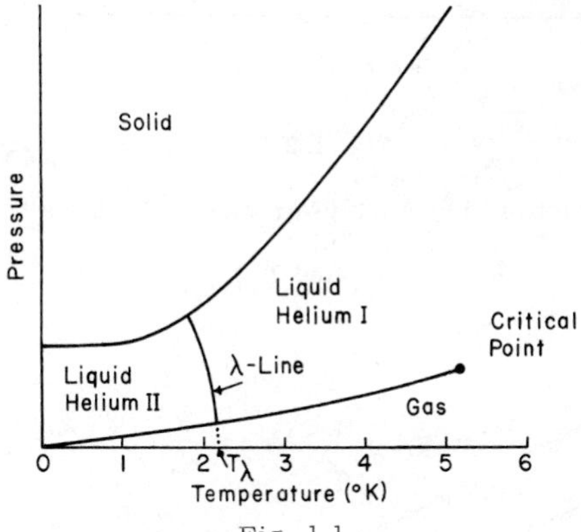

Fig. 1.1.

The normal boiling point is 4.2° K and the critical temperature is 5.19° K(1718mm). Liquid helium exists in two phases, He I and He II, separated by a phase boundary commonly called the λ-line. At saturated vapor pressure this transition occurs when the temperature $T_\lambda = 2.172°$ K, which is termed the λ-point. There is no latent heat associated with this transformation. The specific heat at saturated vapor pressure C_s, as given in Figure 1.2, becomes large as the λ-point is approached from either side.

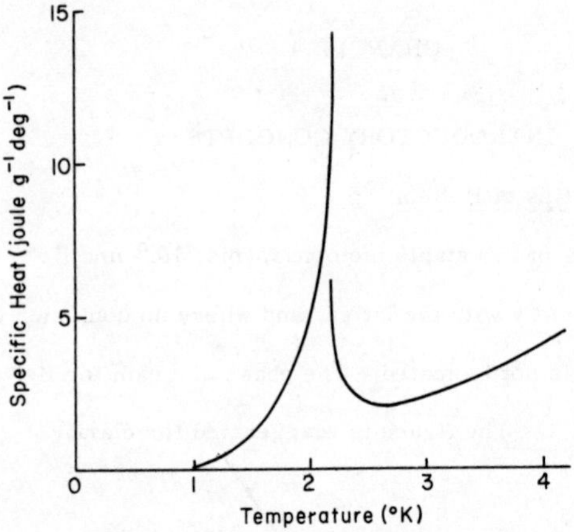

Fig. 1.2.

The log-linear plot in Figure 1.3 (Fairbank 1963) shows that there is a logarithmic discontinuity in C_s and T_λ.

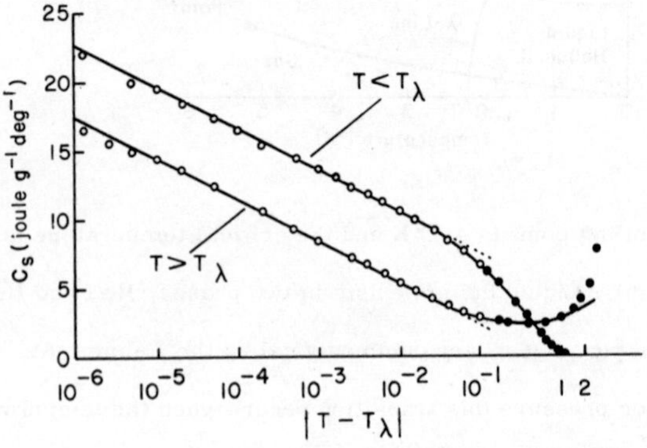

Fig. 1.3.

The expansivity becomes infinite at the λ-point (implying a discontinuity in the slope of the density-temperature curve, as shown in Fig. 1.4.).

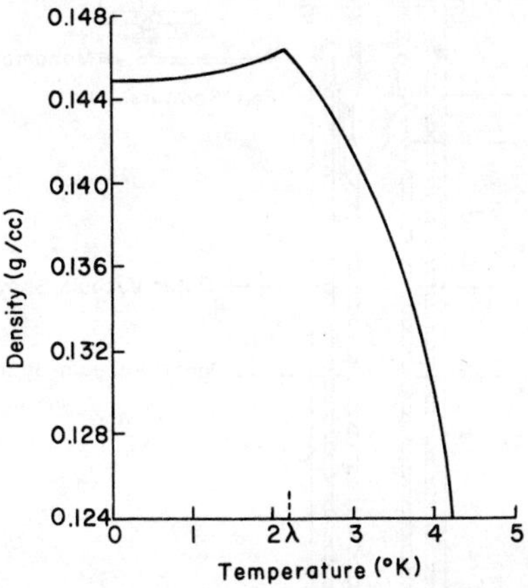

Fig. 1.4.

It should be noted that the maximum in this curve, and the zero in the expansivity, occurs 5 millidegrees above the λ-point (Kerr and Taylor 1964).

It is found that although He I behaves as an ordinary fluid, He II, owing to quantum effects, does not. It is the purpose of these notes to describe and explain some of the unusual properties of He II.

§2. <u>Production of Low Temperatures</u>

An experimental system to be operated at low temperatures is placed in a cryostat--two Dewars, one inside the other, as shown in Figure 1.5.

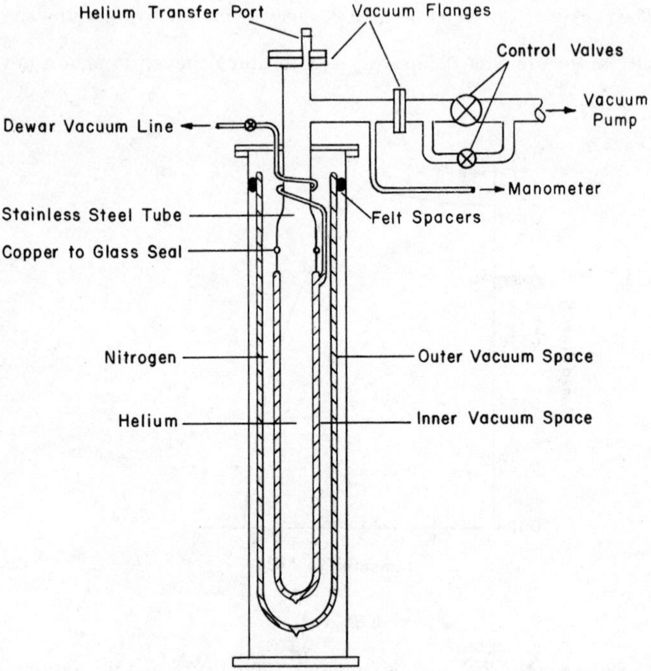

Fig. 1.5.

Liquid nitrogen is placed in the outer Dewar and liquid helium in the inner one. Heat-leaks to the helium bath can occur by conduction along any tubes, wires, etc., leading from the experimental apparatus to the outside. There can also be conduction and convection through the inner vacuum jacket from the nitrogen bath. This actually aids in cooling the apparatus down to liquid nitrogen temperatures. The room temperature pressure in this vacuum space need only be about 1 mm, since any residual gases, except helium, condense when the helium Dewar is filled and produce a very high vacuum. Helium gas tends to diffuse through the glass into the vacuum space when warm. This leaves a partial pressure of helium gas even at low temperatures and can introduce a large heat-leak. For this reason the inner vacuum region is not permanently sealed but is provided with a valve to which a vacuum system may be connected to allow periodic flushing and evacuation of the space. Both Dewars have silver coatings to reduce radiation input through the walls. Visual observation is possible through narrow unsilvered strips left running from top to bottom on opposite sides of the Dewar.

On the top of the helium Dewar a metal flange is attached by means of a copper-to-glass or Kovar seal to allow connection to the metal pipes of a vacuum system. By pumping on the helium bath, the vapor pressure is lowered and thereby reduces the temperature. The temperature range from 4.2° K (760mm) to 1.0°K (0.12mm) can be reached by using large mechanical pumps. Because of the low vapor pressure and film flow (see §4) further reduction in temperature by pumping is quite difficult. Even large booster diffusion pumps achieve temperatures only down to about 0.9° K.

Liquid He^3, however, has a higher vapor pressure than He^4 at a given temperature. A 0.1 mm vapor pressure corresponds to about 1° K for He^4 and 0.47° K for He^3. A He^3 refrigerator making use of this fact is shown in Figure 1.6 (Reif and Meyer 1960).

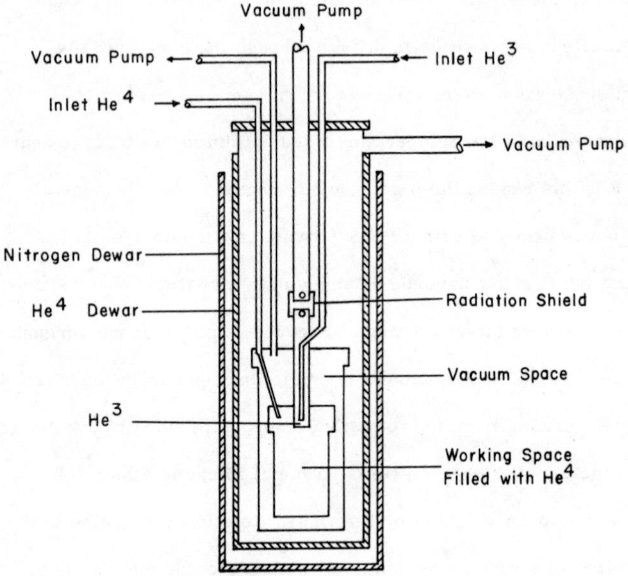

Fig. 1.6.

An additional Dewar is placed in the He^4 Dewar. This contains the experimental apparatus that is in good thermal contact with a liquid He^3 bath. After filling the helium Dewar with liquid helium, the He^3 is allowed to condense, and once sufficient He^3 is collected, it is pumped on to lower the temperature. In practice, temperatures down to 0.3° K can be reached in this manner.

Recently temperatures down to 0.07° K have been attained by means of a mixture refrigerator (Hall, Ford and Thomson 1966). A mixture of He^3 and He^4 can exist in two phases, one having a high concentration of He^3, the other a low concentration.

The conversion of the concentrated phase to the dilute phase requires a heat of dilution so that if the conversion takes place adiabatically the temperature will drop. The refrigerator operates by supplying the concentrated phase to the mixture and extracting the dilute phase. The dilute phase is then isothermally reconcentrated, say, in contact with a separate He^3 bath, and recycled. At present this method is still in an experimental stage but promises to become very useful below 0.3° K.

Temperatures in the millidegree region can be obtained through the adiabatic demagnetization of paramagnetic salts. A paramagnetic salt is first brought to as low a temperature as possible in a He^4 Dewar or He^3 refrigerator. It is then isothermally magnetized, and heat flows from the salt to the surrounding bath. Thermal contact with the bath is then broken, for example, by means of a superconducting heat switch, and the magnetic field is reduced to zero. This adiabatic demagnetization results in a drop in temperature. Low temperatures obtained in this way can be maintained for only short periods of time as compared with the refrigeration methods mentioned above.

§3. Measurement of Temperature

(a) The most common means of measuring the temperature of a sample of liquid helium above 1° K is by use of the liquid He^4 vapor pressure curve, as shown in Figure 1.1. In the case of a He^3 refrigerator, the He^3 vapor pressure is used to measure temperatures down to 0.3° K. Vapor pressures are measured by one of several methods.

Mercury manometers are generally used to measure pressures corresponding to temperatures above the λ-point. For greater sensitivity below T_λ, oil with low vapor pressure and with a specific gravity of about one-fourteenth that of mercury is used in a manometer placed in parallel with the mercury manometer. A more convenient method of vapor pressure measurement is the use of a bourdon type of gauge with mechanical or electrical readout. This avoids the disaster encountered when mercury accidentally enters a metal vacuum system.

(b) Another useful means of temperature measurement takes advantage of the nearly exponential variation in resistance of a semiconductor with temperature. A typical device in practice is an Allen Bradley 56 Ω (nominal) carbon resistor, which has a resistance of about 2,600 Ω at T_λ and about 50,000 Ω at 1° K. Carbon-resistance thermometers are usually calibrated against the helium vapor pressure tables (see Tables 1 and 2 in Appendix A). The resistance can be read with an AC resistance bridge that allows temperature differences of less than 10 μdeg. to be resolved. The bridge can also be connected to a heater in the helium bath through an electronic temperature regulating system, and the temperature can be controlled to within about 20μdeg.

(c) A third method of temperature measurement useful for

temperatures below 0.3°K is based on the assumption of the validity, for temperatures below 0.3°K, of Curie's Law, $\chi = \frac{\lambda}{T}$, relating the magnetic susceptibility of a paramagnetic salt to the temperature. The susceptibility is measured above 0.3°K, λ is computed, and Curie's Law is then used to assign temperatures for lower temperatures. Temperatures obtained in this manner are called magnetic temperatures and are usually denoted by T*.

REFERENCES

Fairbank, W. M. 1963, Proceedings of the International School of Physics, Course XXI, edited by G. Careri (New York: McGraw-Hill).

Hall, H. E., Ford, P. J., and Thomson, K. 1966, Cryogenics, 6, 80.

Kerr, E. C., and Taylor, R. D. 1964, Ann. Physics (N.Y.), 26, 292.

Reif, F., and Meyer, L. 1960, Phys. Rev., 119, 1164.

CHAPTER 2

TWO-FLUID MODEL AND MACROSCOPIC QUANTIZATION

§4. Isothermal Flow Effects

One of the unusual properties of He II is its ability to flow through fine slits and capillaries without producing a pressure gradient. Consider the experimental system illustrated in Figure 2.1 (Hammel and Keller 1965).

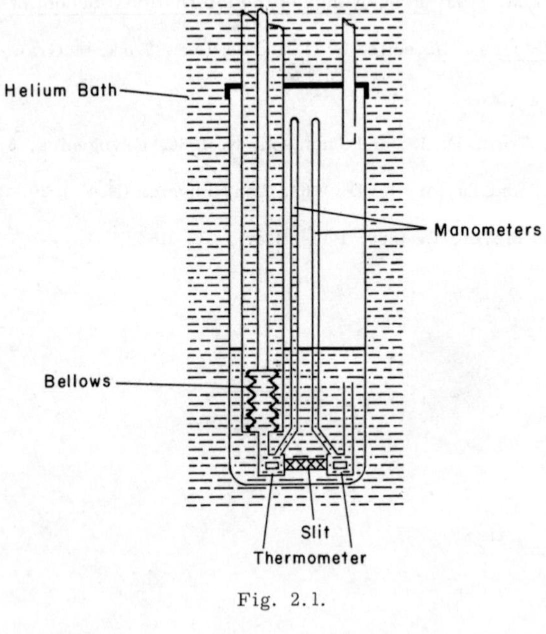

Fig. 2.1.

A constant volume flow rate of He through the slit is established by means of the bellows, the pressure and temperature at each end of the slit being monitored by manometers and thermometers. The slit, illustrated in Figure 2.2, is formed from two concentric cylinders whose diameters are uniform to 0.1 micron.

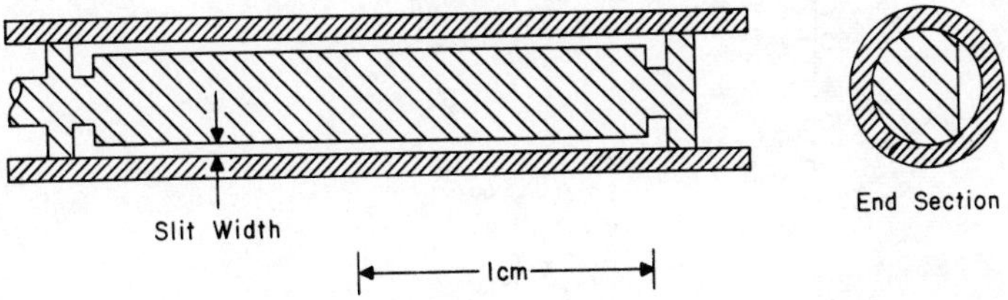

Fig. 2.2.

The slit width, or annular separation, is determined from the viscous flow of air at 300°K and He I at 4°K. The linear flow velocity through the slit, v_s, is computed from the slit width, the diameter of the cylinders, and the volume flow rate. Figure 2.3 shows the induced pressure gradient ∇p across the slit as a function of v_s at a temperature of 1.30° K and a slit width of 3.36×10^{-4} cm. Below a "critical velocity" ($\approx$ 4 cm/sec) no pressure gradient develops and the flow appears to be inviscid. Above critical, a pressure gradient arises, indicating the onset of some dissipative mechanism. It is found that this critical velocity increases with decreasing slit width and decreasing temperature.

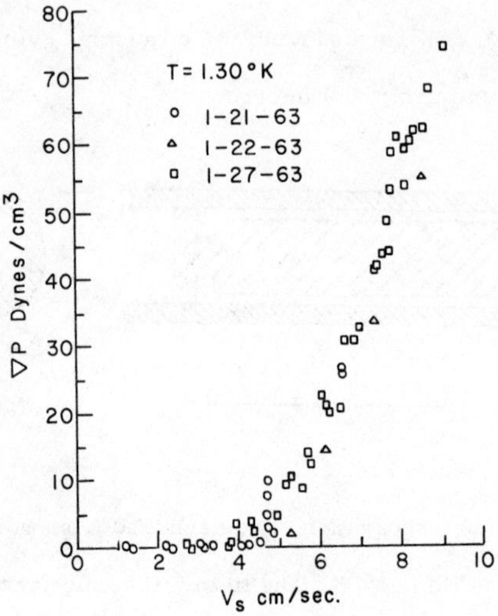

Fig. 2.3

As the λ -point is approached from below, the critical velocity goes to zero as shown by the results of a related experiment. He I, of course, is an ordinary fluid with a viscosity approximately equal to that of He gas, and thus the viscosity of He appears to change discontinuously at the λ -point.

The frictionless flow of He II has been well demonstrated in a persistent current experiment by Reppy and Depatie (1964, 1965). They constructed a torus-shaped channel filled with fibrous foam to form many very narrow channels that allow high critical velocities. Since He II behaves as an inviscid fluid below critical velocities, it is necessary to rotate the torus above critical to set the fluid in motion.

The torus is then stopped, and the fluid velocity decreases until the critical velocity is reached, at which point the dissipative processes cease and a persistent current remains. The presence of this current can be detected by applying a torque to the torus and observing the resultant precession. In the experiment no decrease in the critical flow rate was observed in a twelve-hour period.

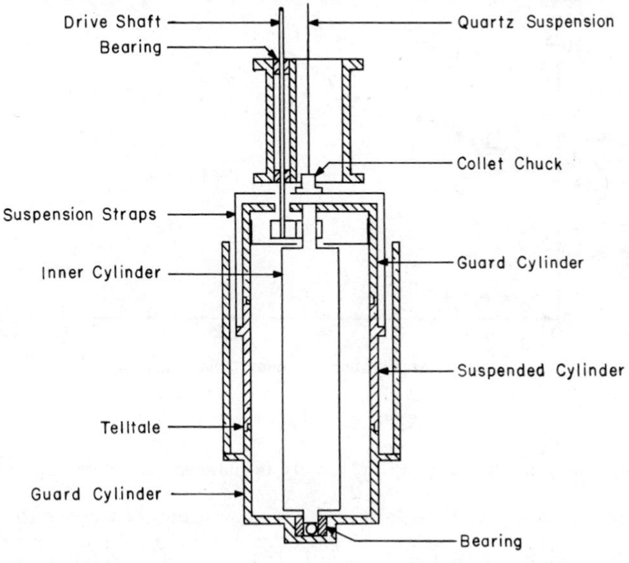

Fig. 2.4.

In experiments on flow through small capillaries, He II behaves like an inviscid fluid for flow velocities below critical. In other experiments, however, He II can behave like a viscous fluid with a viscosity almost equal to that of He I and He gas.

Figure 2.4 shows a rotating viscometer in which the inner cylinder is rotated at constant angular velocity Ω and transmits a torque G through the fluid to the outer cylinder suspended from a fiber. A mirror is fixed to the outer cylinder to reflect a beam of light allowing the angular deflection to be measured, and from the angular deflection, the torque G is computed. The viscosity (proportional to G/Ω) for He II at 1.35°K is shown in Figure 2.5.

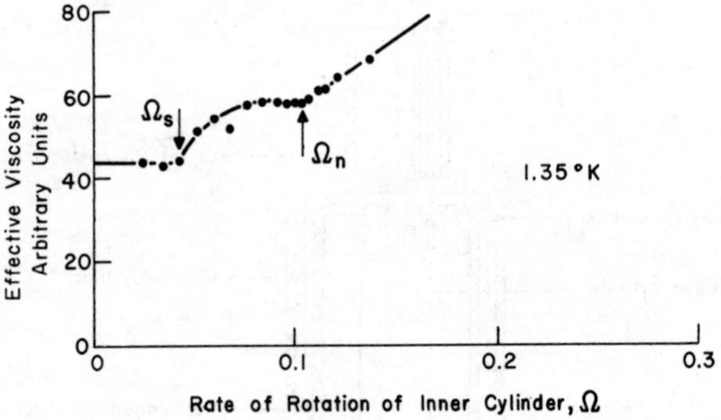

Fig. 2.5.

For viscous laminar flow, the viscosity is independent of velocity, and Figure 2.5 shows that He II behaves as an ordinary viscous fluid below Ω_s, the viscosity being about 10^{-5} poise. (The effects occuring above Ω_s will be discussed later.) It is also found that the viscosity measured in this fashion varies continuously through the λ-point.

In order to explain this seemingly contradictory behavior of He II Tisza (1938) introduced the two-fluid model. This simply assumes that He II consists of two fluids, a normal fluid with viscosity and a superfluid with zero viscosity. Each component is assigned a density, ρ_n and ρ_s, whose sum is the total fluid density $\rho = \rho_n + \rho_s$, and each is assigned its own velocity field $\underset{\sim}{v}_n$ and $\underset{\sim}{v}_s$. In flow through narrow slits, the normal fluid is clamped by its viscosity, and the mass flow is carried entirely by the inviscid superfluid. In the rotating cylinder viscometer, the normal fluid is dragged along by the inner cylinder, transmitting a torque to the outer cylinder while the superfluid is unaffected. It should be noted that the concept of an inviscid superfluid is valid only for flow velocities below critical. As will be discussed later, strong coupling between the two fluids and turbulence may occur at velocities above critical. Such supercritical effects allow the superfluid to be drawn into motion in the persistent current experiment. In this experiment, after dissipation has ceased, the two-fluid model suggests that the normal fluid will be clamped and only the superfluid contributes to the persistent current.

Having assumed a two-fluid model for He II, we now seek its thermodynamic and hydrodynamic properties. Our first concern will be the determination of the two densities, ρ_n and ρ_s. Consider an infinite plane surface in a fluid lying in the x-y plane and oscillating in the x-direction with frequency ω and velocity amplitude v_o. A plane shear wave will propagate in the z-direction with an x-component of velocity given by

$$v = v_o \exp\left\{-\left(\frac{\omega\rho}{2\eta}\right)^{\frac{1}{2}} z + i\left[\omega t - \left(\frac{\omega\rho}{2\eta}\right)^{\frac{1}{2}} z\right]\right\},$$

where ρ is the fluid density and η its shear viscosity. The wave amplitude falls off rapidly in a distance $\delta = \sqrt{2\eta/\rho\omega}$, which may be taken as the thickness of the boundary layer. Thus only the fluid in the immediate vicinity of the surface is moving; the bulk of the fluid is at rest. Now, if a stack of discs separated by a distance much smaller than δ is set into torsional oscillations in a fluid, the fluid between the plates will move with the stack as a solid body (see Fig. 2.6).

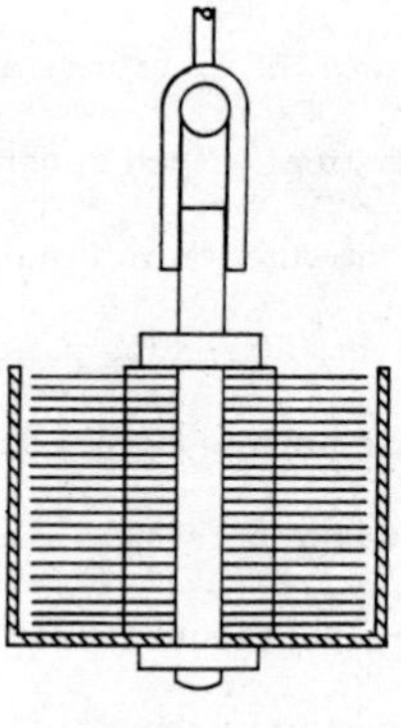

Fig. 2.6.

Thus the moment of inertia, obtained from the frequency of oscillation, will depend on whether the stack is immersed in a fluid or not. A comparison of these two frequencies will then yield the effective mass of the entrained fluid and, from the geometry, the density may be found. Now, if the fluid is He II, only the normal fluid will be entrained and the density found will be the normal fluid density ρ_n. The normal fluid density was first found in this manner by Andronikashvili (1946, 1948). Figure 2.7 shows ρ_n/ρ and $\rho_s/\rho = 1 - \rho_n/\rho$ as a function of temperature (at saturated vapor pressure).

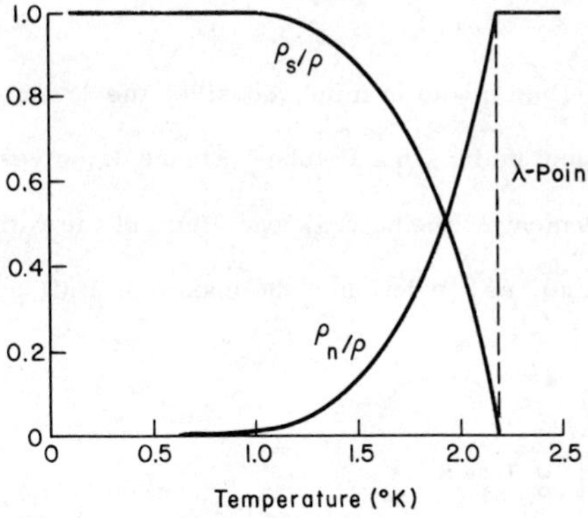

Fig. 2.7.

Measurements of the damping of the torsional oscillations of a single disc depends upon the product $\eta\rho$, and since the viscosity of He II belongs to the normal fluid, the density ρ is taken to be ρ_n. Figure 2.8 shows η as a function of temperature.

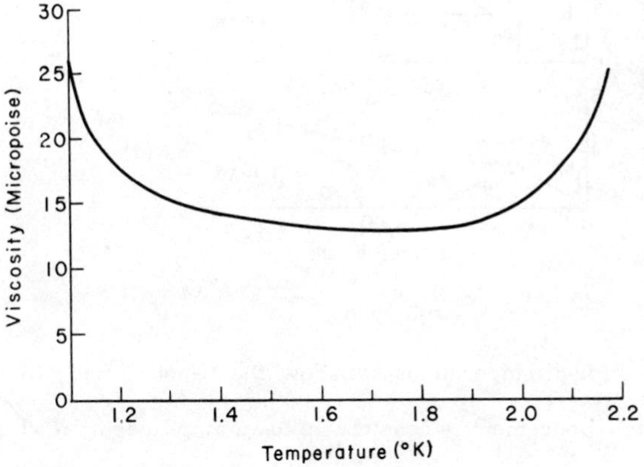

Fig. 2.8.

It should be noted that above 1. 9° K, the viscosity appears gaslike and increases with increasing temperature, while below 1. 9° K it appears liquid-like.

With the two-fluid model in mind, consider the damping of oscillations of liquid helium in a U-tube. Figure 2. 9 gives the logarithmic decrement Δ (the natural logarithim of the ratio of two successive maxima) as a function of the maximum h (Donnelly and Penrose 1956).

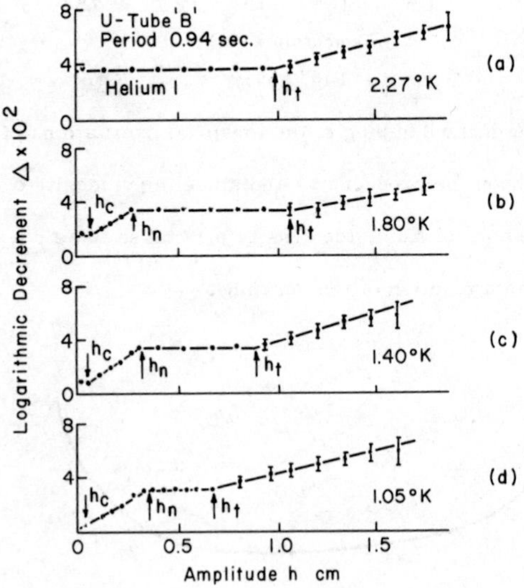

Fig. 2. 9.

Figure 2. 9a is for a temperature just above the λ-point, i. e., He I. The logarithmic decrement is constant up to an amplitude h_t at which point non-linear effects, perhaps associated with turbulence, set in.

Figure 2.9b, which shows results for a temperature just below the λ-point, demonstrates a similar increase in Δ at h_t and is again attributed to turbulence. From h_n to h_t, Δ is the same as for He I, and it is assumed that both the normal fluid and superfluid are moving as a whole, describable in terms of a single-component hydrodynamics. Below h_c there is a second region of constant damping resulting from the normal fluid only. There remains, between h_c and h_n, a transition region between the realms of the two-fluid and single-fluid hydrodynamics. As the temperature is lowered (see Figures 2.9b, 2.9c, and 2.9d), it is seen that for $h < h_c$ Δ decreases, which is in accord with the fact that the product $\rho_n \eta$ decreases with decreasing temperature.

Consider next the torsional oscillations of a sphere in He II. Figure 2.10 shows the logarithm decrement Δ versus the amplitude φ.

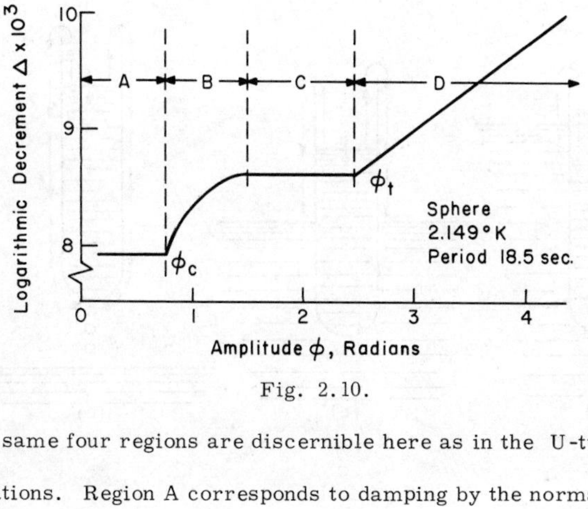

Fig. 2.10.

The same four regions are discernible here as in the U-tube oscillations. Region A corresponds to damping by the normal fluid only, region C damping owing to both fluids moving together, region B the transition region, and region D excess damping owing to turbulence or non-linearities.

As a final example of isothermal flow, we consider the He film. If a solid surface is in contact with a vapor, a thin film will be adsorbed onto it. For helium, if the surface is below the λ-point, the film will be composed of both normal fluid and superfluid. The film thickness is approximately 200 Å, and thus the normal fluid in a film is clamped. The superfluid, however, gives the film a high mobility behaving similarly to He II in narrow slits. (There are differences, of course, because the film has one free surface. In particular, the film can support a peculiar form of wave motion -- see §7 on third sound capillary waves.) Figure 2.11 shows a beaker of He in a bath of He.

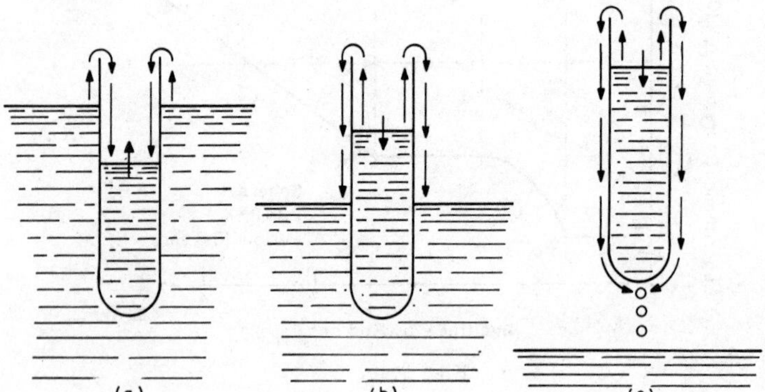

Fig. 2.11.

In Figures 2.11a and 2.11b, owing to the presence of a mobile film, the fluid (superfluid) flows to equalize the two levels. In Figure 2.11c the film flow will completely empty the beaker.

It is found that the linear fluid velocity in the film is not strongly dependent on the level difference. (There is a slight dependence on the vertical distance the film must move, perhaps owing to the changes in film thickness with height.) Figure 2.12 shows the height of the fluid in a beaker as a function of time as the beaker empties nto the bath (Daunt and Mendelssohn 1939).

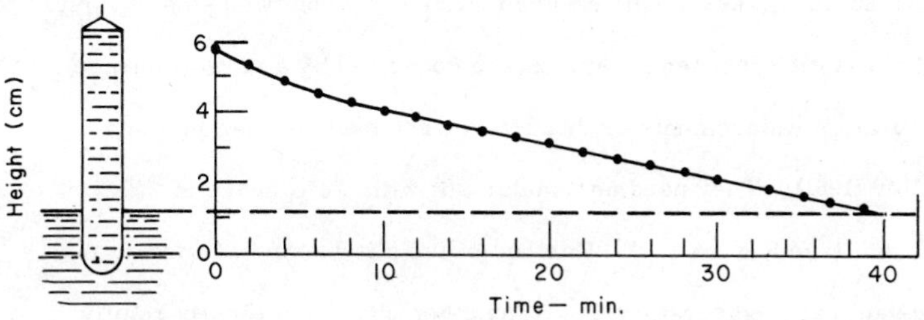

Fig. 2.12.

The critical transfer rate R_c, defined as the ratio of the volume flow rate to the length of perimeter over which the film must pass, has a temperature dependence similar to ρ_s/ρ, which is expected, since only the superfluid flows.

It should be noted that in experiments on superfluid flow in which the flow rate is not controlled externally (as was done in the experiment by Hammel and Keller), the superfluid attains its maximum flow velocity, that is, the critical velocity for the particular experimental system. Thus the film-flow experiment described above involves flow at the critical velocity, whereas Hammel and Keller's experiment involved both subcritical and supercritical flows. A further discussion on these critical velocities will be given in §9.

§5. Thermal Effects

We will now discuss a number of effects involving temperature differences that demonstrate that the entropy is associated with the normal component alone. The first effect is the thermomechanical or "fountain" pressure difference that arises when two baths of liquid helium at different temperatures are connected by a narrow channel. Accurate measurements of this effect were made by Hammel and Keller (1961). They used an annular slit with a clearence of 2.76×10^{-5} cm (see Figure 2.2). One end of the slit was maintained at a constant bath temperature T_o. The other end of the slit, carefully isolated from the bath, was equipped with a heater, thermometer, and pressure transducer. The apparatus is shown schematically in Figure 2.13. The experimental relations between the pressure difference p_f and the temperature T at the hot end for three values of T_o are shown in Figure 2.14.

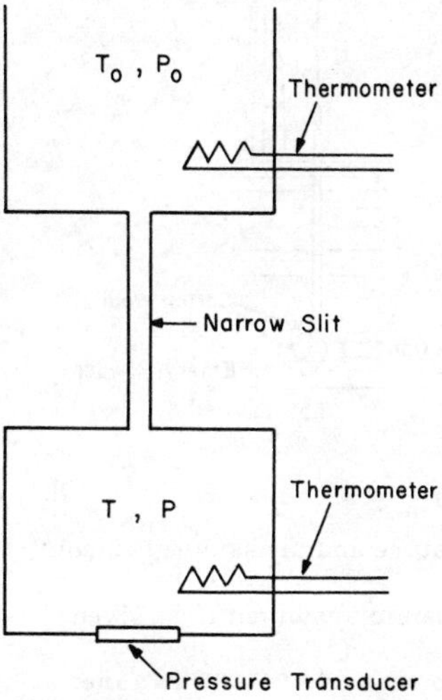

Fig. 2.13.

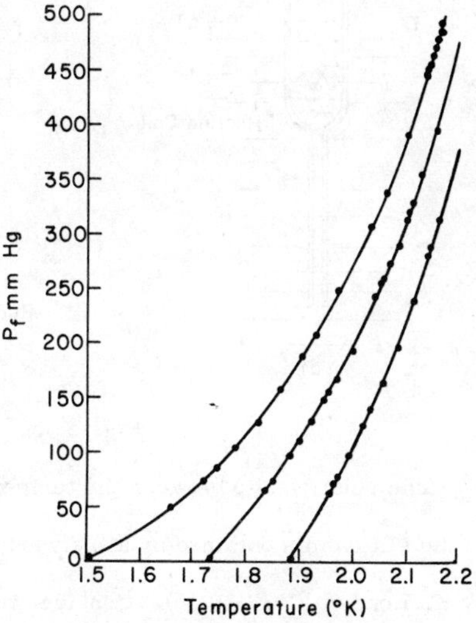

Fig. 2.14.

A dramatic illustration of this effect occurs when the temperature difference is large enough to correspond to a pressure head of 30-50 cm of liquid helium. An appropriate arrangement such as that of Figure 2.15 would then produce a jet of liquid helium justifying the name "fountain effect."

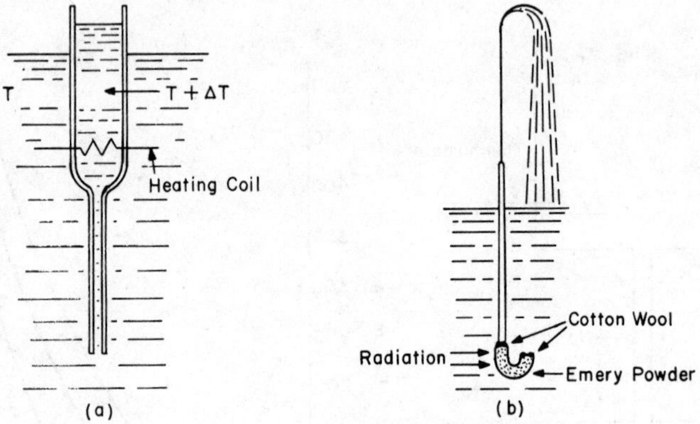

Fig. 2.15.

The relationship between the temperature and pressure gradients in the slit can be obtained by a thermodynamic argument first given by H. London (1938, 1939). Consider two vessels of He II that are separately in thermodynamic equilibrium. If these vessels are connected by a narrow channel, the flow of the normal component between them can be made arbitrarily small, but the superfluid will flow easily and <u>mechanical</u> equilibrium between the baths will be rapidly established. <u>Thermal</u> equilibrium between the baths will not take place if we assume that the entropy is associated with the normal component and that any conduction is negligible. Let us examine the state of equilibrium to which the vessels have come after the superflow has taken place but before significant entropy has been transferred.

Let p_1 and p_2, T_1 and T_2, E_1 and E_2, V_1 and V_2, S_1 and S_2, and M_1 and M_2 be the pressures, temperatures, internal energies per gram, specific volumes, entropies per gram and masses in the two vessels.

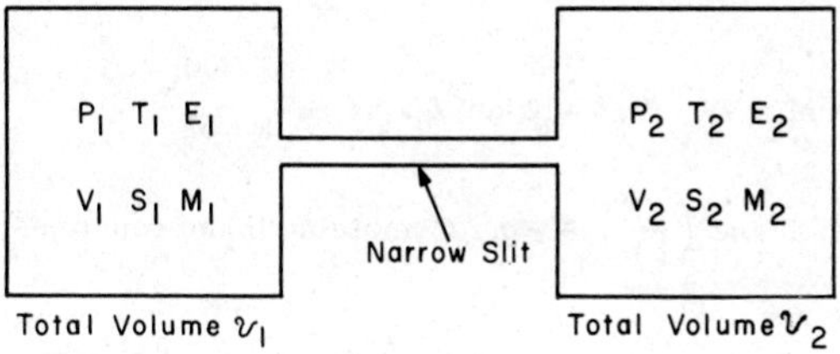

Fig. 2.16.

We are considering the situation as in Figure 2.16 so that superflow occurs with no change in the total entropies or in the total volumes of either bath. The mechanical equilibrium condition is that the sum of the energies of both baths, $\mathcal{E}$, be a minimum with respect to the distribution of mass in the baths. Therefore,

$$O = \delta \mathcal{E} = \sum_{k=1,2} \delta (M_k E_k) = \sum_{k=1,2} \left(E_k \delta M_k + M_k \delta E_k \right), \qquad (2.1)$$

and since $E = E(S, V)$,

$$\delta E_k = \left(\frac{\partial E_k}{\partial S_k} \right)_{V_k} \delta S_k + \left(\frac{\partial E_k}{\partial V_k} \right)_{S_k} \delta V_k , \qquad (2.2)$$

so that

$$O = \sum_{k=1,2} \left\{ E_k \delta M_k + M_k \left[\left(\frac{\partial E_k}{\partial S_k} \right)_{V_k} \delta S_k + \left(\frac{\partial E_k}{\partial V_k} \right)_{S_k} \delta V_k \right] \right\}. \qquad (2.3)$$

The total entropies and volumes in each bath are $\mathcal{S}_k = M_k S_k$ and $\mathcal{V}_k = M_k V_k$. These are held constant so that

$$\delta \mathcal{S}_k = 0 = M_k \delta S_k + S_k \delta M_k \text{ or } \delta S_k = - S_k \frac{\delta M_k}{M_k}, \tag{2.4}$$

and

$$\delta \mathcal{V}_k = 0 = M_k \delta V_k + V_k \delta M_k \text{ or } \delta V_k = - V_k \frac{\delta M_k}{M_k}.$$

Now $\left(\frac{\partial E}{\partial S}\right)_V = T$ and $\left(\frac{\partial E}{\partial V}\right)_S = -p$. Combining these equations, we have

$$0 = \sum_{k=1,2} \left\{ E_k \delta M_k + M_k \left(- T_k S_k \frac{\delta M_k}{M_k} + p_k V_k \frac{\delta M_k}{M_k} \right) \right\} \tag{2.5}$$

$$= \sum_{k=1,2} \left(E_k - S_k T_k + V_k p_k \right) \delta M_k \tag{2.6}$$

$$= \sum_{k=1,2} \Phi_k \delta M_k, \tag{2.7}$$

where Φ is the thermodynamic potential per gram. Since $\delta M_1 = - \delta M_2$, we have $\Phi_2 - \Phi_1 = 0$, and since $\Phi = \Phi(p, T)$,

$$d\Phi = 0 = \left(\frac{\partial \Phi}{\partial p}\right)_T dp + \left(\frac{\partial \Phi}{\partial T}\right)_p dT. \tag{2.8}$$

$\left(\frac{\partial \Phi}{\partial p}\right)_T = \frac{1}{\rho}$ (specific volume), and $\left(\frac{\partial \Phi}{\partial T}\right)_p = -S$, so that

$$\frac{dp}{dT} = \rho S, \tag{2.9}$$

and

$$P_f = \int_{T_0}^{T} \rho S dT \tag{2.10}$$

in the notation of Figure 2.14. The solid lines of Figure 2.14 were obtained from (2.10), which demonstrates excellent agreement with experimental data.

Suppose we consider a situation similar to that used to discuss London's derivation, except that now we relax the condition $\delta v_k = 0$. Equation (2.4) shows that on transfer of δM grams of fluid from container 1 to container 2, the entropy per gram will increase in 1 and decrease in 2. This means that the temperature will increase in 1 by δT_1 and decrease in 2 by δT_2, according to the relations

$$C_1 \delta T_1 = T_1 \delta S_1 = T_1 S_1 \frac{\delta M}{M_1} ,$$

$$C_2 \delta T_2 = T_2 \delta S_2 = -T_2 S_2 \frac{\delta M}{M_2} , \qquad (2.11)$$

where C_1 and C_2 are the specific heats per gram in the two containers.

If, instead of the arrangements above, we put the two containers in contact with reservoirs at temperatures T_1 and T_2, then the entropies per gram will not change in the two containers (since $S = S(p, T)$ and $\delta p = \delta T = 0$). Therefore,

$$\delta \mathcal{S}_1 = -S_1 \delta M = \frac{Q_1}{T}$$

$$\delta \mathcal{S}_2 = S_2 \delta M = \frac{Q_2}{T} , \qquad (2.12)$$

so that a transfer of δM grams from a bath results in an amount of heat $Q = TS\delta M$ removed from that bath.

The temperature changes described by (2. 11) describe the "mechano-caloric" effect, which was first observed by Daunt and Mendelssohn (1939) and is illustrated in Figure 2. 17.

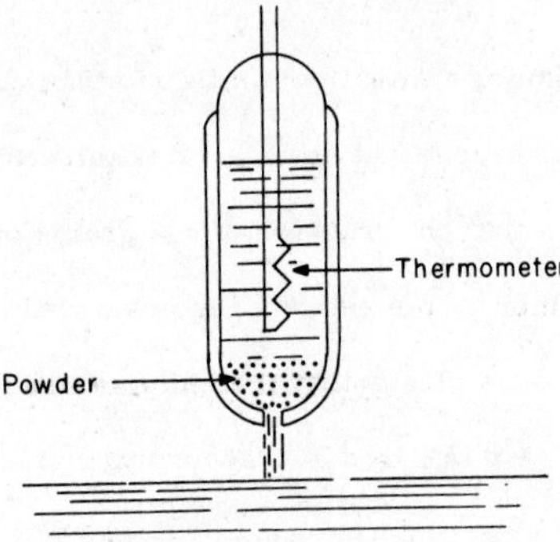

Fig. 2. 17.

A small insulated container, plugged at the bottom with fine emery powder, was arranged so that it could be raised or lowered into a bath of He II. It was found that when liquid flowed into the container, the temperature dropped about 10^{-2} °K, and when liquid flowed out, the temperature rose by the same amount. This qualitatively confirms (2. 11). Quantitative confirmation of (2. 12) to within a few per cent were made by means of a direct measurement of the quantity $\frac{Q}{\delta M} = Q^*$ (Brewer and Edwards 1958).

We conclude from this discussion that in the two-fluid theory, the assumption that the entropy of He II is associated with the normal component rests on a firm experimental foundation.

§6. Internal Convection and the Equations of Motion in the Two-fluid Model

Consider the hypothetical experiment of Figure 2. 18.

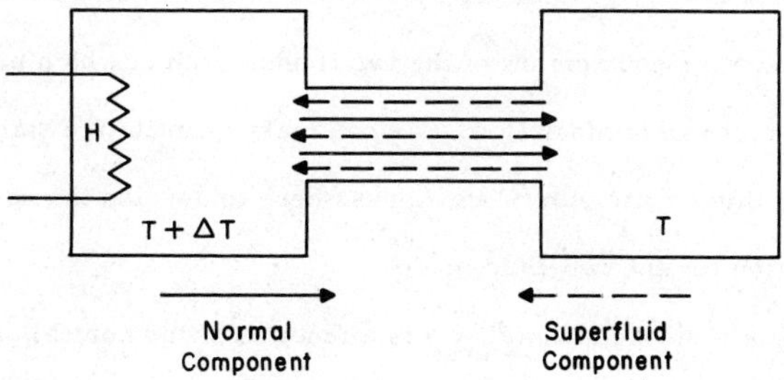

Fig. 2.18.

We have a closed tube containing He II with a heater on one end and a reservoir in contact with the other. In an ordinary fluid, such as HeI, the heat will pass from left to right by thermal conduction, providing care is taken to prevent convection (for example, by mounting the low density end upward). Under these circumstances, the heat flux is proportional to the temperature gradient and there is a well-defined thermal conductivity. Early experiments with He II, however, seemed to indicate that the thermal conductivity became infinite in the limit of small heat flux. It is evident that this anomalous behavior must be described by a mechanism different from conduction.

The explanation in terms of the two-fluid theory is indicated by the arrows in Figure 2.19. The superfluid in contact with the heater absorbs heat, becomes normal fluid, and flows toward the cool end where it gives it up. The flow of superfluid in the tube, by continuity, is toward the heater. It is clear that this internal convection is not the result of a density gradient or hydrodynamic instability, but instead is a peculiar counterflow of the two fluids, each of which may be pictured as being in laminar flow. We can make quantitative statements about this counterflow if we digress here to develop the equations of motion for the two-fluid model.

The mass flow of fluid $\underset{\sim}{j}(\underset{\sim}{v}_n, \underset{\sim}{v}_s)$ is a function of the normal and superfluid velocity fields. If we assume the velocities are small (compared, say, with the velocity of sound), $\underset{\sim}{j}$ may be expanded in a power series, and we have

$$\underset{\sim}{j} = \rho_s \underset{\sim}{v}_s + \rho_n \underset{\sim}{v}_n + \ldots \ , \tag{2.13}$$

where ρ_s and ρ_n are formally identified with the superfluid and normal components of the mass density. We assume there is no source or sink of mass, so that

$$\operatorname{div} \underset{\sim}{j} + \frac{\partial \rho}{\partial t} = 0 \ . \tag{2.14}$$

The conservation of momentum may be written

$$\frac{\partial j_i}{\partial t} + \frac{\partial \pi_{ki}}{\partial x_k} = 0, \tag{2.15}$$

where the tensor summation convention is used and where π_{ik} is the momentum flow density tensor,

$$\pi_{ik} = p\delta_{ik} + \rho_s v_{si} v_{sk} + \rho_n v_{ni} v_{nk} - \eta \left(\frac{\partial v_{ni}}{\partial x_k} + \frac{\partial v_{nk}}{\partial x_i} \right) , \tag{2.16}$$

and p is the pressure. Equation (2.16) is written for an incompressible fluid and hence neglects second and other coefficients of viscosity. It is a natural generalization of the ordinary momentum flow density tensor

$$\pi_{ik} = p\,\delta_{ik} + \rho v_i v_k - \eta\left(\frac{\partial v_i}{\partial x_k} + \frac{\partial v_k}{\partial x_i}\right) \tag{2.17}$$

(see Landau and Lifshitz 1959, §15). Since viscous dissipation varies as v_n^2, we may write an equation for conservation of entropy correct to first order,

$$\frac{\partial(\rho S)}{\partial t} + \mathrm{div}(\rho S \underset{\sim}{v}_n) = 0 \;. \tag{2.18}$$

Note that all the entropy flow is associated with the normal component. The heat transport per unit volume is therefore

$$\underset{\sim}{q} = \rho S T \underset{\sim}{v}_n \;. \tag{2.19}$$

At this point, we make the assumption that

$$\mathrm{curl}\, \underset{\sim}{v}_s = 0 \;. \tag{2.20}$$

That this is true is made plausible by the fact that a classical inviscid fluid obeys curl $\underset{\sim}{v}$ = constant, the law of conservation of vorticity.

The final relation comes from equating the force acting on a unit mass of superfluid with the resulting acceleration $\frac{dv_s}{dt}$. We present here an argument based on one originally advanced by Landau. A rigorous (but more mathematical) argument will be presented in Chapter 4. Consider the transfer of ΔM grams of superfluid from point 1 to point 2, a distance $\delta \underset{\sim}{x}$ away. This is to be done in such a way that the normal component is undisturbed with the result that the entropy and the momentum of the normal mass of the liquid relative to the superfluid remain constant. In addition, the volume of the liquid is considered a constant. Since we are moving superfluid, we assume that the total energy of the fluid is unchanged by this transfer (i. e., there is nothing like viscous dissipation). The kinetic energy of the superfluid can be subtracted out, so that

$$\mathcal{E} = \mathcal{E}_{s,\,kin.} + \mathcal{E}' \quad ,$$

where $\mathcal{E}_{s,\,kin.}$ is the kinetic energy of the superfluid and $\mathcal{E}'$ is the energy of the fluid with the superfluid at rest. As a result of the transfer, we then have

$$\begin{aligned} \delta \mathcal{E} = 0 &= \delta \mathcal{E}_{s,\,kin.} + \delta \mathcal{E}' \\ &= \delta \left(\tfrac{1}{2} \Delta M \underset{\sim}{v}_s^{\,2}\right) + \left[\left(\frac{\partial \mathcal{E}'}{\partial M}\right)_{2\,S,V} - \left(\frac{\partial \mathcal{E}'}{\partial M}\right)_{1\,S,V}\right] \Delta M \\ &= \Delta M \frac{d\underset{\sim}{v}_s}{dt} \cdot \delta \underset{\sim}{x} + \Delta M\, \nabla \left(\frac{\delta \mathcal{E}'}{\delta M}\right)_{S,V} \cdot \delta \underset{\sim}{x} \end{aligned} \qquad (2.21)$$

so that

$$\frac{d\underset{\sim}{v}_s}{dt} = -\underset{\sim}{\nabla} \left(\frac{\delta \mathcal{E}'}{\delta M}\right)_{S,V} \quad . \qquad (2.22)$$

We know from thermodynamics that $\left(\frac{\partial \mathcal{E}'}{\partial M}\right)_{S,V} = \left(\frac{\partial (M\Phi)}{\partial M}\right)_{p,T}$. Now $\mathcal{E}'$ does not include the superfluid kinetic energy but does include the relative kinetic energy of the normal fluid, and we can write

$$M\Phi = M\Phi_o + \frac{\underset{\sim}{P}^2}{2M_n} , \qquad (2.23)$$

where $\underset{\sim}{P}$ is the conserved momentum $M_n(\underset{\sim}{v}_n - \underset{\sim}{v}_s)$ and M_n is the normal fluid mass $\frac{\rho_n}{\rho} M$. We then have

$$\frac{\partial (M\Phi)}{\partial M} = \Phi_o - \frac{\rho_n}{2\rho}(\underset{\sim}{v}_n - \underset{\sim}{v}_s)^2 , \qquad (2.24)$$

so that

$$\frac{d\underset{\sim}{v}_s}{dt} = - \text{grad}\left[\Phi_o - \frac{\rho_n}{2\rho}(\underset{\sim}{v}_n - \underset{\sim}{v}_s)^2\right] . \qquad (2.25)$$

Now $\frac{\partial \underset{\sim}{v}_s}{\partial t}$ is computed relative to a fixed frame by

$$\frac{d\underset{\sim}{v}_s}{dt} = \frac{\partial \underset{\sim}{v}_s}{\partial t} + (\underset{\sim}{v}_s \cdot \nabla)\underset{\sim}{v}_s ,$$

or from (2.20)

$$\frac{d\underset{\sim}{v}_s}{dt} = \frac{\partial \underset{\sim}{v}_s}{\partial t} + \nabla\left(\frac{v_s^2}{2}\right) ,$$

so that

$$\frac{\partial \underset{\sim}{v}_s}{\partial t} = -\text{grad}\left[\Phi_o + \frac{v_s^2}{2} - \frac{\rho_n}{2\rho}(\underset{\sim}{v}_n - \underset{\sim}{v}_s)^2\right]. \qquad (2.26)$$

Note that we could define a more general thermodynamic potential for the superfluid, including the $(\underset{\sim}{v}_n - \underset{\sim}{v}_s)^2$ term, so that, for example, there is a force on superfluid elements toward regions of high counter-flow. When equilibrium prevails, $\frac{d\underset{\sim}{v}_s}{dt} = 0$, and we regain the condition for the thermomechanical effect, (2. 8).

We now develop the two-fluid equations for incompressible flow. Assuming ρ, ρ_s, ρ_n, and S are constant, we have from (2.14) and (2.18)

$$\operatorname{div} \underset{\sim}{v}_n = \operatorname{div} \underset{\sim}{v}_s = 0 . \tag{2. 27}$$

Substituting (2.16) in (2.15) and using (2. 27), we find

$$\rho_s \frac{\partial \underset{\sim}{v}_s}{\partial t} + \rho_n \frac{\partial \underset{\sim}{v}_n}{\partial t} + \rho_s (\underset{\sim}{v}_s \cdot \nabla)\underset{\sim}{v}_s + \rho_n (\underset{\sim}{v}_n \cdot \nabla)\underset{\sim}{v}_n = -\nabla p + \eta \nabla^2 \underset{\sim}{v}_n . \tag{2. 28}$$

Since

$$\begin{aligned} \nabla \Phi_0 &= -S\nabla T + V\nabla p \\ &= -S\nabla T + \frac{\nabla p}{\rho} , \end{aligned} \tag{2. 29}$$

(2. 25) gives

$$\rho_s \frac{d\underset{\sim}{v}_s}{dt} = \frac{\rho_s}{\rho} \nabla p + \rho_s S \nabla T + \frac{\rho_n \rho_s}{2\rho} \nabla (\underset{\sim}{v}_n - \underset{\sim}{v}_s)^2 . \tag{2. 30}$$

By substituting in (2. 28), we get

$$\rho_n \frac{d\underset{\sim}{v}_n}{dt} = \frac{\rho_n}{\rho} \nabla p - \rho_s S \nabla T - \frac{\rho_n \rho_s}{2\rho} \nabla (\underset{\sim}{v}_n - \underset{\sim}{v}_s)^2 + \eta \nabla^2 \underset{\sim}{v}_n , \tag{2. 31}$$

where

$$\frac{d\underset{\sim}{v}_n}{dt} = \frac{\partial \underset{\sim}{v}_n}{\partial t} + (\underset{\sim}{v}_n \cdot \nabla)\underset{\sim}{v}_n . \tag{2. 32}$$

Equations (2.30) and (2.31) are Landau's equations of motion for He II.

Now let us look into the boundary conditions at a stationary surface. The perpendicular component of the mass flux must vanish,

$$\underset{\sim}{j}_{\perp} = \rho_s \underset{\sim}{v}_{s\perp} + \rho_n \underset{\sim}{v}_{n\perp} = 0 . \tag{2.33}$$

The individual $\underset{\sim}{v}_{s\perp}$ and $\underset{\sim}{v}_{n\perp}$ need not vanish since heat may be transferred between the liquid and surface. The parallel component of $\underset{\sim}{v}_n$ obeys the "no-slip" condition for an ordinary fluid,

$$\underset{\sim}{v}_{n\parallel} = 0 . \tag{2.34}$$

The normal component of the heat flux must be continuous,

$$\underset{\sim}{q}_{\perp} = -K \nabla T_{solid} , \tag{2.35}$$

where grad T_{solid} is the gradient of temperature in the boundary and K is the thermal conductivity. Application of (2.35) is complicated by the experimental observation that when heat flows across a surface between liquid helium and a solid, a temperature discontinuity appears across the boundary. This "Kapitza resistance" is not a phenomenon peculiar to He II.

When heat transfer into the surface is zero,

$$\underset{\sim}{v}_{n\parallel} = \underset{\sim}{v}_{n\perp} = \underset{\sim}{v}_{s\perp} = 0 . \tag{2.36}$$

We can return now to the description of thermal counterflow. In a closed tube there is obviously no net mass flow, so that by (2.13),

$$\underset{\sim}{v}_s = -\frac{\rho_n}{\rho_s}\underset{\sim}{v}_n . \tag{2.37}$$

The equations of motion reduce, after linearization and the assumptions of steady flow and small velocities, to

$$-\frac{1}{\rho}\underset{\sim}{\nabla} p + S\underset{\sim}{\nabla} T = 0 , \tag{2.38}$$

and

$$-\frac{1}{\rho}\underset{\sim}{\nabla} p - \frac{\rho_s}{\rho_n} S\underset{\sim}{\nabla} T + \frac{\eta}{\rho_n}\underset{\sim}{\nabla}^2 \underset{\sim}{v}_n = 0 . \tag{2.39}$$

Subtracting these equations and using (2.19), we obtain

$$\underset{\sim}{\nabla}^2 \underset{\sim}{q} = \Lambda \underset{\sim}{\nabla} T , \tag{2.40}$$

where

$$\Lambda = \rho^2 S^2 T \eta^{-1} . \tag{2.41}$$

Consider a two-dimensional slit with walls at $z = \pm d/2$. We suppose that the heat flows in the x-direction and depends only upon z. Then, since $\underset{\sim}{q}_{\parallel} = \rho S T \underset{\sim}{v}_{n\parallel} = 0$ at $z = \pm \frac{d}{2}$, we have

$$\underset{\sim}{q} = \frac{1}{2}\Lambda \underset{\sim}{\nabla} T (z^2 - \frac{d^2}{4}) , \tag{2.42}$$

and an average heat flow,

$$\bar{\underset{\sim}{q}} = -\Lambda \frac{d^2}{12}\underset{\sim}{\nabla} T . \tag{2.43}$$

We also have, then,

$$\bar{\underset{\sim}{v}}_n = -\rho_s d^2 \frac{\underset{\sim}{\nabla} T}{12\eta} , \tag{2.44}$$

and from (2.37)

$$\bar{\underset{\sim}{v}}_s = \frac{\rho_n}{\rho_s}\,\frac{\rho S d^2 \underset{\sim}{\nabla} T}{12\eta} \, . \qquad (2.45)$$

We thus have an effective conductivity in the slit,

$$K_{eff} = \frac{|\bar{\underset{\sim}{q}}|}{|\underset{\sim}{\nabla} T|} = \frac{\Lambda d^2}{12} \, , \qquad (2.46)$$

which has the approximate empirical value,

$$K_{eff} \approx 1.2 \times 10^5 \, T^{12.2} \, d^2 \, . \qquad (2.47)$$

By comparison, the ordinary heat conductivity of He I at 3.3° K is only

$$K_{He\,I} \cong 6 \times 10^5 \text{ cal/deg/cm/sec} \, ,$$

so that in slit only 10^{-3} cm wide, the effective conductivity of He II is about 10^7 times larger.

Careful heat-conductivity experiments using annular slits have been reported by Craig, Keller, and Hammel (1963). Their data for $d = 2.13 \times 10^{-4}$ cm is illustrated in Figure 2.19, where the heat flux is presented as a function of the temperature T of the hot end of the slit for various bath temperatures T_o. The theoretical curves are obtained by integrating (2.43) from T_o to T and suitably adjusted for the heat flux owing to the stainless steel from which the slits were fabricated. It may be seen that, except for the lowest temperatures, (2.43) holds true over temperature differences as large as 300 mdeg.

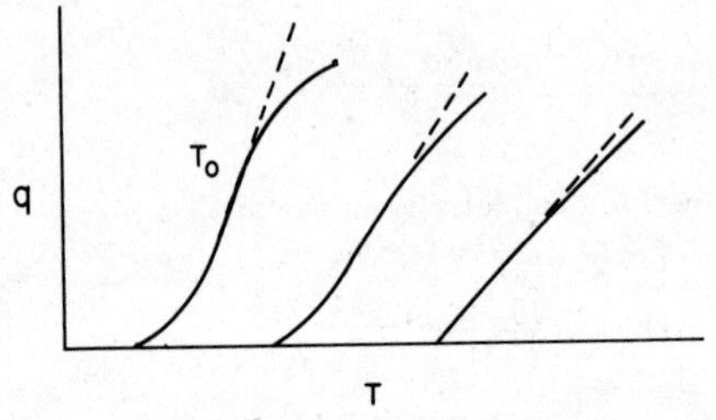

Fig. 2.19.

To account for the effective conductivity at higher temperature differences, Gorter and Mellink (1949) proposed an empirical set of equations,

$$\rho_s \frac{\partial \underset{\sim}{v}_s}{\partial t} = \frac{\rho_s}{\rho} \nabla p + \rho_s S \nabla T - \rho_n \rho_s A (\underset{\sim}{v}_s - \underset{\sim}{v}_n)^3 , \tag{2.48a}$$

and

$$\rho_n \frac{\partial \underset{\sim}{v}_n}{\partial t} = - \frac{\rho_n}{\rho} \nabla p - \rho_s S \nabla T + \rho_n \rho_s A (\underset{\sim}{v}_s - \underset{\sim}{v}_n)^3 + \eta \nabla^2 \underset{\sim}{v}_n , \tag{2.48b}$$

which introduced the $(\underset{\sim}{v}_s - \underset{\sim}{v}_n)^3$ term often referred to as "mutual friction." A is found empirically to be a rising function of temperature (Vinen 1957) and of order 50 cm sec/gm. Solving these equations in the slit geometry used above, we obtain

$$|\underset{\sim}{v}_n| = -(d^2 - 4z^2) \frac{|\nabla p|}{8\eta} , \tag{2.49a}$$

and

$$|\underset{\sim}{v}_s| = |\underset{\sim}{v}_n| - \left| \frac{\underset{\sim}{\nabla} p - \rho S \underset{\sim}{\nabla} T}{A \rho \rho_n} \right|^{1/3} . \tag{2.49b}$$

We see first of all that $\underset{\sim}{q}$, which is proportional to $\underset{\sim}{v}_n$, is proportional to ∇p even for large temperature differences. We also obtain, using the zero net mass flow condition,

$$|\underset{\sim}{\nabla} T| = \frac{|\underset{\sim}{\nabla} p|}{\rho_s} + \frac{A\rho_n}{S} \left| \frac{\rho d^2 \cdot \underset{\sim}{\nabla} p}{12\eta\rho_s} \right|^{1/3} \tag{2.50}$$

and

$$\underset{\sim}{\nabla} T = \frac{-12\eta}{d^2(\rho S)^2 T}\bar{\underset{\sim}{q}} - \frac{A\rho_n \bar{\underset{\sim}{q}}^3}{\rho_s^2 S^4 T^3} . \tag{2.51}$$

These equations have been verified by Craig, Keller, and Hammel (1963) over a wide range of temperature differences.

§7. The Propagation of Sound in Helium II

We now discuss the propagation of sound in He II in terms of a linearized set of equations that include, of course, compressibility. Suppose $\underset{\sim}{v}_n$ and $\underset{\sim}{v}_s$ are small quantities varying only with the oscillations. Let us write

$$\rho = \rho_o + \rho', \; p = p_o + p', \; S = S_o + S', \; T = T_o + T' \; . \; . \; . \tag{2.52}$$

where ρ_o, p_o, S_o, and T_o are equilibrium values of these quantities and the primed symbols represent changes owing to the wave motion. We then have from (2.14), (2.18), and (2.26)

$$\frac{\partial \rho'}{\partial t} + \mathrm{div}\,(\rho_{so}\underset{\sim}{v}_s + \rho_{no}\underset{\sim}{v}_n) = 0 , \tag{2.53}$$

$$S_o \frac{\partial \rho}{\partial t} + \rho_o \frac{\partial S'}{\partial t} + \rho_o S_o \operatorname{div} \underset{\sim}{v}_n = 0 , \qquad (2.54)$$

and

$$\frac{\partial \underset{\sim}{v}_s}{\partial t} + \frac{1}{\rho_o} \nabla p' - S_o \nabla T' = 0 \qquad (2.55)$$

to the first order. We neglect viscosity so that the linearized momentum flow density tensor is

$$\pi_{ik} = p\delta_{ik} , \qquad (2.56)$$

so that (2.15) becomes

$$\frac{\partial}{\partial t}(\rho_{s_o} \underset{\sim}{v}_s + \rho_{n_o} \underset{\sim}{v}_n) + \nabla p' = 0 . \qquad (2.57)$$

Differentiating (2.53) and (2.57), we have

$$\frac{\partial^2 \rho'}{\partial t^2} = \nabla^2 p' . \qquad (2.58)$$

Combining (2.53) and (2.57), we have

$$\rho_{n_o} \frac{\partial}{\partial t}(\underset{\sim}{v}_n - \underset{\sim}{v}_s) + \rho_o S_o \nabla T' = 0 . \qquad (2.59)$$

Taking the divergence of this and using

$$\nabla \cdot (\underset{\sim}{v}_n - \underset{\sim}{v}_s) = - \frac{\rho_o}{\rho_o S_o} \frac{\partial S'}{\partial t} \qquad (2.60)$$

(which comes from [2.53] and [2.54]), we obtain

$$\frac{\partial^2 S'}{\partial t^2} = \frac{\rho_{s_o} S_o^2}{\rho_{n_o}} \nabla^2 T' \tag{2.61}$$

We now let $\rho = \rho(p, T)$ and $S = S(p, T)$, so that

$$\rho' = \left(\frac{\partial\rho}{\partial p}\right)_T p' + \left(\frac{\partial\rho}{\partial T}\right)_p T' ,$$

$$S' = \left(\frac{\partial S}{\partial p}\right)_T p' + \left(\frac{\partial S}{\partial T}\right)_p T' . \tag{2.62}$$

We then have from (2.58) and (2.61)

$$\left(\frac{\partial\rho}{\partial p}\right)_T \frac{\partial^2 p'}{\partial t^2} - \nabla^2 p' + \left(\frac{\partial\rho}{\partial T}\right)_p \frac{\partial^2 T'}{\partial t^2} = 0 \tag{2.63}$$

and

$$\left(\frac{\partial S}{\partial p}\right)_T \frac{\partial^2 p'}{\partial t^2} - \frac{S_o^2 \rho_{s_o}}{\rho_{n_o}} \nabla^2 T' + \left(\frac{\partial S}{\partial T}\right)_p \frac{\partial^2 T'}{\partial t^2} = 0 . \tag{2.64}$$

Let us assume solutions of (2.63) and (2.64) in the form of plane waves, so that p' and T' vary as $\exp i\omega(t - \frac{x}{u})$, where u is the velocity of propagation. We then have

$$p'\left[\frac{1}{u^2} - \left(\frac{\partial\rho}{\partial p}\right)_T\right] - T'\left(\frac{\partial\rho}{\partial T}\right)_p = 0 , \tag{2.65}$$

and

$$-p'\left(\frac{\partial S}{\partial p}\right)_T + T'\left[\frac{S_o^2 \rho_{s_o}}{\rho_{n_o} u^2} - \left(\frac{\partial S}{\partial T}\right)_p\right] = 0 . \tag{2.66}$$

The condition for compatibility of (2.65) and (2.66) is that the determinant of the coefficients of T' and p' must vanish, so that

$$u^4 \frac{\partial(S,\rho)}{\partial(T,p)} - u^2 \left[\left(\frac{\partial S}{\partial T}\right)_p + S_o^{\ 2} \frac{\rho_{s_o}}{\rho_{n_o}} \left(\frac{\partial \rho}{\partial p}\right)_T \right] + \frac{\rho_{s_o}}{\rho_{n_o}} S_o^2 = 0, \quad (2.67)$$

where $\frac{\partial(S,\rho)}{\partial(T,p)}$ is the Jacobian of the transformation of S, ρ with respect to T and p.

From thermodynamics, we have

$$\frac{\partial(S,\rho)}{\partial(T,p)} = \frac{C_V}{T} \left(\frac{\partial \rho}{\partial p}\right)_T \qquad (2.68)$$

and

$$\left(\frac{\partial S}{\partial T}\right)_p \frac{T}{C_V} \left(\frac{\partial p}{\partial \rho}\right)_T = \left(\frac{\partial p}{\partial \rho}\right)_S, \qquad (2.69)$$

so that (2.67) reduces to

$$u^4 - u^2 \left[\left(\frac{\partial p}{\partial \rho}\right)_S + \frac{\rho_{s_o}}{\rho_{n_o}} \frac{TS^2}{C_V} \right] + \frac{\rho_s TS^2}{\rho_n C_V} \left(\frac{\partial p}{\partial \rho}\right)_T = 0 . \qquad (2.70)$$

Equation (2.70) determines two propagating velocities of sound in He II. At all temperatures, $C_p \approx C_V = C$, and by (2.68) $\left(\frac{\partial p}{\partial \rho}\right)_S \approx \left(\frac{\partial p}{\partial \rho}\right)_T = \frac{\partial p}{\partial \rho}$, so that (2.70) gives

$$u_1 = \left(\frac{\partial p}{\partial \rho}\right)^{\frac{1}{2}}, \quad u_2 = \left(\frac{TS^2 \rho_s}{C\rho_n}\right)^{\frac{1}{2}}. \qquad (2.71)$$

Thus u_1 is essentially constant and is the velocity of ordinary sound, whereas u_2 is a strong function of temperature becoming zero at the λ-point. The velocity u_2 is plotted against temperature in Figure 2.20a and u_1 against temperature in Figure 2.20b.

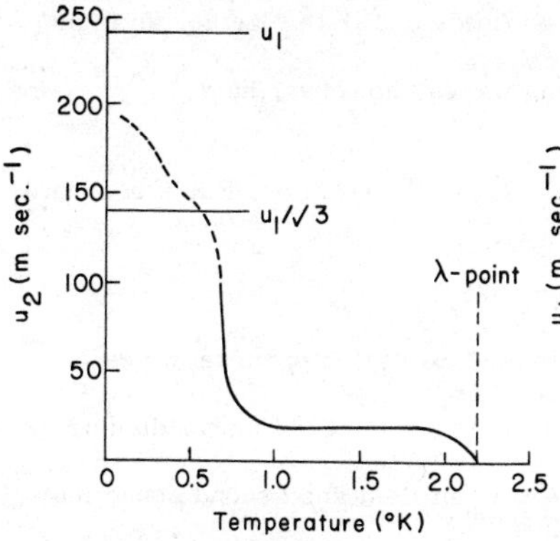

Fig. 2.20a.

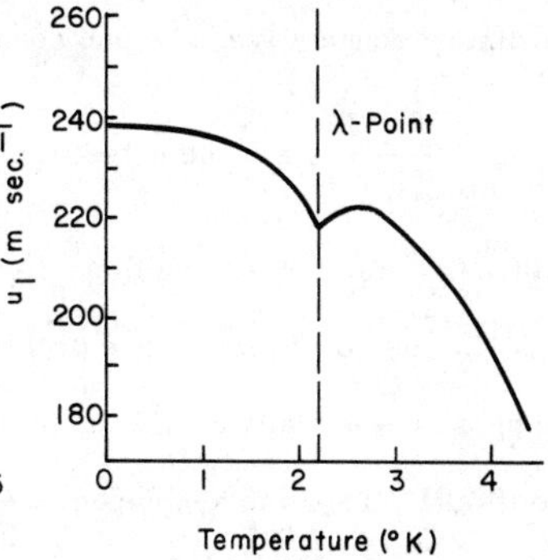

Fig. 2.20b.

The nature of the two forms of sound in He II may be appreciated by considering a plane sound wave. In such a wave, we can write

$$v_n = a v_s, \quad p' = b v_s, \quad T' = c v_s \quad . \tag{2.72}$$

Using equations (2.14), (2.52), (2.54), (2.55), and (2.56), Lifshitz and Andronikashvili (1949)have shown that to first order in the coefficient of thermal expansion

$$\alpha = -\rho^{-1}\left(\frac{\partial \rho}{\partial T}\right)_p$$

$$a_1 = 1 + \frac{\alpha \rho}{S \rho_s} \frac{u_1^2 u_2^2}{(u_1^2 - u_2^2)}, \quad b_1 = \rho u_1, \quad c_1 = \frac{\alpha T}{C} \frac{u_1^3}{(u_1^2 - u_2^2)}, \tag{2.73}$$

for first sound, and that

$$a_2 = -\frac{\rho_s}{\rho_n} + \frac{\alpha p}{S\rho_n}\frac{u_1^2 u_2^2}{(u_1^2 - u_2^2)}, \quad b_2 = \frac{\alpha\rho u_1^2 u_2^3}{S(u_1^2 - u_2^2)}, \quad c_2 = \frac{-u_2}{S}, \tag{2.74}$$

for second sound. Since α is a very small quantity, we see that for first sound $\underset{\sim}{v}_n \approx \underset{\sim}{v}_s$, so that the two fluids oscillate together as in an ordinary sound wave. Second sound waves, however, have $\underset{\sim}{v}_n \approx -\frac{\rho_s}{\rho_n}\underset{\sim}{v}_s$, and the mass flux $\underset{\sim}{j} \approx 0$. Here the two fluids oscillate "through" each other and there is no net flow.

Let us now consider the problem of excitation of these waves. Suppose a y-z plane oscillates in x-direction (that is, perpendicular to itself). Then the x-components of v_s in first and second sound may be written

$$v_{s1} = A_1 \exp\left[-i\omega(t - \frac{x}{u_1})\right] \tag{2.75}$$

and

$$v_{s2} = A_2 \exp\left[-i\omega(t - \frac{x}{u_2})\right]. \tag{2.76}$$

If the plane oscillates with velocity $v_o \cos \omega t$, then the boundary conditions $v_{nx} = v_{sx} = 0$ yield

$$A_1 + A_2 = v_o, \quad A_1 a_1 + A_2 a_2 = v_o, \tag{2.77}$$

so that

$$\frac{A_2}{A_1} = -\frac{1-a_1}{1-a_2} \approx \frac{\alpha \rho_n u_2^2}{\rho_s S} , \tag{2.78}$$

where we have neglected u_2^2 in comparison with u_1^2.

Since for small oscillations the average kinetic and potential energy densities are equal, the total energy density in the wave is (Landau and Lifshitz 1959, §64)

$$\overline{E} = \rho_s \overline{v_s^2} + \rho_n \overline{v_n^2} = \frac{1}{2} A^2 (\rho_s + \rho_n a^2) , \tag{2.79}$$

and the intensity is $\overline{E} u = I$. For the two sound waves then,

$$\frac{I_2}{I_1} = \frac{u_2 A_2^2 (\rho_s + \rho_n a_2^2)}{u_1 A_1^2 (\rho_s + \rho_n a_1^2)} \approx \frac{\alpha^2 u_2^3 T}{C u_1} . \tag{2.80}$$

Since α is small, I_2 is much less than I_1. At 2° K, for example, the ratio of the intensity of second to that of first sound $\frac{I_2}{I_1} \approx 2 \times 10^{-6}$.

The sound waves above were generated by means of an oscillating plane. Suppose we keep the plane steady and instead let the temperature of the plane oscillate according to $T = T_o \cos \omega t$. The condition $j_1 = 0 = \rho_s v_{sx} + \rho_n v_{nx}$ gives

$$\rho_s (A_1 + A_2) + \rho_n (a_1 A_1 + a_2 A_2) = 0 , \tag{2.81}$$

so that

$$\left|\frac{A_2}{A_1}\right| = \frac{\rho_n a_1 + \rho_s}{\rho_n a_z + \rho_s} \approx \frac{S}{\alpha u_2^2} \tag{2.82}$$

and

$$\frac{I_2}{I_1} \approx \frac{C}{T\alpha^2 u_1 u_2} \ . \tag{2.83}$$

This ratio is 5×10^3 at 2° K so that this is an efficient means of radiating second sound.

Experimentally, all one needs for observation of second sound is a resonant cavity with a heater on one wall and a thermometer on the other. Snyder (1963) used fired lava stone in the form of a hollow cube with aquadag coatings as thermometers and achieved a Q-factor of 4,000 at 2.5 kc and 2° K.

If sound is propagated through a narrow channel of width d such that $d << \left(\frac{2\eta}{\rho_n \omega}\right)^{\frac{1}{2}}$, then the normal fluid is effectively clamped by its viscosity and we have the phenomenon of "fourth sound."

The velocity of fourth sound can be obtained from linearized equations with $\underset{\sim}{v}_n = 0$. Thus (2.53), (2.54), and (2.55) become

$$\frac{\partial \rho'}{\partial t} + \rho_s \operatorname{div} \underset{\sim}{v}_s = 0 \ , \tag{2.84}$$

$$S_o \frac{\partial \rho'}{\partial t} + \rho_o \frac{\partial S'}{\partial t} = 0. \tag{2.85}$$

and

$$\frac{\partial \underset{\sim}{v}_s}{\partial t} + \frac{1}{\rho} \nabla p' - S_o \nabla T' = 0 . \qquad (2.86)$$

Eliminating $\underset{\sim}{v}_s$ between (2.84) and (2.86), we obtain

$$\frac{\partial^2 \rho'}{\partial t^2} = \frac{\rho_{so}}{\rho_o} \nabla^2 p' - S_o \rho_{so} \nabla^2 T' . \qquad (2.87)$$

Now take the Laplacian of (2.85), expand ρ' and S' in terms of p' and T', and neglect thermal expansivity (and hence also $\left[\frac{\partial S}{\partial p}\right]_T$), so that we have

$$\frac{\partial}{\partial t}\left[S_o \left(\frac{\partial p}{\partial \rho}\right)_T \nabla^2 p' + \rho_o \left(\frac{\partial S}{\partial T}\right)_p \nabla^2 T' \right] = 0 . \qquad (2.88)$$

The term in the brackets may then be taken to be zero. Eliminating $\nabla^2 T'$ between (2.87) and (2.88), we obtain

$$\frac{\partial^2 p'}{\partial t^2} = \frac{\rho_{so}}{\rho_o} \left(\frac{\partial p}{\partial \rho}\right)_T + \frac{\rho_{so} S_o^2}{\rho_o \, \partial S/\partial T_p} \nabla^2 p' , \qquad (2.89)$$

so that for fourth sound

$$u_4^2 = \frac{\rho_s}{\rho} u_1^2 + \frac{\rho_n}{\rho} u_2^2 , \qquad (2.90)$$

where u_1 and u_2 are given by (2.71).

Fourth sound was experimentally studied by Shapiro and Rudnick (1965) using solid dielectric transducers at both ends of a standing wave tube that was packed with a superleak material such as rouge (Fig. 2.21). The velocity of fourth sound was measured as a function of temperature and the results are shown in Figure 2.22 in excellent agreement with (2.90).

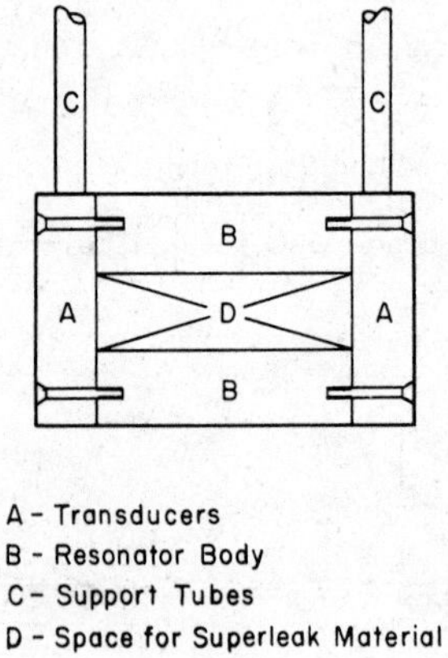

Fig. 2.21.

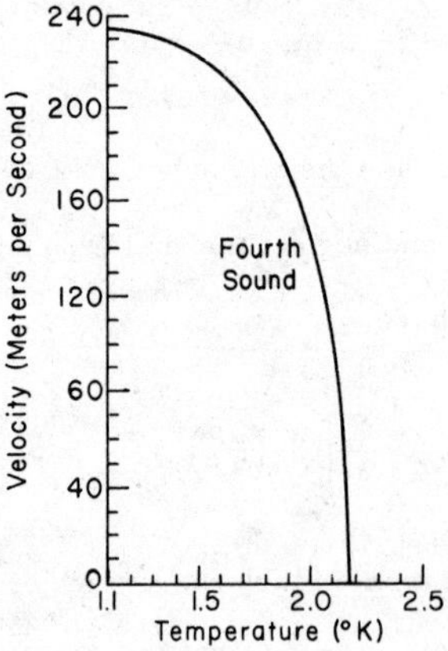

Fig. 2.22.

Another form of wave propagation in He II is capillary or surface tension waves on the free surface of the liquid. Let the free surface be the plane normal to the z-axis and let ζ be the deviation of the z-component of the coordinates of points on the surface from their equilibrium values. We have no net mass flux across the surface so that

$$j'_z = \rho_{no} v_{nz} + \rho_{so} v_{sz} + \rho_o \dot{\xi} \tag{2.91}$$

(see Landau and Lifshitz 1959, §12 and §61). Pressure fluctuations are caused by the surface tension and

$$p' = \nu\left(\frac{\partial^2 \xi}{\partial x^2} + \frac{\partial^2 \xi}{\partial y^2}\right) , \qquad (2.92)$$

where ν is the surface-tension coefficient. The heat flux across the surface must vanish so that

$$\rho ST(v_{nz} - \dot{\xi}) = 0 \quad \text{or}$$

$$(2.93)$$

$$v_{nz} = \dot{\xi} .$$

Combining with (2.91), we obtain

$$v_{sz} = \dot{\xi} . \qquad (2.94)$$

Let us guess a solution of (2.57) such that all quantities vary as $\exp[kz - i(\omega t - kx)]$. We then find, using (2.91) and (2.92),

$$\omega^2 = \nu k^3 / \rho . \qquad (2.95)$$

For the case of waves propagating along a He II film, for wavelengths longer than the thickness of the film d, the normal fluid will be effectively damped so that $v_n = 0$ and we have "third sound." In this case, (2.95) becomes

$$\omega^2 = \frac{\rho_s}{\rho} \frac{\nu k^3}{\rho} \tanh kd \qquad (2.96)$$

so that

$$u_3^2 = \frac{\omega^2}{k^2} = \frac{\rho_s}{\rho} \frac{\nu k}{\rho} \tanh kd . \qquad (2.97)$$

Third sound was observed experimentally by Everitt, Atkins, and Denenstein (1964). A narrow strip of film was periodically evaporated with pulses of infrared radiation and oscillations in the thickness of the film were observed. Typical velocities of third sound were of order 100 cm/sec.

§8. Breakdown of the Simple Two-fluid Model: Macroscopic Quantum Effects

Consider the equilibrium configuration of He II in a rotating cylindrical container. A fundamental assumption of the two-fluid model was that $\nabla \times \underset{\sim}{v}_s = 0$ (2.20). In the simply connected region considered here, this implies that $\underset{\sim}{v}_s = 0$. If (2.30) and (2.31) are then solved for the configuration of the surface, we find

$$Z = \frac{\rho_n}{\rho} \frac{\Omega^2 r^2}{2g} , \tag{2.98}$$

where Z is the height of the surface along the axis of symmetry (which is the axis of rotation), Ω is the angular velocity of the container, r is the perpendicular distance from the axis of rotation, and g is the gravitational constant. This reduces to the classical limit when $\rho_n \to \rho$ and $\rho_s \to 0$,

$$Z = \frac{\Omega^2 r^2}{2g} . \tag{2.99}$$

Equation (2.98) has a very strong temperature dependence and at

$1.5^\circ K$ there is an order of magnitude difference between it and the classical result. The first experimental observation was that of Osborne (1950), who showed that (2.99) was right rather than (2.98). It was then suggested that a critical velocity had been exceeded below which $\nabla \times \underset{\sim}{v}_s = 0$. Careful optical methods were used by Meservey (1964) for angular velocities as low as 0.29 rad/sec in a 1.26 cm radius container to show that the classical result was still correct. We thus have a situation where it appears that the superfluid component rotates as a solid body with curl $\underset{\sim}{v}_s = 2\Omega \hat{1}_z$.

We can account for this effect if we make some changes in the two-fluid theory. We amend (2.20) to read curl $\underset{\sim}{v}_s = 0$ except perhaps at isolated singular lines in the fluid. In the cylindrical container considered above, if such a singular line --a vortex filament --were placed on the axis of rotation, the only non-zero velocity field possible is of vortex form $\underset{\sim}{v}_s = \frac{A}{r} \hat{1}_\theta$, where A is some constant. Note that we are faced with the non-physical situation of the velocity increasing indefinitely as the origin is approached so that something must be said about the fluid in the immediate vicinity of $r = 0$. For the purposes of this discussion, we can assume that the superfluid rotates as a solid body in the "core" from $r = 0$ to $r = a$.

We now appeal to a rough quantum mechanical argument to determine the value of the constant A. In analogy with the Bohr-Sommerfeld criterion for an electron's motion about a nucleus, we require that the action of a helium atom about the vortex core be quantized in units of h, so that

$$\oint \underset{\sim}{P}_s \cdot d\underset{\sim}{\ell} = \ell h \quad \ell = 0, 1, 2, \ldots, \tag{2.100}$$

or

$$\oint \underset{\sim}{v}_s \cdot d\ell = \ell (h/m) . \tag{2.101}$$

This is equivalent to requiring an integral number of De Broglie wavelengths about the core. We then have

$$A = \frac{\ell}{2\pi}\left(\frac{h}{m}\right)$$

and

$$\underset{\sim}{v}_s = \frac{\ell \kappa}{2\pi r} \hat{1}_\theta , \tag{2.102}$$

where $\kappa = \frac{h}{m}$ is called the "strength" of a singly quantized vortex. The energy associated with this vortex motion per unit length of vortex line is obviously the kinetic energy per unit length,

$$\epsilon = \int_o^{2\pi} \int_o^R \tfrac{1}{2} \rho_s v_s^2 \, r dr d\theta$$

$$= \frac{\rho_s \kappa^2 \ell^2}{4\pi} \left(\ln \frac{R}{a} + \tfrac{1}{4} \right) , \tag{2.103}$$

where R is the radius of the container. The angular momentum per atom outside the core is

$$\underset{\sim}{L} = \underset{\sim}{r} \times \underset{\sim}{P}$$

$$= \ell h \hat{1}_\theta . \tag{2.104}$$

One might infer from (2.103) that for a given angular momentum, it is "cheaper" to produce several singly quantized vortices than one multiply quantized vortex, and we can assume $\ell = 1$ for each vortex.

If we assume a uniform distribution of vortices in the cylindrical container considered above, classical rotation would be imitated if the density of lines n_o were

$$n_o = \frac{2\Omega}{\kappa} \, , \tag{2.105}$$

or since $\kappa = 9.97 \times 10^{-4}\ cm^2/sec$, $n_o \cong 2{,}000$ vortex lines per cm^2 for one radian per second rotation (see Figure 2.23).

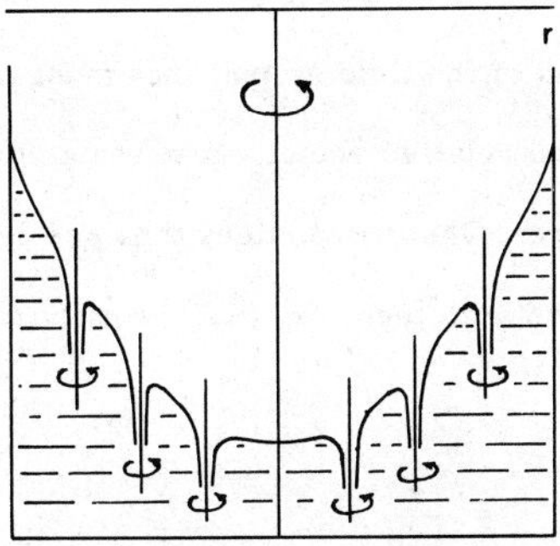

Fig. 2.23.

These quantized vortices are thought to obey essentially classical hydrodynamics except for the quantization of strength. Vortices must then terminate either on the boundaries of the fluid or on themselves in the form of vortex rings. The properties of vortex rings can be understood as follows: consider two oppositely oriented parallel vortex lines a distance 2R apart as in Figure 2.24.

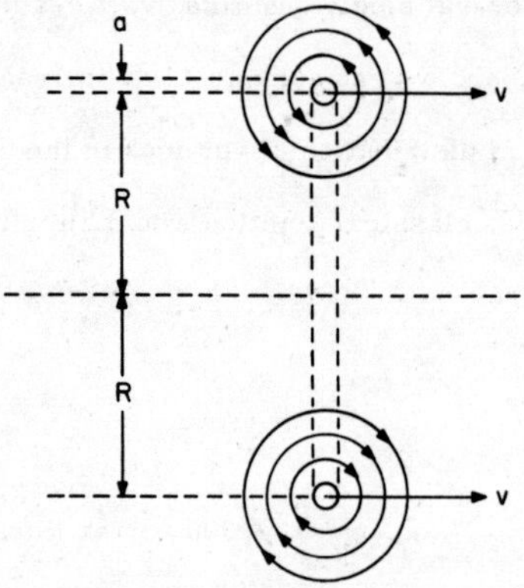

Fig. 2.24.

Vortices are excitations of the fluid so that they must travel with the fluid and there can be no relative velocity between a vortex core and fluid velocity at the core. The two vortices then see each other's velocity fields and travel with them, so that the pair travel with the velocity

$$v_{pair} = \frac{\kappa}{4\pi R} \qquad (2.106)$$

with respect to the fluid velocity far from the pair. In a vortex ring we must consider contributions to the velocity field at a point on the core from all the elements of the ring. For a ring of radius R, the velocity is

$$v_{ring} = \frac{\kappa}{4\pi R}\left(\ln\frac{8R}{a} - \frac{1}{4}\right) . \qquad (2.107)$$

From (2.103) we see that the energy of a vortex line is almost proportional to its length, so that for a ring the energy is

$$\mathcal{E} = \tfrac{1}{2}\rho_s \kappa^2 R \left(\ln\frac{8R}{a} - \frac{7}{4}\right). \qquad (2.108)$$

The velocity of a vortex ring is then approximately inversely proportional to its radius and hence approximately inversely proportional to its energy. A force exerted on the ring would then tend to make it grow in size increasing its energy and decreasing its velocity.

A demonstration of the grainy structure of Figure 2.23 in rotating helium was made by Tanner, Springett, and Donnelly (1965). The apparatus of Figure 2.25 was used.

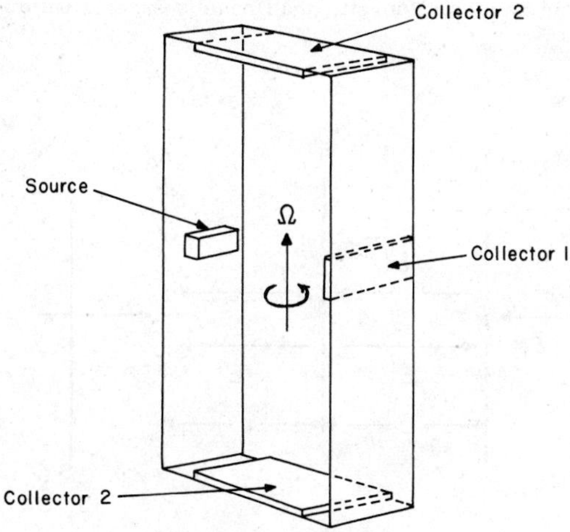

Fig. 2.25.

A radioactive source was used to produce many ion pairs in the liquid helium. Some of these pairs are separated by an electric field, and a current is set up along the electric field lines and measured at collector 1. It was found that when the apparatus was rotated about an axis perpendicular to the electric field, the ion current was attenuated with almost all of the lost current appearing at collector 2 perpendicular to the axis of rotation. The nature of the ions and of the attenuation mechanism is discussed in Chapter 6.

Quantized vortex rings were first observed by Rayfield and Reif (1964). The apparatus used was a time of flight velocity spectrometer (see Figure 2.26). The operation of the velocity spectrometer is based on the presumption that very little dissipation of the energy of the charge carriers occurs in the region $A_1 A_2$. This presumption is not true for the Tanner, Springett, and Donnelly experiment quoted above.

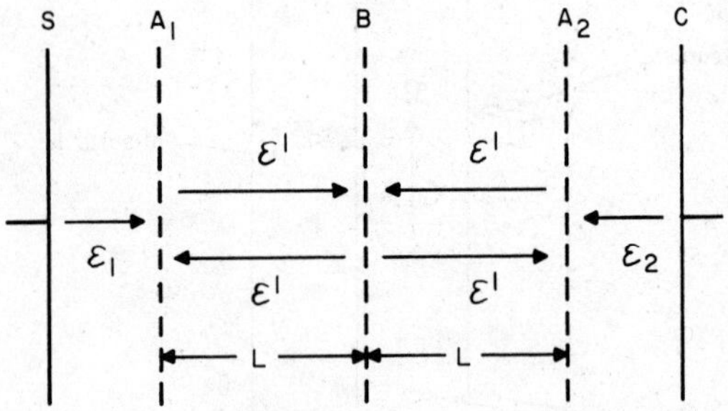

Fig. 2.26.

A potential V is applied between the radioactive source S and grid A_1. The charge carrier then arrives at A_1 with an energy $E = eV$ and some velocity v. It is prevented from reaching the collecting electrode C by a retarding potential ($\approx -V$) applied between A_2 and C. A small square wave potential of frequency ν is applied to grid B, and small electric fields $\mathcal{E}'$ alternately directed toward and away from B are produced in the region $A_1 A_2$ (free of d. c. fields). If v is such that the time of flight $\frac{L}{v}$ of the charge carrier through the distance L from A_1 to B is just equal to the time $(2\nu)^{-1}$ between field reversals, then the carrier remains in synchronism with this field and thus gains from it a small net amount of energy sufficient to overcome the retarding potential between A_2 and C to reach the collector C. At the frequency $\nu = \frac{1}{2}\left(\frac{v}{L}\right)$, therefore, the collected current will exhibit a resonance maximum. It was found that at low enough temperatures and at high enough E the carriers indeed exhibited negligible dissipation in $A_1 A_2$. Plotting E versus v obtained by the above method, we see that v does decrease with E and that the plot agrees extremely well with the theoretical values obtained by eliminating R between (2. 107) and (2. 108) and by letting $a \approx 1$ Å. A comparison of the theoretical and experimental values are shown in Figure 2. 27. We have thus demonstrated that the charge carriers behave exactly like vortex rings with strength $\kappa = \frac{h}{m}$.

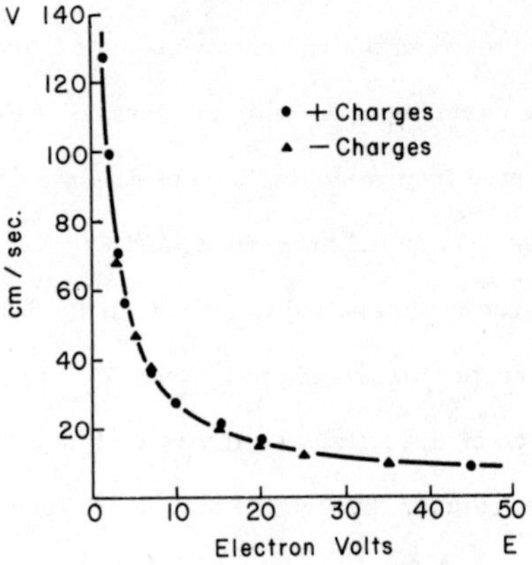

Fig. 2.27.

§9. Critical Velocities Owing to Vortex Generation

In §4 we noted that for low fluid velocity, the superfluid passes through a narrow channel without producing any pressure gradient across the channel and hence dissipating no energy. At a certain critical velocity, however, a pressure gradient does develop and somehow energy is dissipated. In this section, we present several possible reasons for the presence of a critical velocity.

Consider the flow of He II through a narrow two-dimensional channel of width d and length L. Feynman (1955) has shown that if Ψ is the ground state wave function for the superfluid, the wave function describing the flow of superfluid from left to right will be

$$\psi = \Psi \exp i\underset{\sim}{k} \cdot \underset{\sim}{r} = \Psi \exp i\varphi \,, \tag{2.109}$$

and the current density will be

$$\underset{\sim}{J} = \frac{\hbar}{m}\psi\psi^*\nabla\varphi = \left(\frac{\hbar}{m}\right)\rho_s\underset{\sim}{\nabla}\varphi = \rho_s\underset{\sim}{v}_s , \qquad (2.110)$$

where the phase φ acts as a velocity potential for the flow. Neglecting end effects, the current density in the slit and the phases φ_1 and φ_2 in the baths at each end of the slit are related by

$$J = \rho_s\underset{\sim}{v}_s = \rho_s\left(\frac{\hbar}{m}\right)\frac{\varphi_2 - \varphi_1}{L} . \qquad (2.111)$$

This is the situation for pure superflow where no thermodynamic potential difference occurs between the ends of the slit.

Beliaev (1958) has shown that the wave function contains a phase factor $\exp(-i\mu t/\hbar)$, where $\mu(=m\Phi)$ is the chemical potential. Thus the superfluid behaves like an external field with frequency $\omega = \mu/\hbar$. If baths 1 and 2 have a chemical potential difference between them, the coupling through the slit will induce a beat frequency,

$$\Delta\omega = \Delta\mu/\hbar , \qquad (2.112)$$

which may be interpreted (Richards and Anderson 1965) as a phase slip that produces a quantized vortex line every time the phase slips by 2π between the baths. Indeed integration of (2.110) in the presence of a quantized vortex line yields a difference of 2π in the phase at a given point depending on which side of the vortex line the path of integration lies. Thus vortices are produced at a rate

$$\nu = \Delta\omega/2\pi = \Delta\mu/2\pi\hbar \ . \tag{2.113}$$

The magnitude of ν may be appreciated by noting that a level difference z between baths corresponds to $\Delta\mu$ = mgz and ν = 980 kc for z = 1 cm.

The energy per unit length ϵ of each quantized vortex line is given by (2.103). The dissipation of energy per unit length of slit owing to vortex production is $\epsilon\nu$, which must be supplied by the energy gained by the superfluid flowing through the potential difference $\Delta\Phi$. Thus

$$\rho_s v_c d\Delta\varphi = \epsilon\nu = \epsilon m\Delta\varphi/2\pi\hbar \ , \tag{2.114}$$

and

$$v_c d = \frac{\kappa}{4\pi}\left(\ln\frac{d}{a} + \tfrac{1}{4}\right) , \tag{2.115}$$

where v_c is the critical velocity. This discussion that indicates fair order of magnitude agreement with experiment was suggested by Donnelly (1965).

Donnelly (1965) has also suggested a more direct and intuitive though less rigorous explanation for the critical velocity. In a subcritical flow, the De Broglie wavelength associated with the superflow is $\lambda = \frac{\kappa}{v}$, and low velocities correspond to long wavelengths in the channel. The De Broglie wavelength criterion that gives essentially the same results as the phase-slip argument states that quantum instability will be expected when the De Broglie wavelength of the moving superfluid is comparable with the scale of velocity disturbances in the flow. For a narrow channel, this scale is of order d, so that

$$\lambda_c = \frac{\kappa}{v_c} \approx d \,, \qquad (2.116)$$

which gives almost the same result as (2.115).

Let us examine the application of the wavelength criterion to a different experiment. Reif and Meyer (1960) have shown that positive ions have a limiting velocity of about 4×10^3 cm/sec at temperatures below 1°K. If we try to increase the velocity of the ions beyond this value, quantized vortex rings are formed, as discussed in §9. If we apply our wavelength criterion, we should expect such a phenomenon to be possible if

$$\lambda = \frac{\kappa}{v_c} \approx 2R \,, \qquad (2.117)$$

where R is the radius of the ion. Putting R ≈ 12Å (see Chapter 6 for a discussion of ions), we indeed find $v_c \approx 4 \times 10^3$ cm/sec.

Another approach to critical velocities has been suggested by Glaberson and Donnelly (1966). Consider a narrow tube containing vortex lines pinned to protuberances in the walls of the tube. For this discussion, we can neglect the effects of the wall on the vortex line. At zero velocity of the superfluid in the tube, the vortex has the shape of a straight line. As the fluid velocity is slightly increased, the vortex bows out into a circular section (if the vortex were free, it would move with the fluid--see §9--a pinned vortex will bow so that self-induced velocities cancel external flow velocities producing a stable configuration). As the velocity is further increased, the vortex bows out still further approaching the shape of a semicircle. At this point the vortex behaves very much like a free vortex ring, and the external fluid flow is inversely proportional to the radius of curvature of the vortex. The minimum radius of curvature and hence the maximum fluid flow for which a stable configuration is possible occurs when the vortex is in the shape of a semicircle. If the fluid-flow velocity is increased beyond this point, the vortex bows out still more, increasing its radius curvature and producing an unstable configuration and a free growth of vortex line. From (2. 107) then

$$\begin{aligned} v_c &= \frac{\kappa}{4\pi R_{min}} \left(\ln \frac{8R_{min}}{a} - \tfrac{1}{4} \right) \\ &= \frac{\kappa}{2\pi \ell} \left(\ln \frac{4\ell}{a} - \tfrac{1}{4} \right), \end{aligned} \tag{2. 118}$$

where ℓ is the distance between the pins holding the vortex. If there are many such pinned vortices, the state of marginal stability is produced by the longest ℓ or for $\ell = 2r$ where r is the radius of the tube. We then have

$$v_c \approx \frac{\kappa}{4\pi r} \left(\ln \frac{8r}{a} - \tfrac{1}{4} \right), \tag{2. 119}$$

which is the same as the velocity of a vortex ring of radius equal to the radius of the tube.

REFERENCES

Beliaev, S. T. 1958, Zh. Eksperim. i. Teor. Fiz., 34, 417.

Brewer, D. F., and Edwards, D. O. 1958, Proc. Phys. Soc. 71, 117-125.

Craig, P. O., Keller, W. E., and Hammel, E. F. 1963, Ann. of Phys. (N.Y.), 21, 72.

Daunt, J. G. 1939, Nature, 143, 719.

Daunt, J. G., and Mendelssohn, K. 1939, Proc. Roy. Soc. (London), A170, 423 and 439.

Donnelly, R. J. 1959, Phys. Rev. Letters, 3, 507.

——————— 1965, Phys. Rev. Letters, 14, 939.

Donnelly, R. J., and Penrose, O. 1956, Phys. Rev., 103, 1137.

Everitt, C. W. F., Atkins, K. R., and Denenstein, A. 1964, Phys. Rev., 136, A1494.

Feynman, R. P. 1955, Progress in Low Temperature Physics, edited by C. J. Gorter (Amsterdam: North-Holland Pub. Co.), Vol. I.

Glaberson, W. I., and Donnelly, R. J. 1966, Phys. Rev., 141, 208.

Gorter, C. J., and Mellink, J. H. 1949, Physica 15, 285.

Hammel, E. F. 1965, private communication.

Keller, W. E., and Hammel, E. F. 1961, Phys. Rev., 124, 1641.

Landau, L. D., and Lifshitz, E. M. 1959, Fluid Mechanics (New York: Pergamon Press).

Lifshitz, E. M., and Andronikashivili, E. L. 1949, A Supplement to Helium (New York: Consultants Bureau).

London, H. 1938, Nature, 142, 612.

——— 1939, Proc. Roy. Soc. (London), A171, 484.

Meservey, R. 1964, Phys. Rev., 133, A1471.

Osborne, D. V. 1950, Proc. Phys. Soc. (London), 63, 909.

Rayfield, G. W., and Reif, F. 1964, Phys. Rev., 136, A1194.

Reif, F., and Meyer, L. 1960, Phys. Rev., 119, A1164.

Reppy, J. D., and Depatie, P. A. 1964, Phys. Rev. Letters, 12, 187.

——— 1965, Phys. Rev. Letters, 14, 733.

Richards, P. L., and Anderson, P. W. 1965, Phys. Rev. Letters, 14, 540.

Shapiro, K. A., and Rudnick, I. 1965, Phys. Rev., 137, A1383.

Snyder, H. 1963, Phys. Fluids, 6, 755.

Tanner, D. J., Springett, B. E., and Donnelly, R. J. 1965, Low Temperature Physics, LT-9, edited by J. G. Daunt, D. O. Edwards, F. J. Milford, and M. Yaqub (New York: Plenum Press).

Tisza, L. 1938, Nature, 141, 913.

Vinen, W. F. 1957, Proc. Roy. Soc. (London), A240, 114.

CHAPTER 3

QUASI PARTICLE MODEL FOR HELIUM

§ 10. Excitation Spectrum of He II

In order to calculate the thermodynamic properties of He II from statistical mechanics, the energy spectrum must be known. For low temperatures (below 0.4° K), the specific heat is proportional to T^3, which is characteristic of phonon excitations as in solids. At higher temperatures, there is an additional contribution to the specific heat proportional to $e^{-\frac{\Delta}{kT}}$, Δ a constant, which is characteristic of a spectrum having an energy gap Δ. Landau (1941) proposed that there were two branches to the dispersion curve as sketched in Figure 3.1.

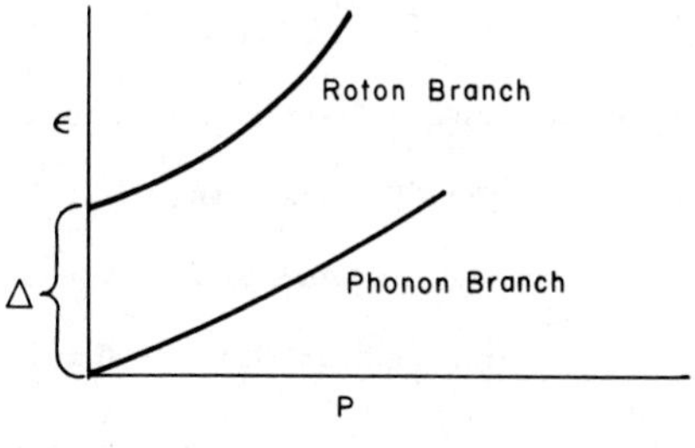

Fig. 3.1.

The excitations for the lower branch were taken to be compressional waves in the fluid or phonons, while the excitations for the upper branch were believed to be related to rotational motions of small clusters of He atoms and were termed rotons. Second sound velocities predicted from this spectrum failed to agree with the measured values of Peshkov (1946), and Landau (1947) modified the spectrum as shown in Figure 3.2.

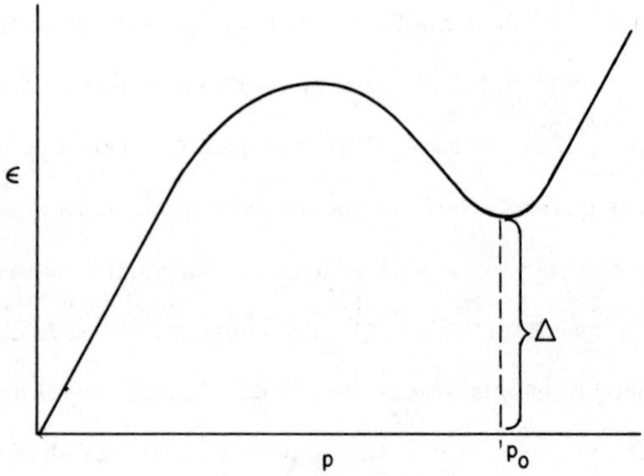

Fig. 3.2.

As seen, the roton minimum has been shifted to p_o, and the roton and phonon parts have been joined to form a single branch. The distinction between these two regions of the spectrum is still useful, however, as it will be shown that the thermodynamic functions depend principally on the regions of the spectrum near $p \approx 0$ and $p \approx p_o$ and that the contributions from these two parts are additive. Furthermore, although the structure of phonon excitations is well understood, being compressional waves, the motion associated with the short-wavelength rotons is still in question. It should be noted that the wavelength of the excitations of momentum p_o is about 2Å and is smaller than the average interparticle separation of 4.4Å.

The energy spectrum has now been obtained directly through inelastic neutron scattering, the data presented below owing to the researches of Yarnell, Arnold, Bendt, and Kerr (1959). If a neutron scatters inelastically from liquid helium at very low temperatures, the most probable result is the creation of a single excitation, whose momentum and energy can be inferred from the momentum and energy of the neutron before and after scattering (Cohen and Feynman 1957). If λ_i and λ_s are the incident and scattered neutron wavelengths, energy and momentum conservation require

$$\epsilon = h^2(\lambda_i^{-2} - \lambda_s^{-2})/2m$$

$$p^2 = h^2(\lambda_i^{-2} + \lambda_s^{-2} - 2\lambda_i^{-1}\lambda_s^{-1}\cos\varphi), \qquad (3.1.)$$

where ϵ and p are the energy and momentum of the excitation and φ the scattering angle. In the experiment, a thermal reactor was used to produce an intense neutron flux. This method, however, also gives a Maxwellian distribution in wavelengths. All neutrons with a wavelength shorter than a cutoff wavelength λ_c were removed by Bragg scattering from a polycrystaline filter. The incident wavelength distribution then possessed a sharp edge at λ_c, and if the scattering results in the creation of an excitation, the scattered beam has a sharp cutoff at a longer wavelength. Thus, by measuring λ_i, λ_s, and φ, the energy spectrum of the liquid can be found from (3.1). The results are shown in Figure 3.3.

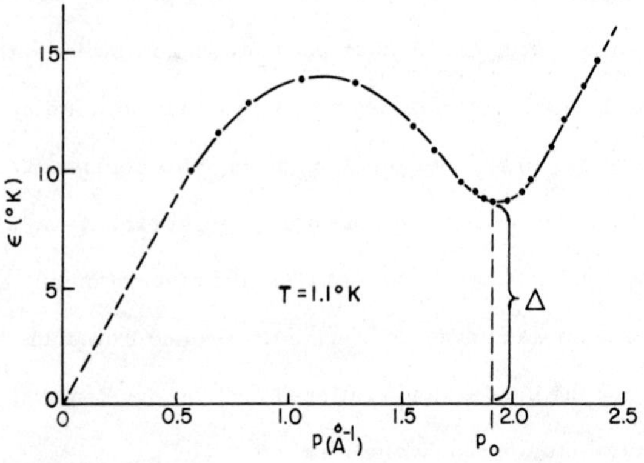

Fig. 3.3.

The dotted line drawn from the origin to the experimental point of lowest momentum has a slope of 239 ± 5 m/sec in excellent agreement with Van Itterbeek's (1957) first sound velocity at 1.1° K of 237 ± 0.6 m/sec. Near p_o, the spectrum can be represented by

$$\varepsilon(p) = \Delta + \frac{(p-p_o)^2}{2\mu_o}, \qquad (3.2)$$

with

$$\frac{p_o}{\hbar} = 1.92 \pm 0.01 \text{Å}^{-1},$$

$$\frac{\Delta}{k} = 8.65 \pm 0.04^\circ \text{K}, \text{ and}$$

$$\mu_o = (0.16 \pm 0.01) m_{He}.$$

It is found that Δ decreases with increasing temperature, according to the empirical relation

$$\frac{\Delta}{k} = 8.68 - 0.0084\ T^{7}\ {}^{\circ}K\ , \tag{3.3}$$

and is attributed to the fact that at higher temperatures the density of excitations is becoming large and interactions between excitations become important.

A theoretical approach for deriving the energy spectrum from the liquid structure factor obtained from X-ray or neutron scattering has been given by Feynman (1954) and Feynman and Cohen (1956). They obtained the energies of the excited states through variation of a trial wave function deduced from physical arguments concerning the microscopic motion of the particles. We present here a simplified treatment from Abrikosov, Gorkov, and Dzyaloshinski (1963), which parallels that of Pitaevskii (1956), and reproduces Feynman's results for small momenta. Near $0^{\circ}K$, the energy E of the liquid is a functional of the density and velocity fields $\rho(\underset{\sim}{r})$, $\underset{\sim}{v}(\underset{\sim}{r})$ only (at higher temperature a dependence on an additional thermodynamic variable is needed). This energy is just the sum of the kinetic and potential energies

$$E(\rho, \underset{\sim}{v}) = \tfrac{1}{2} \int \rho \underset{\sim}{v}^{2} d^{3}\underset{\sim}{r} + E^{(1)}(\rho). \tag{3.4}$$

At absolute zero, the density field will not be uniform owing to the zero-point motion; assuming this variation to be small, however, the density field will differ only slightly from its average value ρ_0 by an amount $\delta\rho(\underset{\sim}{r})$,

$$\rho(\underset{\sim}{r}) = \rho_0 + \delta\rho(\underset{\sim}{r}) . \tag{3.5}$$

By definition of the average density, we must have $\int \rho(\underset{\sim}{r}) d^3\underset{\sim}{r} = \int \rho_0 d^3\underset{\sim}{r}$, and thus

$$\int \delta\rho(\underset{\sim}{r}) d^3\underset{\sim}{r} = 0. \tag{3.6}$$

$\underset{\sim}{v}(\underset{\sim}{r})$ and $\delta\rho(\underset{\sim}{r})$ are taken to be of the same order of magnitude, and the energy is expanded to second order. The kinetic energy is then $\frac{1}{2}\rho_0 \int \underset{\sim}{v}^2 d^3\underset{\sim}{r}$, and the potential energy becomes

$$\begin{aligned} E^{(1)}(\rho) = E^{(1)}(\rho_0) &+ \int \psi(\underset{\sim}{r}) \delta\rho(\underset{\sim}{r}) d^3\underset{\sim}{r} \\ &+ \tfrac{1}{2} \int \varphi(\underset{\sim}{r}, \underset{\sim}{r}') \delta\rho(\underset{\sim}{r}) \delta\rho(\underset{\sim}{r}') d^3\underset{\sim}{r}\, d^3\underset{\sim}{r}' , \end{aligned} \tag{3.7}$$

where the expansion functions ψ and φ are determined from the equilibrium properties of the fluid. Since the fluid is homogeneous in equilibrium, $\psi(\underset{\sim}{r})$ is a constant, and since the fluid is isotropic in equilibrium, $\varphi(\underset{\sim}{r}, \underset{\sim}{r}')$ can be a function only of the distance $|\underset{\sim}{r} - \underset{\sim}{r}'|$ between elements. The second term on the right-hand side of (3.7) then becomes $\psi \int \delta\rho(\underset{\sim}{r}) d^3\underset{\sim}{r}$ and is zero by (3.6). Thus

$$\begin{aligned} E(\rho, \underset{\sim}{r}) = E^{(1)}(\rho_0) &+ \tfrac{1}{2}\rho_0 \int \underset{\sim}{v}^2(\underset{\sim}{r}) d^3\underset{\sim}{r} \\ &+ \tfrac{1}{2} \int \varphi(|\underset{\sim}{r} - \underset{\sim}{r}'|) \delta\rho(\underset{\sim}{r}) \delta\rho(\underset{\sim}{r}') d^3\underset{\sim}{r}\, d^3\underset{\sim}{r}' . \end{aligned} \tag{3.8}$$

$\delta\rho$, $\underset{\sim}{v}$, and φ are now expanded in Fourier series:

$$\delta\rho(\underset{\sim}{r}) = \frac{1}{V}\sum_{\underset{\sim}{k}} \rho_{\underset{\sim}{k}}\, e^{i\underset{\sim}{k}\cdot\underset{\sim}{r}}, \tag{3.9}$$

$$\underset{\sim}{v}(\underset{\sim}{r}) = \frac{1}{V}\sum_{\underset{\sim}{k}} \underset{\sim}{v}_{\underset{\sim}{k}}\, e^{i\underset{\sim}{k}\cdot\underset{\sim}{r}}, \tag{3.10}$$

$$\varphi\left(|\underset{\sim}{r}-\underset{\sim}{r}'|\right) = \frac{1}{V}\sum_{\underset{\sim}{k}} \varphi_{\underset{\sim}{k}}\, e^{i\underset{\sim}{k}\cdot(\underset{\sim}{r}-\underset{\sim}{r}')}, \tag{3.11}$$

where V is the volume of fluid and $\underset{\sim}{k}$ the excitation wave vector. Since $\delta\rho, \underset{\sim}{r}$ and φ are all real, $\rho_{\underset{\sim}{k}} = \rho^*_{-\underset{\sim}{k}}$, $\underset{\sim}{v}_{\underset{\sim}{k}} = \underset{\sim}{v}^*_{-\underset{\sim}{k}}$, and $\varphi_{\underset{\sim}{k}} = \varphi^*_{-\underset{\sim}{k}}$. Also, since φ depends only on the magnitude of $\underset{\sim}{r}-\underset{\sim}{r}'$, φ_k must be real. Substituting (3.9, 3.10, and 3.11) in (3.8) yields

$$E(\rho, \underset{\sim}{v}) = \frac{1}{2V}\sum_{\underset{\sim}{k}} \left(\rho_o|\underset{\sim}{v}_{\underset{\sim}{k}}|^2 + \varphi_{\underset{\sim}{k}}|\rho_{\underset{\sim}{k}}|^2\right). \tag{3.12}$$

$\underset{\sim}{v}_{\underset{\sim}{k}}$ can be expressed in terms of $\dot{\rho}_{\underset{\sim}{k}}$ through the continuity equation $\dot{\rho} + \nabla\cdot(\rho\underset{\sim}{v}) = 0$. To first order, this becomes

$$\frac{\partial}{\partial t}(\delta\rho) + \rho_o\nabla\cdot\underset{\sim}{v} = 0\,. \tag{3.13}$$

The second-order terms need not be retained since they introduce terms of order higher than second in (3.12). Equation (3.13) with (3.9) and (3.10) yields

$$\underset{\sim}{v}_{\underset{\sim}{k}} = i\frac{\dot{\rho}_{\underset{\sim}{k}}}{\rho_o}\frac{\underset{\sim}{k}}{k^2}. \tag{3.14}$$

Using this, (3.12) becomes

$$E(\rho, \underset{\sim}{v}) = E^{(1)}(\rho_o) + \frac{1}{2V} \sum_{\underset{\sim}{k}} \left(\frac{|\dot{\rho}_{\underset{\sim}{k}}|^2}{\rho_o k^2} + \varphi_{\underset{\sim}{k}} |\rho_{\underset{\sim}{k}}|^2 \right). \quad (3.15)$$

Thus the energy has been reduced to a sum over normal modes with frequencies $\omega_{\underset{\sim}{k}}$,

$$\omega_{\underset{\sim}{k}}^2 = \rho_o k^2 \varphi_{\underset{\sim}{k}} , \quad (3.16)$$

and these modes are quantized with energies

$$E_{\underset{\sim}{k}} = \hbar \omega_{\underset{\sim}{k}} (n_{\underset{\sim}{k}} + \tfrac{1}{2}), \; n_{\underset{\sim}{k}} = 0, 1, 2, \cdots . \quad (3.17)$$

The ground-state energy of the liquid is then

$$E_o = E^{(1)}(\rho_o) + \tfrac{1}{2} \sum_{\underset{\sim}{k}} \hbar \omega_{\underset{\sim}{k}} . \quad (3.18)$$

Assuming the fluid to be in its ground state, the mean of (3.15) is equated to this last expression, giving

$$\hbar \omega_{\underset{\sim}{k}} = \frac{\overline{|\dot{\rho}_{\underset{\sim}{k}}|^2}}{\rho_o k^2} + \varphi_{\underset{\sim}{k}} \overline{|\rho_{\underset{\sim}{k}}|^2} = 2\varphi_{\underset{\sim}{k}} \overline{|\rho_{\underset{\sim}{k}}|^2} . \quad (3.19)$$

The last step follows from the fact that the average kinetic and potential energies are equal. Eliminating $\varphi_{\underset{\sim}{k}}$ from (3.19) by (3.16) and solving for $\hbar \omega_{\underset{\sim}{k}}$ yields

$$\hbar \omega_{\underset{\sim}{k}} = \frac{\hbar^2 k^2 V \rho_o}{2 \overline{|\rho_{\underset{\sim}{k}}|^2}} , \quad (3.20)$$

which is just the energy of an excitation with wave vector $\underset{\sim}{k}$, and the energy spectrum for the excitation can be written

$$\epsilon(\underset{\sim}{k}) = \frac{\hbar^2 k^2}{2mS(\underset{\sim}{k})} , \tag{3.21}$$

where m is the mass of the helium atom and

$$S(\underset{\sim}{k}) = \frac{\overline{|\rho_{\underset{\sim}{k}}|^2}}{m\rho_o V} \tag{3.22}$$

is the structure factor. From (3.9), we have

$$\rho_{\underset{\sim}{k}} = \int \delta\rho(\underset{\sim}{r}) e^{-i\underset{\sim}{k}\cdot\underset{\sim}{r}} d^3\underset{\sim}{r} . \tag{3.23}$$

Thus

$$S(\underset{\sim}{k}) = \frac{1}{m\rho_o V} \overline{\int \delta\rho(\underset{\sim}{r})\delta\rho(\underset{\sim}{r}') e^{-i\underset{\sim}{k}\cdot(\underset{\sim}{r}'-\underset{\sim}{r})} d^3\underset{\sim}{r}\, d^3\underset{\sim}{r}'} ,$$

$$= \frac{1}{m\rho_o} \int \overline{\delta\rho(\underset{\sim}{r})\delta\rho(\underset{\sim}{r}+\underset{\sim}{R})} e^{-\underset{\sim}{k}\cdot\underset{\sim}{R}} d^3\underset{\sim}{R} , \tag{3.24}$$

$$= \frac{1}{Vn_o} \int \overline{\delta n(\underset{\sim}{r})\delta n(\underset{\sim}{r}+\underset{\sim}{R})} e^{-i\underset{\sim}{k}\cdot\underset{\sim}{R}} d^3\underset{\sim}{R} ,$$

where $\underset{\sim}{R} = \underset{\sim}{r}' - \underset{\sim}{r}$ and the particle number densities $n_o = \rho_o/m$ and $\delta n(\underset{\sim}{r}) = \delta\rho(\underset{\sim}{r})/m$ have been introduced. Thus $S(\underset{\sim}{k})$ is the Fourier transform of the function $S(\underset{\sim}{R})$, related to the pair correlation function $g(\underset{\sim}{R})$ by

$$S(\underset{\sim}{R}) = \frac{\overline{\delta n(\underset{\sim}{r})\delta n(\underset{\sim}{r}+\underset{\sim}{R})}}{n_o} = \delta(\underset{\sim}{R}) + g(\underset{\sim}{R})n_o\ , \qquad (3.25)$$

$\delta(\underset{\sim}{R})$ being the ordinary delta function.

Thus, from the measured structure factor from neutron or X-ray scattering, the energy spectrum can be found from (3.21). The derivation of (3.21) has been founded on a continuum model of liquid helium and is expected to be valid for long-wavelength excitations or phonons. For small k, then, it is expected that $\epsilon(k) = u_1 \hbar k$ and $S(k) = \frac{\hbar k}{2mu_1}$, where u_1 is the velocity of ordinary sound. For very large momenta, the Fourier transform of the pair correlation function g(R) in (3.25) tends to zero, since $g(\underset{\sim}{R})$ is a continuous function; therefore, $S(k) \approx 1$ and $\epsilon(k) \approx \frac{\hbar^2 k^2}{2m}$, which is the dispersion relation for a free particle. For the roton region of the spectrum, the above analysis fails due to the breakdown of the continuum model for short-wavelength excitations; (3.21), however, can be used as an interpolation formula between the limits of short and long wavelengths. This, of course, leaves uncertain the resulting roton spectrum. Feynman and Cohen's (1956) analysis corrects the short-wavelength region, and fairly good agreement with the spectrum of Figure 3.3 has been found (Miller, Pines, and Nozieres 1962). Figure 3.4a shows the structure factor i(s) + 1 from neutron diffraction as a function of $s = \frac{4\pi}{\lambda} \sin \varphi/2$, where λ is the neutron wavelength and φ is the scattering angle (Henshaw and Woods 1960). Figure 3.4b then gives the resulting dispersion curve compared with that of Figure 3.3.

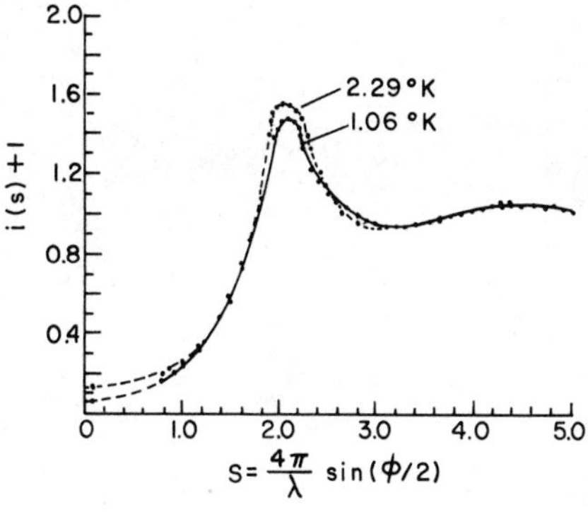

Fig. 3.4a.

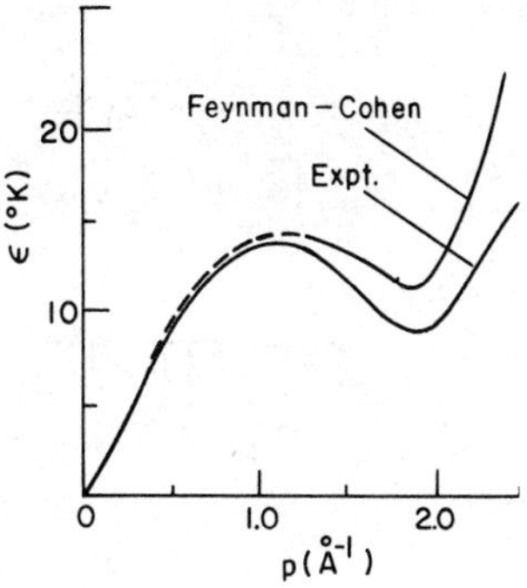

Fig. 3.4b.

Indeed the agreement is excellent for the phonon region and is qualitatively correct near p_o.

§ 11. Thermodynamic Properties of He II

Because of the low temperatures, the thermodynamic properties of He will depend only on the regions of the energy spectrum near $p \approx 0$ and $p \approx p_o$ (although the roton region has a large energy gap, the density of states being proportional to $\frac{dp}{d\epsilon}$ becomes large near p_o and the roton region contributes strongly above 0.8° K).

If there are $N_{\underset{\sim}{p}}$ excitations with momentum $\underset{\sim}{p}$ and energy $\epsilon(\underset{\sim}{p})$, the total energy of the fluid is

$$E\{N_{\underset{\sim}{p}}\} = E_o + \sum_{\underset{\sim}{p}} N_{\underset{\sim}{p}} \epsilon(\underset{\sim}{p}) , \qquad (3.26)$$

where E_o is the ground-state energy and $\{N_{\underset{\sim}{p}}\}$ denotes the entire set of occupation numbers. The partition function for the fluid is then (with $\beta = \frac{1}{kT}$)

$$
\begin{aligned}
Z &= Z_o \sum_{\{N_{\underset{\sim}{p}}\}} e^{-\beta E\{N_{\underset{\sim}{p}}\}}, \\
&= Z_o \sum_{\{N_{\underset{\sim}{p}}\}} \prod_{\underset{\sim}{p}} e^{-\beta N_{\underset{\sim}{p}} \epsilon(\underset{\sim}{p})}, \\
&= Z_o \prod_{\underset{\sim}{p}} \sum_{N_{\underset{\sim}{p}}} e^{-\beta N_{\underset{\sim}{p}} \epsilon(\underset{\sim}{p})}, \\
&= Z_o \prod_{\underset{\sim}{p}} \left[1 - e^{-\frac{\epsilon(p)}{kT}}\right]^{-1} \quad \text{(for Bose particles)},
\end{aligned}
\tag{3.27}
$$

and the Helmholtz free energy F is

$$
F = -kT \log Z + F_o , \tag{3.28}
$$

where $F_o = -kT \log Z_o$, and is the contribution due to the ground state. The ground-state contribution to the thermodynamic variables will always be additive and will not be carried through the equations. From (3.27) and (3.28) then

$$F = -kT \sum_{\underset{\sim}{p}} \log \left[1 - e^{-\frac{\epsilon(p)}{kT}} \right]^{-1} ,$$

$$= -\frac{kTV}{h^3} \int \log \left[1 - e^{-\frac{\epsilon(p)}{kT}} \right]^{-1} d^3 \underset{\sim}{p} . \qquad (3.29)$$

The last step comes from an assumed continuum distribution of states and lets $\sum_{\underset{\sim}{p}} \Rightarrow \frac{V}{h^3} \int d^3 \underset{\sim}{p}$.

It is convenient to express the thermodynamic functions in terms of the number density of phonons and rotons, so that we first derive the average number of excitations with momentum $\underset{\sim}{p}'$ per unit volume, $n(\underset{\sim}{p}')$,

$$n(\underset{\sim}{p}') = \frac{1}{VZ} \sum_{\{N_{\underset{\sim}{p}}\}} N_{\underset{\sim}{p}'} \, e^{-\beta E\{N_{\underset{\sim}{p}}\}} ,$$

$$= \frac{1}{VZ} \sum_{\{N_{\underset{\sim}{p}}\}} N_{\underset{\sim}{p}'} \prod_{\underset{\sim}{p}} e^{-\beta N_{\underset{\sim}{p}} \epsilon(\underset{\sim}{p})} ,$$

$$= -\frac{1}{\beta VZ} \frac{\partial}{\partial \epsilon(\underset{\sim}{p}')} \sum_{\{N_{\underset{\sim}{p}}\}} \prod_{\underset{\sim}{p}} e^{-\beta N_{\underset{\sim}{p}} \epsilon(\underset{\sim}{p})} , \qquad (3.30)$$

$$= -\frac{1}{\beta VZ} \frac{\partial Z}{\partial \epsilon(\underset{\sim}{p}')} ,$$

$$= \frac{1}{V} \frac{\partial F}{\partial \epsilon(\underset{\sim}{p}')} .$$

From (3.29) this is

$$n(\underset{\sim}{p}) = \frac{1}{h^3}\left[e^{\frac{\epsilon(p)}{kT}} - 1\right]^{-1}. \quad (3.31)$$

The total number, N, of excitations per unit volume is then

$$N = \frac{1}{h^3}\int\left[e^{\frac{\epsilon(p)}{kT}} - 1\right]^{-1} d^3\underset{\sim}{p}. \quad (3.32)$$

This integral extends over all values of momenta but, as we mentioned previously, only two small regions of the spectrum contribute. Thus, splitting the integral into two parts, we have

$$N = N_{ph} + N_r , \quad (3.33)$$

where

$$N_{ph} = \frac{4\pi}{h^3}\int\left(e^{\frac{u_1 p}{kT}} - 1\right)^{-1} p^2\,dp$$

(Phonon region) (3.34)

$$N_r = \frac{4\pi}{h^3}\int\left[e^{\frac{\Delta}{kT} + \frac{(p-p_o)^2}{2mkT}} - 1\right]^{-1} p^2\,dp$$

(Roton region) (3.35)

In both integrals, the integrand depends only on the magnitude of $\underset{\sim}{p}$, and we have taken $d^3\underset{\sim}{p} = 4\pi p^2\,dp$. Because of the extremely low temperature, the integrand in (3.34) becomes quite small except near $p \approx 0$, so that the upper limit may be extended to ∞ with little error,

$$N_{ph} = \frac{4\pi}{h^3} \int_0^\infty \left(e^{\frac{u_1 p}{kT}} - 1 \right)^{-1} p^2 dp \,. \tag{3.36}$$

Letting $x = \frac{u_1 p}{kT}$, we get

$$N_{ph} = 4\pi \left(\frac{kT}{hu_1}\right)^3 \int_0^\infty \frac{x^2 dx}{e^x - 1} \,. \tag{3.37}$$

But $\int_0^\infty \frac{x^2 dx}{e^x - 1} = 2\zeta(3)$, where $\zeta(3) = 1.202$ (Landau and Lifshitz 1958). Thus

$$N_{ph} = \frac{1}{\pi^2} \left(\frac{kT}{\hbar u_1}\right)^3 \zeta(3) \,. \tag{3.38}$$

For the same reasons as given above, the phonon contribution to the free energy from (3.29) becomes

$$F_{ph} = \frac{4\pi kTV}{h^3} \int_0^\infty \log\left(1 - e^{-\frac{u_1 p}{kT}}\right) p^2 dp \,. \tag{3.39}$$

Letting $x = \frac{u_1 p}{kT}$ and integrating by parts, we get

$$\begin{aligned} F_{ph} &= 4\pi kTV \left(\frac{kT}{hu_1}\right)^3 \int_0^\infty \log(1 - e^{-x}) x^2 dx \,, \\ &= -\frac{4\pi V (kT)^4}{3(hu_1)^3} \int_0^\infty \frac{x^3 dx}{e^x - 1} \,. \end{aligned} \tag{3.40}$$

But $\int_0^\infty \frac{x^3 dx}{e^x - 1} = \frac{(2\pi)^4}{240}$ (Landau and Lifshitz 1958). Then,

$$F_{ph} = \frac{\pi^2 V(kT)^4}{90(\hbar u_1)^3} = -\frac{\pi^4}{90\zeta(3)} kTVN_{ph} . \qquad (3.41)$$

Some of the other thermodynamic functions are now readily found,

$$S_{ph} = -\left(\frac{\partial F_{ph}}{\partial T}\right)_V = \frac{\pi^2 Vk^4 T^3}{15(\hbar u_1)^3} = \frac{\pi^4}{15\zeta(3)} kVN_{ph} , \qquad (3.42)$$

$$E_{ph} = F_{ph} + TS_{ph} = \frac{\pi^2 V(kT)^4}{30(\hbar u_1)^3} = \frac{\pi^4}{30\zeta(3)} kTVN_{ph} , \qquad (3.43)$$

and

$$C_{V_{ph}} = \left(\frac{\partial E_{ph}}{\partial T}\right)_V = \frac{2\pi^2 Vk^4 T^3}{15(\hbar u_1)^3} = \frac{2\pi^4}{15\zeta(3)} kVN_{ph} , \qquad (3.44)$$

For the roton contribution, we first compute N_r from (3.35). Since Δ is large compared to kT, the integrand may be expanded, retaining only the first term,

$$N_r = \frac{4\pi}{h^3} e^{-\frac{\Delta}{kT}} \int\limits_{\text{(Roton region)}} e^{-\frac{(p-p_0)^2}{2\pi kT}} p^2 dp \qquad (3.45)$$

Since the major contribution comes from $p \approx p_0$, the limits of integration are taken as $\pm\infty$ and the p^2 factor is replaced with $p_0{}^2$,

$$N_r = \frac{4\pi p_0^2}{h^3} e^{-\frac{\Delta}{kT}} \int_{-\infty}^{\infty} e^{-\frac{(p-p_0{}^2)}{2\mu kT}} dp . \qquad (3.46)$$

Letting $x^2 = \frac{(p-p_0)^2}{2\mu kT}$, we get

$$N_r = \frac{4\pi p_0^2}{h^3} (2\mu kT)^{\frac{1}{2}} e^{-\frac{\Delta}{kT}} \int_{-\infty}^{\infty} e^{-x^2} dx . \qquad (3.47)$$

The integral equals $\sqrt{\pi}$, so that

$$N_r = \frac{2(\mu kT)^{\frac{1}{2}} p_0^2}{(2\pi)^{3/2} \hbar^3} e^{-\frac{\Delta}{kT}} . \qquad (3.48)$$

The roton free energy is found from (3. 29). Again, because of the large excitation energy, the logarithm is expanded to first order,

$$\log\left(1-e^{-\frac{\epsilon}{kT}}\right) \approx -e^{-\frac{\epsilon}{kT}} . \qquad (3.49)$$

Thus

$$F_r = -\frac{4\pi kTV}{h^3} e^{-\frac{\Delta}{kT}} \int_{-\infty}^{\infty} e^{-\frac{(p-p_0)^2}{2\mu kT}} p^2 dp . \qquad (3.50)$$

Comparing this to (3. 45), we have

$$F_r = -kTVN_r , \qquad (3.51)$$

and we find

$$S_r = -\left(\frac{\partial F_r}{\partial T}\right)_V = kVN_r \left(\frac{3}{2} + \frac{\Delta}{kT}\right) , \qquad (3.52)$$

$$E_r = F_r + TS_r = kTVN_r (\tfrac{1}{2} + \frac{\Delta}{kT}) \qquad (3.53)$$

and

$$C_{V_r} = \left(\frac{\partial E_r}{\partial T}\right)_V = kVN_r\left[\frac{3}{4} + \frac{\Delta}{kT} + \left(\frac{\Delta}{kT}\right)^2\right]. \tag{3.54}$$

Bendt, Cowan, and Yarnell (1959) have used the expressions obtained above and the corresponding expressions retaining higher order terms to compare the inelastic neutron scattering data (Figure 3.3) with the calometrically determined values and have found excellent agreement.

§ 12. Calculation of ρ_n and ρ_s

The number density N given by (3.32) is not to be confused with the density of normal fluid. From the two-fluid model, the momentum density is defined (for small velocities) as

$$\underset{\sim}{j} = \rho_n \underset{\sim}{v}_n + \rho_s \underset{\sim}{v}_s . \tag{3.55}$$

In this expression, $\underset{\sim}{v}_n$ is to be taken as the average drift velocity of the excitations and $\underset{\sim}{v}_s$ as the velocity of the background medium. It should be noted that the excitation spectrum $\varepsilon(p)$ as given in Figure 3.3 holds only in a frame of reference moving with the background medium. Thus $\underset{\sim}{v}_s$ is defined as the velocity of that frame of reference in which this excitation spectrum is valid. Also, from the two-fluid model, we have $\rho = \rho_n + \rho_s$. From this and (3.55) we see that ρ_n (and thus ρ_s) can be found by determining the momentum density.

Consider two coordinate systems K_o and K, K_o moving with velocity $\underset{\sim}{v}$ with respect to K. The energy and momentum as viewed in the two frames are related by

$$p_o = \underset{\sim}{p} - M\underset{\sim}{v} \tag{3.56}$$

and

$$E_o = E - \underset{\sim}{v} \cdot \underset{\sim}{p} + \tfrac{1}{2} M\underset{\sim}{v}^2 . \tag{3.57}$$

Here E_o and $\underset{\sim}{p}_o$ are the energy and momentum as seen in K_o; E and $\underset{\sim}{p}$ are the energy and momentum seen in K, and M is the total mass of the system. Consider the background medium (superfluid) at rest in K and the excitation gas moving with an average drift velocity $\underset{\sim}{v}$. As we have noted, the energy spectrum $\epsilon(p)$ for the excitations is given in the frame moving with the superfluid K; however, the energy ϵ_o, which appears in the distribution function (3.31),

$$n(\epsilon_o) = \frac{1}{h^3} \left(e^{\frac{\epsilon_o}{kT}} - 1 \right)^{-1} , \tag{3.58}$$

is the energy of excitations as seen in the frame moving with the excitations, K_o. To express ϵ_o in terms of $\epsilon(p)$, consider the creation of an excitation of momentum $\underset{\sim}{p}$ and energy $\epsilon(p)$ as viewed in K. From (3.56) and (3.57) the change in momentum and energy as seen in K_o are

$$\underset{\sim}{p}_o = \underset{\sim}{p} \tag{3.59}$$

and

$$\varepsilon_o = \varepsilon(p) - \underset{\sim}{v} \cdot \underset{\sim}{p} \,. \tag{3.60}$$

Thus the distribution function (3.58) becomes

$$n(\varepsilon - \underset{\sim}{v} \cdot \underset{\sim}{p}) = \frac{1}{h^3}\left(e^{\varepsilon - \underset{\sim}{v} \cdot \underset{\sim}{p}} - 1\right)^{-1} . \tag{3.61}$$

The average momentum of the excitations $\underset{\sim}{j}$ per unit volume as seen in K is then

$$\underset{\sim}{j} = \int \underset{\sim}{p}\, n(\varepsilon - \underset{\sim}{v} \cdot \underset{\sim}{p}) d^3 \underset{\sim}{p} \,. \tag{3.62}$$

Assuming $\underset{\sim}{v}$ to be small, we expand $n(\varepsilon - \underset{\sim}{v} \cdot \underset{\sim}{p}) \approx n(\varepsilon) - \underset{\sim}{v} \cdot \underset{\sim}{p} \frac{dn(\varepsilon)}{d\varepsilon}$, and thus

$$\underset{\sim}{j} = \int \underset{\sim}{p}\, n(\varepsilon) d^3 \underset{\sim}{p} - \int (\underset{\sim}{v} \cdot \underset{\sim}{p}) \underset{\sim}{p} \frac{dn(\varepsilon)}{d\varepsilon} d^3 \underset{\sim}{p} \,. \tag{3.63}$$

The first term is zero, since $n(\varepsilon)$ is isotropic in momentum space, and the second term can be written in dyadic notation as

$$\underset{\sim}{j} = -\underset{\sim}{v} \cdot \int \underset{\sim}{p}\underset{\sim}{p} \frac{dn(\varepsilon)}{d\varepsilon} d^3 \underset{\sim}{p} \,. \tag{3.64}$$

Since $n(\varepsilon)$ is isotropic, so is $\frac{dn(\varepsilon)}{d\varepsilon}$; the off-diagonal elements of $\int \underset{\sim}{p}\underset{\sim}{p} \frac{dn(\varepsilon)}{d\varepsilon} d^3 \underset{\sim}{p}$ will vanish, and the diagonal elements will be equal to each other and to $\frac{1}{3}$ the average of p^2. Thus

$$\underset{\sim}{j} = -\frac{1}{3} \underset{\sim}{v} \int p^2 \frac{dn(\varepsilon)}{d\varepsilon} d^3 \underset{\sim}{p} \,. \tag{3.65}$$

Now we have assumed that the superfluid is at rest in K, thus the momentum density in K from (3.55) becomes

$$\underset{\sim}{j} = \rho_n \underset{\sim}{v} . \tag{3.66}$$

Comparing this to (3.65), we find

$$\rho_n = \frac{4\pi}{3} \int \frac{dn}{d\epsilon} p^4 dp . \tag{3.67}$$

The phonon contribution is

$$\rho_{nph} = -\frac{4\pi}{3u_1} \int_0^\infty \frac{dn}{dp} p^4 dp , \tag{3.68}$$

where in $n(\epsilon)$ the energy is taken as the phonon energy only $\epsilon = u_1 p$ and $\frac{dn}{dp} = u_1 \frac{dn}{d\epsilon}$. Integrating by parts then

$$\rho_{nph} = \frac{16\pi}{3u_1} \int_0^\infty np^3 dp ,$$

$$= \frac{16\pi}{3u_1 h^3} \int_0^\infty \frac{p^3 dp}{e^{\frac{u_1 p}{kT}} - 1} . \tag{3.69}$$

Letting $x = \frac{u_1 p}{kT}$, we get

$$\rho_{nph} = \frac{16\pi}{3u_1 h^3} \left(\frac{kT}{u_1}\right)^4 \int_0^\infty \frac{x^3 ds}{e^x - 1} . \tag{3.70}$$

But $\int_0^\infty \frac{x^3 dx}{e^x - 1} = \frac{(2\pi)^4}{240}$ (Landau and Lifshitz 1958). Thus

$$\rho_{nph} = \frac{2\pi^2 (kT)^4}{45\hbar^3 u_1^5} = \frac{2\pi^4 (kT)}{45 u_1^2 \zeta(3)} N_{ph} . \qquad (3.71)$$

For the roton part, take $n = \frac{1}{h^3} e^{-\left[\Delta + \frac{(p-p_o)^2}{kT}\right]}$ in (3.67), then

$$\rho_{nr} = \frac{4\pi}{3kTh^3} e^{-\frac{\Delta}{kT}} \int_{-\infty}^{\infty} e^{-\frac{(p-p_o)^2}{2\mu kT}} p^4 dp$$

$$\approx \frac{4\pi p_o^{\ 4}}{3kTh^3} e^{-\frac{\Delta}{kT}} \int_{-\infty}^{\infty} e^{-\frac{(p-p_o)^2}{2MkT}} dp . \qquad (3.72)$$

Comparing this to (3.46) for the number of rotons, we find

$$\rho_{nr} = \frac{2\mu^{1/2} p_o^{\ 4}}{3(2\pi)^{3/2} (kT)^{1/2} \hbar^3} e^{-\frac{\Delta}{kT}} = \frac{p_o^{\ 3}}{3kT} N_r . \qquad (3.73)$$

The total normal fluid density is the sum of the phonon and roton contributions,

$$\rho_n = \frac{2\pi^2 (kT)^4}{45\hbar^3 u_1^{\ 5}} + \frac{2\mu^{1/2} p_o^{\ 4}}{3(2\pi)^{3/2} (kT)^{1/2} \hbar^3} e^{-\frac{\Delta}{kT}} , \qquad (3.74)$$

and the superfluid density is defined by $\rho_s = \rho - \rho_n$.

In the two-fluid model, emphasis is placed on two fluids with individual density and velocity fields. By analogy with ordinary fluids, the total mass and momentum densities are thus defined by $\rho = \rho_n + \rho_s$ and $\underset{\sim}{j} = \rho_n \underset{\sim}{v}_n + \rho_s \underset{\sim}{v}_s$. From the Landau model, however, it is seen that this division does not reflect the fundamental physical processes.

In the Landau model, the momentum density is more appropriately taken as $\underset{\sim}{j} = \rho \underset{\sim}{v}_s + \rho_n(\underset{\sim}{v}_n - \underset{\sim}{v}_s)$ in which the superfluid density is suppressed. The second term is the momentum density of the excitations seen in a system moving with the background medium, while the first term is the momentum density due to the motion of the fluid as a whole with velocity $\underset{\sim}{v}_s$. As will be shown in the next chapter, the term $\rho \underset{\sim}{v}_s$ results solely from the Galilean transformation connecting the momentum density $\underset{\sim}{j}$, as seen in the laboratory, to the momentum density $\rho_n(\underset{\sim}{v}_n - \underset{\sim}{v}_s)$, as seen by an observer moving with the background medium. It is not too difficult to see the origin or this background medium or superfluid. In a solid, the background medium is the lattice upon which excitations exist. All regions of the lattice, however, are fixed relative to each other and thus $\underset{\sim}{v}_s = 0$ throughout. In He II, on the other hand, the background medium is locally mobile, so that $\underset{\sim}{v}_s$ must be specified at each point in the fluid. It will be seen that this interpretation underlies the derivation of the generalized hydrodynamic equations presented in the next chapter.

§13. Condition for Superfluidity

By superfluidity, it is simply meant that the superfluid can flow past objects without exerting a drag or that objects can move through the superfluid without slowing down. It is known that this property holds only for relative velocities below certain critical values. Consider an object such as an ion moving through He at 0° K with energy E and momentum $\underset{\sim}{P}$ (at higher temperature, drag forces will be present because of the normal fluid). For the ion to lose energy and momentum to the fluid, an excitation of momentum $\underset{\sim}{p}$ and energy $\epsilon(p)$ must be created. Thus, if the final energy and momentum of the ion are E' and $\underset{\sim}{P}'$, energy and momentum conservation require

$$E = E' + \epsilon \tag{3.75}$$

and

$$\underset{\sim}{P} = \underset{\sim}{P}' + \underset{\sim}{p} . \tag{3.76}$$

Thus $(\underset{\sim}{P} - \underset{\sim}{p})^2 = \underset{\sim}{P}'^2$, or

$$\underset{\sim}{p} \cdot \underset{\sim}{P} = \tfrac{1}{2} \underset{\sim}{p}^2 + \tfrac{1}{2} \underset{\sim}{P}^2 - \tfrac{1}{2} \underset{\sim}{P}'^2 . \tag{3.77}$$

Assuming the dispersion relation $E = \Gamma + \frac{\underset{\sim}{P}^2}{2M}$ for the ion, where M is its mass and Γ is a constant, we have from (3.75)

$$\tfrac{1}{2} \underset{\sim}{P}^2 - \tfrac{1}{2} \underset{\sim}{P}'^2 = M(E-E') = M\epsilon . \tag{3.78}$$

Substituting this in (3.77), we find

$$pP\cos\theta = \tfrac{1}{2} \underset{\sim}{p}^2 + M\epsilon , \tag{3.79}$$

where θ is the angle between $\underset{\sim}{p}$ and $\underset{\sim}{P}$. Now the ion velocity is $\underset{\sim}{v} = \frac{\partial E}{\partial \underset{\sim}{P}} = \frac{\underset{\sim}{P}}{M}$ and thus (3.79) gives

$$Mpv\cos\theta = \tfrac{1}{2} p^2 + M\epsilon . \tag{3.80}$$

Since $\cos\theta \leq 1$, we find

$$v \geq \frac{\epsilon}{p} + \frac{p}{2M} \, . \tag{3.81}$$

Thus if the ion velocity is less than $\frac{\epsilon}{p} + \frac{p}{2M}$, energy - momentum conservation would be violated to create an excitation of energy ϵ and momentum p. Assuming for simplicity that the ion is sufficiently massive for the second term on the right-hand side of (3.81) to be neglected, then $v \geq \frac{\epsilon}{p}$. Thus, to create a phonon for which $\frac{\epsilon}{p} = u_1$, the ion must move faster than the speed of first sound ($\approx$ 237 m/sec for $T < 1^\circ K$). There is, however, a minimum to $\frac{\epsilon}{p}$ smaller than u_1 given by

$$\frac{d}{dp}\left(\frac{\epsilon}{p}\right) = 0 = \frac{1}{p^2}\frac{d\epsilon}{dp} - \frac{\epsilon}{p^2} \, , \tag{3.82}$$

or at

$$\frac{d\epsilon}{dp} = \frac{\epsilon}{p} \, . \tag{3.83}$$

That is, $\left(\frac{\epsilon}{p}\right)_{min}$ is the slope of a line from the origin and tangent to the dispersion curve. This point turns out to be slightly greater than the roton minimum p_0 of Figure 3.3 and $\left(\frac{\epsilon}{p}\right)_{min} \approx 58$ m/sec. Similar arguments show that this same criteria is found for superfluid flow in narrow channels. The critical velocity in narrow channels, however, is much smaller than this value and is a function of the channel size. We have here, of course, considered only phonons and rotons as available excitations, and it has been shown in §9 that the critical velocities arise from the creation of vortex lines or rings. The point to be made, however, is that although the values for critical velocities are not quantitatively obtained from these arguments alone, nevertheless the nature of superfluidity is brought out. Indeed, if the dispersion curve were to approach zero momentum with zero slope (say, for free particles for which $\varepsilon = \frac{p^2}{2M}$), then energy-momentum conservation could be maintained for vanishingly small velocities and superfluidity would not occur.

§ 14. Mobility of Ions

In the previous section and in § 9, it was shown that ions moving through the superfluid would produce excitations, such as vortex rings, if the critical velocity were exceeded. Above 1° K and for relatively small electric fields, however, the ion, due to collisions with the quasi-particles, will not gain sufficient energy in a mean free path to produce these rings. Under these conditions, the ion will move with a steady-drift velocity u given by

$$u = \mu(\mathcal{E})\mathcal{E} , \qquad (3.84)$$

where $\mathcal{E}$ is the field strength and $\mu(\mathcal{E})$ is the mobility. Reif and Meyer (1960, 1961) have measured the mobilities of both positive and negative ions as functions of temperature, pressure, and electric field. The mobility was determined from the time of flight for ions between two grids in a drift-velocity spectrometer shown in Figure 3.5.

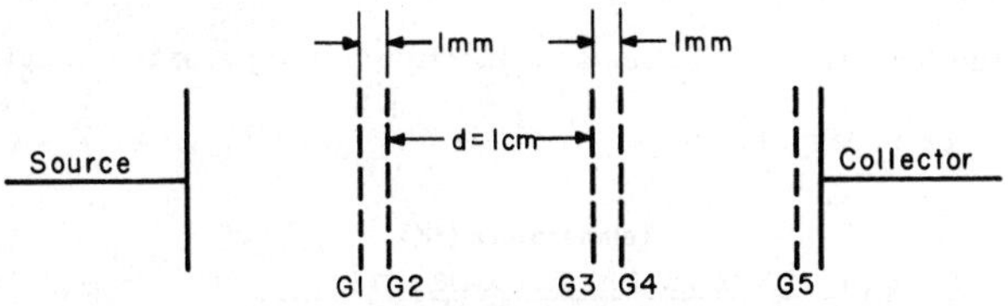

Fig. 3.5.

Ions are produced at the source by α emitting p_o^{210}. These α's have a range in He of about 0.3 mm producing a large number of ion pairs. Although most of these ion pairs recombine, a beam of either positive or negative ions may be drawn through the liquid to the collector by appropriate electric fields. The resulting currents are of the order of 10^{-13} amp and are measured with a vibrating reed electrometer. Square-wave voltages are synchronously applied to the two pairs of grids G_1 - G_2 and G_3 - G_4, acting as gates to the ion beam. In order for a current to be seen, the ions passed by gate G_1 - G_2 must arrive at gate G_3 - G_4, when the latter is open. This will occur when the time of flight τ for the ions to traverse the space d is an integral number of periods ν^{-1} of the gating signals, ν being the frequency of the gates. The final grid G_5 (a Frisch grid) is present merely to isolate the collector and thus the electrometer from the gating signals and the images of approaching charges.

At low-field strengths, the mobility of both positive and negative ions is found to be independent of field strength. By low fields, it is simply meant that the energy $e\mathcal{E}\ell$ acquired by the ion in one mean free path ℓ is small compared to the thermal energy kT. Figure 3.6

shows the low-field mobilities as a function of temperature at saturated vapor pressure.

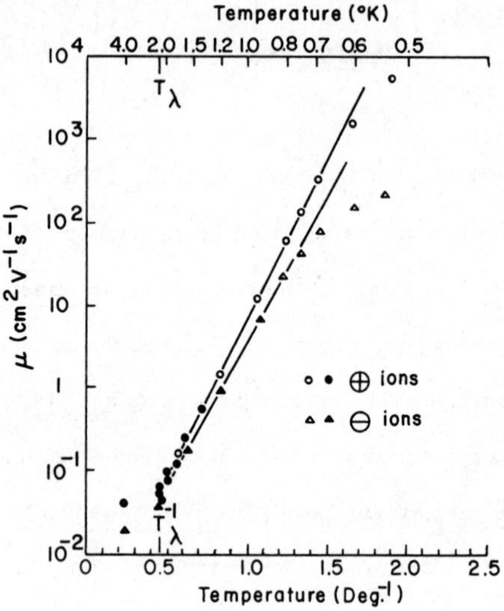

Fig. 3.6.

The straight lines through the points are given by

$$\mu = \mu' e^{\frac{\Delta}{kT}} , \qquad (3.85)$$

with $\frac{\Delta}{k}$ = 8.8° K for the positive ions and $\frac{\Delta}{k}$ = 8.1° K for the negative ions. The temperature dependence is quite similar to that of the roton number density, and it is expected that rotons determine the mobility at high temperatures. Following Reif and Meyer, it is assumed that the mobility can be obtained through simple kinetic theory. In one mean-free path, the ion acquires a momentum $e\mathcal{E}\tau$ in the field direction, where τ is the mean time between collisions. If an average fraction f of this forward momentum is lost at each collision, then the average ion velocity u is given by

$$fMu = e\mathcal{E}\tau , \tag{3.86}$$

where M is the ion mass. Thus the mobility is

$$\mu = \frac{u}{\mathcal{E}} = \frac{1}{f}\left(\frac{e}{M}\right)\tau . \tag{3.87}$$

But $\tau = \ell \langle v_{ir} \rangle^{-1}$, where $\langle v_{ir} \rangle$ is the average relative ion-roton velocity and $\ell = (N_r \sigma_{ir})^{-1}$, where N_r is the density of rotons and σ_{ir} is the ion-roton scattering cross section. Thus

$$\mu = \frac{1}{f}\left(\frac{e}{M}\right)\left(N_r \sigma_{ir}\right)^{-1} \langle v_{ir} \rangle^{-1} . \tag{3.88}$$

Neglecting the small difference between the mean and rms values, we consider

$$\langle v_{ir}^2 \rangle = \langle (\underset{\sim}{v}_i - \underset{\sim}{v}_r)^2 \rangle = \langle v_i^2 \rangle + \langle v_r^2 \rangle . \tag{3.89}$$

For low fields, the ion may be assumed to be in thermal equilibrium and the equipartition theorem yields $\langle v_i^2 \rangle = \frac{3kT}{M}$. For the roton we take

$$\langle v_r^2 \rangle = \frac{4\pi}{N_r} \int v_r^2 n_r p^2 dp , \tag{3.90}$$

where N_r is the roton density given by (3.48) and n_r is the roton distribution function from (3.31).

$$n_r(P) = \frac{1}{h^3} \exp\left\{-\frac{1}{kT}\left[\Delta + \frac{(p-p_o)^2}{2\mu_o}\right]\right\}. \tag{3.91}$$

The roton velocity is taken as the group velocity,

$$v_r = \frac{\partial \epsilon}{\partial p} = \frac{p-p_o}{\mu_o}, \tag{3.92}$$

and (3.90) becomes

$$\langle v_r^2 \rangle = \frac{4\pi p_o^2}{N_r \mu_o^2 h^3} e^{-\frac{\Delta}{kT}} \int_{-\infty}^{\infty} e^{-\frac{(p-p_o)^2}{2\mu_o kT}} (p-p_o)^2 dp \tag{3.93}$$

in the same approximations used in § 12. Carrying out the integrations yield $\langle v_r^2 \rangle = \frac{kT}{\mu_o}$, and thus

$$\langle v_{ir} \rangle \approx \sqrt{\langle v_{ir}^2 \rangle} = \left(\frac{kT}{\mu_o}\right)^{\frac{1}{2}} \left(1 + \frac{3\mu_o}{M}\right)^{\frac{1}{2}}. \tag{3.94}$$

Thus we have

$$\mu = \frac{(2\pi)^{3/2} \hbar^3}{2 f p_o^2 kT \sigma_{ir}} \left(\frac{e}{M}\right)\left(1 + \frac{3\mu_o}{M}\right)^{-\frac{1}{2}} e^{\frac{\Delta}{kT}}. \tag{3.95}$$

Reif and Meyer assumed a δ-function interaction between ion and roton to estimate $f = \frac{2}{3}$, so that

$$\mu = \frac{3(2\pi)^{3/2} \hbar^3}{4 p_o^2 kT \sigma_{ir}} \left(\frac{e}{M}\right)\left(1 + \frac{3\mu_o}{M}\right)^{-\hbar} e^{\frac{\Delta}{kT}}. \tag{3.96}$$

From the measured mobility values and the ion mass, the cross section can be found. Because of the uncertainties in the assumed hard-sphere interaction between ion and roton and the uncertainties in the ionic mass, the cross sections will not be given here. The significant fact is the temperature dependence of the mobility, which essentially agrees with the measured values above 1° K.

Figure 3.7 shows the pressure dependence of the mobilities.

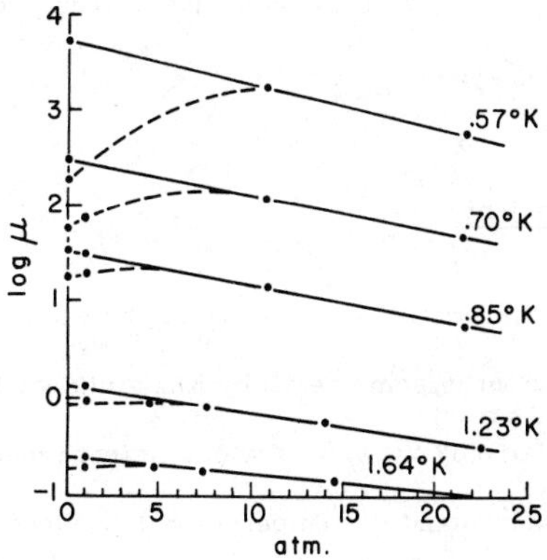

Fig. 3.7.

As the pressure increases, the positive ion mobilities fall off; the negative ion mobilities first rise almost to the positive ion mobility values and then follow the positive ion mobilities down. Except for the initial increase in the negative ion mobility (which is probably the result of compression of the negative ion itself), the decrease in mobilities are accountable within experimental error by the pressure dependence of Δ as measured by Henshaw and Woods (1960).

Two other effects should be noted. In Figure 3.6 the low-temperature mobilities begin falling away from the straight lines. At these temperatures where the roton contribution is becoming small, scattering by phonons and He^3 impurities become important. Also, as the field strengths are increased, the mobilities begin to fall off, possibly indicating the onset of scatterings with the creation of excitations. At low temperatures with long ion mean-free path and at high fields, these excitations are, as previously discussed, predominately vortex rings.

§ 15. Viscosity Coefficient

A derivation of the kinetic coefficients for the excitation gas in He II has been carried out in some detail by Khalatnikov (1952). We will, however, consider only the viscosity coefficient from a simplified point of view to understand its temperature dependence. Following Lifshitz and Andronikashvili (1959), we assume the viscosity to be given from the elementary kinetic theory

$$\eta \propto mnv\ell \ , \tag{3.97}$$

where m is the mass of the particles, n the particle number density, v the mean particle velocity, and ℓ the mean-free path. Furthermore, we assume that the viscosity can be written as the sum of phonon and roton contributions

$$\eta = \eta_{ph} + \eta_r \ . \tag{3.98}$$

For the roton contribution, we take mn, the mass density, in (3.97) to equal ρ_{nr}, as given by (3.73),

$$mn = \rho_{nr} \propto T^{-1} N_r \,. \qquad (3.99)$$

Also, the mean roton velocity is given from (3.93),

$$v \propto \sqrt{T} \,, \qquad (3.100)$$

so that

$$\eta_r \propto T^{-\frac{1}{2}} N_r \ell \,. \qquad (3.101)$$

To determine the mean-free path of a roton, we must consider both elastic and inelastic scatterings of rotons with rotons and phonons. It can be shown that the elastic processes are much more important than the inelastic ones, and thus for high temperatures (> 1° K), where the roton density is much larger than the phonon density, we assume that only elastic roton-roton scatterings need be considered. Then the mean-free path is given by

$$\ell = \frac{1}{N_r \sigma_{rr}} \,, \qquad (3.102)$$

where σ_{rr} is the elastic roton-roton scattering cross section and (3.101) becomes

$$\eta_r \propto \frac{1}{\sqrt{T}\sigma_{rr}} \,. \qquad (3.103)$$

Further arguments, assuming a δ-function interaction between rotons, shows σ_{rr} to be proportional to $1/\sqrt{T}$, and thus

$$\eta_r \approx \text{const} \ . \tag{3.104}$$

For the phonon contribution, it is again found that elastic scattering predominates. Above $\approx 0.8^\circ$ K, because of the high roton density, phonon-roton scatterings dominate, while below 0.8° K, phonon-phonon scattering becomes important. In (3.97) we now take $mn = \rho_{ph} \propto T^4$ and $v = u_1$, which is temperature independent, so that

$$\eta_{ph} \propto T^4 \ell \ . \tag{3.105}$$

Above 0.8° K, we have $\ell = \frac{1}{N_r \sigma_{phr}} \propto \frac{1}{\sqrt{T}\sigma_{phr}} e^{\frac{\Delta}{kT}}$. Thus

$$\eta_{ph} \propto \frac{T^4}{\sqrt{T}\sigma_{phr}} e^{\frac{\Delta}{kT}} \ . \tag{3.106}$$

At these temperatures, the phonons will have small momenta, while the rotons with which they collide will have momenta $\approx p_o$. Therefore, the scattering of the phonons should be similar to the scattering of long-wavelength sound waves from rigid spheres, for which the scattering cross section is inversely proportional to the fourth power of the wavelength. For phonons then, $\sigma_{phr} \propto p^4 \propto T^4$, since $p = \frac{\epsilon}{u_1} \approx \frac{kT}{u_1}$. Thus

$$\eta_{ph} \propto T^{-\frac{1}{2}} e^{\frac{\Delta}{kT}} \ . \tag{3.107}$$

For phonon-phonon scattering at a lower temperature (below 0.8° K), it is found that

$$\eta_{ph} \propto T^{-5} . \qquad (3.108)$$

From Figure 2.8 it is seen that the viscosity is roughly temperature independent between 1.6° K to 1.9° K, indicating that only the roton contribution is important. Below 1.6° K, however, the viscosity increases rapidly, as expected from (3.107) and (3.108) for the phonon contribution. Above 1.9° K the viscosity increases, and it is assumed that this is because of the increase in the number of excitations making the gaslike approximations invalid.

REFERENCES

Abrikosov, A. A., Gorkov, L. P., and Dzyaloshinski, J. E. 1963, Methods of Quantum Field Theory in Statistical Physics (Englewood Cliffs, N. J.: Prentice-Hall).

Bendt, P. J., Cowan, R. D., and Yarnell, J. L. 1959, Phys. Rev., 113, 1386.

Cohen, M., and Feynman, R. P. 1957, Phys. Rev., 107, 13.

Feynman, R. P. 1954, Phys. Rev., 94, 262.

Feynman, R. P., and Cohen, M. 1956, Phys. Rev., 102, 1189.

Henshaw, D. G., and Woods, A. D. B. 1960, Proceedings of the Seventh International Conference on Low Temperature Physics, edited by G. M. Graham and A. C. Hollis Hallet (Toronto:

University of Toronto Press), p. 64.

Henshaw, D. G., and Woods, A. D. B. 1961, Phys. Rev., 121, 1266.

Khalatnikov, I. M. 1965, Introduction to the Theory of Superfluidity (New York: Benjamin).

Landau, L. D. 1941, J. Phys. USSR, 5, 71. Translated in Khalatnikov, I. M. 1965, Introduction to the Theory of Superfluidity (New York: Benjamin).

——— 1947, ibid, 11, 91. Translated in Khalatnikov, I. M. 1965, Introduction to the Theory of Superfluidity (New York: Benjamin).

Landau, L. D., and Lifshitz, E. M. 1958, Statistical Physics (Reading, Mass.: Addison-Wesley), p. 164.

Lifshitz, E. M., and Andronikashvili, E. L. 1959, A Supplement to Helium (London: Chapman and Hall), p. 46.

Meyer, L., and Reif, F. 1961, Phys. Rev., 123, 727.

Miller, A., Pines, D., and Nozieres, P. 1962, Phys. Rev., 127, 1452.

Peshkov, V. P. 1946, J. Phys. USSR, 10, 389.

Pitaevskii, L. P. 1956, J. Phys. USSR, 31, 536. Translated in 1956, Soviet Phys. JETP, 4, 439.

Reif, F., and Meyer, L. 1960, Phys. Rev., 119, 1164.

Van Itterbeek, A., and Forrez, G. 1954, Physica, 20, 133.

Van Itterbeek, A., Forrez, G., and Teirlinck, M. 1957, Physica, 23, 63 and 905.

Yarnell, J. L., Arnold, G. P., Bendt, P. J., and Kerr, E. C. 1959, Phys. Rev., 113, 1379.

CHAPTER 4

GENERALIZED HYDRODYNAMIC EQUATIONS

§16. Landau's Hydrodynamic Equations

Theoretical and experimental evidence has been given to show that circulation in the superfluid must be quantized (§8, see also Chester 1963 and Lin 1963). The source of this circulation can be either potential flow ($\underset{\sim}{\nabla} \times \underset{\sim}{v} = 0$) in multiply connected regions or quantized vortices. The former introduces no vorticity in the fluid while the latter does, the vorticity being localized to the vortex cores. In this section vortices will be assumed absent, and thus $\underset{\sim}{\nabla} \times \underset{\sim}{v}_s = 0$ everywhere. In addition, energy dissipation will be neglected (both superfluid vorticity and dissipation will be included in §17).

The basic hydrodynamic equations come from the laws of mass, momentum, and energy conservation just as for an ordinary fluid. Since dissipation is neglected, entropy is also conserved, and for convenience, we choose entropy conservation rather than energy conservation as the third fundamental equation. The three conservation laws then are

$$\dot{\rho} + \underset{\sim}{\nabla} \cdot \underset{\sim}{j} = 0, \tag{4.1}$$

$$\dot{\underset{\sim}{j}} + \underset{\sim}{\nabla} \cdot \pi = 0, \tag{4.2}$$

and

$$\dot{\sigma} + \underset{\sim}{\nabla} \cdot \underset{\sim}{F} = 0, \quad (4.3)$$

where

ρ	=	mass density
$\underset{\sim}{j}$	=	momentum density or mass flux
π	=	momentum flux
σ	= ρS =	entropy density
$\underset{\sim}{F}$	=	entropy flux.

A complete hydrodynamic description of a classical fluid is obtained once the momentum density $\underset{\sim}{j}$ and two thermodynamic variables, such as ρ and σ, are known (an equation of state is assumed). Five equations are needed to determine these five unknowns and thus the three conservation laws form a complete set. Being complete, these equations must imply energy conservation:

$$\dot{E} + \underset{\sim}{\nabla} \cdot \underset{\sim}{Q} = 0, \quad (4.4)$$

where E is the energy density and $\underset{\sim}{Q}$ the energy flux.

Now consider two coordinate systems, the laboratory system K in which the variables appearing in the last four equations are defined, and a system K_o moving with velocity $\underset{\sim}{v}_s$. The quantities appearing in (4.1) through (4.4) can be expressed in terms of the corresponding quantities as seen in K_o, the latter being identified by a subscript zero. In particular, we will need,

$$\underset{\sim}{j} = \rho \underset{\sim}{v}_s + \underset{\sim}{j}_o , \quad (4.5)$$

$$\pi = \rho \underset{\sim}{v}_s \underset{\sim}{v}_s + \underset{\sim}{v}_s \underset{\sim}{j}_o + \pi_o , \quad (4.6)$$

$$E = \tfrac{1}{2}\rho v_s^2 + \underset{\sim}{v}_s \cdot \underset{\sim}{j}_o + E_o , \tag{4.7}$$

$$\underset{\sim}{Q} = (\tfrac{1}{2}\rho v_s^2 + \underset{\sim}{v}_s \cdot \underset{\sim}{j}_o + E_o)\underset{\sim}{v}_s + \tfrac{1}{2} v_s^2 \underset{\sim}{j}_o + \pi_o \cdot \underset{\sim}{v}_s + \underset{\sim}{Q}_o , \tag{4.8}$$

and

$$\underset{\sim}{F} = \sigma \underset{\sim}{v}_s + \underset{\sim}{F}_o . \tag{4.9}$$

These transformations are consequences solely of Galilean relativity and must hold regardless of the system considered, that is, they must be valid for classical fluids as well as He II. The simplest way to derive these transformations is to begin with the classical expressions (see Landau and Lifshitz 1959, Chapter 1):

$$\underset{\sim}{j} = \rho \underset{\sim}{v} , \tag{4.10}$$

$$\pi = \rho \underset{\sim}{v}\,\underset{\sim}{v} + p\delta , \tag{4.11}$$

$$E = \rho(\tfrac{1}{2} v^2 + e) , \tag{4.12}$$

$$\underset{\sim}{Q} = \rho \underset{\sim}{v}(\tfrac{1}{2} v^2 + e + \frac{p}{\rho}) , \tag{4.13}$$

and

$$\underset{\sim}{F} = \sigma \underset{\sim}{v} , \tag{4.14}$$

where p is the pressure, e the internal energy per unit mass, and δ the unit dyadic (for a summary of the dyadic notation used here see Appendix A). Let $\underset{\sim}{v}$ and $\underset{\sim}{v}_o$ be the velocity of a fluid element as seen in K and K_o, respectively. They are connected by $\underset{\sim}{v} = \underset{\sim}{v}_s + \underset{\sim}{v}_o$. The momentum density $\underset{\sim}{j}$ from (4.10) then becomes

$$\underset{\sim}{j} = \rho \underset{\sim}{v}_s + \rho \underset{\sim}{v}_o = \rho \underset{\sim}{v}_s + \underset{\sim}{j}_o , \tag{4.15}$$

where $\underset{\sim}{j}_o = \rho \underset{\sim}{v}_o$. The momentum flux π also becomes

$$
\begin{aligned}
\pi &= \rho(\underset{\sim}{v}_s + \underset{\sim}{v}_o)(\underset{\sim}{v}_s + v_o) + p\delta \\
&= \rho \underset{\sim}{v}_s \underset{\sim}{v}_s + \rho \underset{\sim}{v}_s \underset{\sim}{v}_o + \rho \underset{\sim}{v}_o \underset{\sim}{v}_o + p\delta ,
\end{aligned}
\tag{4.16}
$$

and identifying $\underset{\sim}{j}_o = \rho \underset{\sim}{v}_o$ and $\pi_o = \rho \underset{\sim}{v}_o \underset{\sim}{v}_o + p\delta$, we obtain equation (4. 6). The remaining three transformation equations may be found in the same manner.

Now, assume that the transformation carries us to a frame in which the fluid is locally at rest. Since the fluid is at rest, the mass flux $\underset{\sim}{j}_o$, energy flux $\underset{\sim}{Q}_o$, and entropy flux $\underset{\sim}{F}_o$ are zero (since dissipation is neglected energy and entropy flux can only result from a mass flux). Furthermore, in this frame, the energy density is just the thermodynamic internal energy density ρe and the momentum flux is just $p\delta$. It is also obvious that the velocity $\underset{\sim}{v}_s$ in the transformation equations is just the fluid velocity $\underset{\sim}{v}$. Making the substitutions indicated above in the transformation equations (4. 5) through (4. 9), we see that they reduce to equation (4. 10) through (4. 14). In other words, if the transformation equations are assumed, the form for the hydrodynamical variables can be derived from fundamental physical assumptions in a frame in which the fluid is at rest. Then one transforms to the laboratory system.

The transformation equations as we noted above must also hold for He II. In He II, however, there are two velocity fields to consider: the background velocity field $\underset{\sim}{v}_s$ and the drift velocity field $\underset{\sim}{v}_n$ of the excitation gas. We choose to transform to a frame in which the background fluid is at rest. In this frame, the fluxes are not zero. From § 12 we know, for example, that $\underset{\sim}{j}_o = \rho_n(\underset{\sim}{v}_n - \underset{\sim}{v}_s)$. In general in frame K_o, the fluxes will involve both thermodynamic quantities and the velocity $\underset{\sim}{v}_n - \underset{\sim}{v}_s$. The thermodynamic variables, however, are defined for a unit mass of total fluid, whereas the velocity $\underset{\sim}{v}_n - \underset{\sim}{v}_s$ refers only to some "partial motion" of the fluid. Thus there is some ambiguity even in frame K_o as to the form of the fluxes. In addition, even if these fluxes could be deduced, an equation describing the field $\underset{\sim}{v}_s$ would not readily follow. We can take a slightly different approach by noting that since dissipation is neglected, the fluxes cannot depend on the gradients of the thermodynamic variables or on velocity gradients. The variables defined in K will be expressed in terms of those in K_o and substituted into the energy conservation equation. From this equation it will be evident that certain relations must exist in order that the apparent dependence of the fluxes on the thermodynamic and velocity gradients vanish.

Since the superfluid is assumed to be irrotational, $\underset{\sim}{v}_s$ and thus $\dot{\underset{\sim}{v}}_s$ must be derivable from some potential that, for convenience, is taken as $\frac{1}{2}v_s^2 + \psi$. Thus

$$\dot{\underset{\sim}{v}}_s + \underset{\sim}{\nabla}(\tfrac{1}{2}v_s^2 + \psi) = 0. \tag{4.17}$$

Now in frame K_o the energy density is given by

$$dE_o = \Phi d\rho + T d\sigma + (\underset{\sim}{v}_n - \underset{\sim}{v}_s)\cdot d\underset{\sim}{j}_o, \tag{4.18}$$

where Φ is the thermodynamic potential and T the temperature. The first two terms comprise the thermodynamic internal energy of the fluid element as a whole while the last term gives the additional kinetic energy due to the motion of the excitations within the element. Moreover, we may simply take (4. 18) as defining the velocity $(\underset{\sim}{v}_n - \underset{\sim}{v}_s)$ as the velocity conjugate to $\underset{\sim}{j}_o$. Thus from (4. 7) and (4. 18)

$$\dot{E} = (\tfrac{1}{2}v_s^2 + \Phi)\dot{\rho} + (\underset{\sim}{j}_o + \rho\underset{\sim}{v}_s)\cdot\dot{\underset{\sim}{v}}_s + \underset{\sim}{v}_n\cdot\dot{\underset{\sim}{j}}_o + T\dot{\sigma} \,. \tag{4. 19}$$

Noting from (4. 5) that $\dot{\underset{\sim}{j}}_o = \dot{\underset{\sim}{j}} - \dot{\rho}\underset{\sim}{v}_s - \rho\dot{\underset{\sim}{v}}_s$, the time derivatives in (4. 19) can be eliminated by (4.1), (4. 2), (4. 3), and (4. 17).

$$\begin{aligned}\dot{E} = &- (\tfrac{1}{2}\underset{\sim}{v}_s^2 + \Phi - \underset{\sim}{v}_n\cdot\underset{\sim}{v}_s)\underset{\sim}{\nabla}\cdot\underset{\sim}{j} \\ &- (\underset{\sim}{j}_o + \rho\underset{\sim}{v}_s - \rho\underset{\sim}{v}_n)\cdot\underset{\sim}{\nabla}(\tfrac{1}{2}v_s^2 + \psi) \\ &- \underset{\sim}{\nabla}\cdot\pi\cdot\underset{\sim}{v}_n - T\underset{\sim}{\nabla}\cdot\underset{\sim}{F} \,.\end{aligned} \tag{4. 20}$$

$\underset{\sim}{j}$, π, and $\underset{\sim}{F}$ are now replaced with their values from (4. 5), (4. 6), and (4. 9).

$$\begin{aligned}\dot{E} = &- (\tfrac{1}{2}v_s^2 + \Phi - \underset{\sim}{v}_n\cdot\underset{\sim}{v}_s)\,\underset{\sim}{\nabla}\cdot(\underset{\sim}{j}_o + \rho\underset{\sim}{v}_s) \\ &- (\underset{\sim}{j}_o + \rho\underset{\sim}{v}_s - \rho\underset{\sim}{v}_n)\cdot\underset{\sim}{\nabla}(\tfrac{1}{2}v_s^2 + \psi) \\ &- \underset{\sim}{\nabla}\cdot(\rho\underset{\sim}{v}_s\underset{\sim}{v}_s + \underset{\sim}{v}_s\underset{\sim}{j}_o + \underset{\sim}{j}_o\underset{\sim}{v}_s)\cdot\underset{\sim}{v}_n \\ &- \underset{\sim}{\nabla}\cdot\pi_o\cdot\underset{\sim}{v}_n - T\underset{\sim}{\nabla}\cdot(\sigma\underset{\sim}{v}_s + \underset{\sim}{F}_o) \,.\end{aligned} \tag{4. 21}$$

Next, calculate $\underset{\sim}{\nabla}\cdot\underset{\sim}{Q}$ from (4. 8):

$$\begin{aligned}\underset{\sim}{\nabla}\cdot\underset{\sim}{Q} = &\underset{\sim}{\nabla}\cdot\left[(\tfrac{1}{2}\rho v_s^2 + \underset{\sim}{v}_s\cdot\underset{\sim}{j}_o)\underset{\sim}{v}_s\right] + E_o\underset{\sim}{\nabla}\cdot\underset{\sim}{v}_s + \underset{\sim}{v}_s\cdot\underset{\sim}{\nabla}E_o \\ &+ \underset{\sim}{\nabla}\cdot(\tfrac{1}{2}v_s^2\underset{\sim}{j}_o) + \underset{\sim}{\nabla}\cdot(\pi_o\cdot\underset{\sim}{v}_s) + \underset{\sim}{\nabla}\cdot\underset{\sim}{Q}_o \,.\end{aligned} \tag{4. 22}$$

From (4.18) we see that

$$\underline{\nabla} E_o = \Phi \underline{\nabla} \rho + T \underline{\nabla} \sigma + \underline{\nabla} \underline{j}_o \cdot (\underline{v}_n - \underline{v}_s) . \qquad (4.23)$$

Using (4.21), (4.22), and (4.23), form $\dot{E} + \underline{\nabla} \cdot Q = 0$ and solve for $\underline{\nabla} \cdot \underline{Q}_o$:

$$\underline{\nabla} \cdot \underline{Q}_o = (\tfrac{1}{2} v_s^2 + \Phi - \underline{v}_n \cdot \underline{v}_s) \underline{\nabla} \cdot (\underline{j}_o + \rho \underline{v}_s)$$

$$+ (\underline{j}_o + \rho \underline{v}_s - \rho \underline{v}_n) \cdot \nabla (\tfrac{1}{2} v_s^2 + \psi)$$

$$+ \underline{\nabla} \cdot (\rho \underline{v}_s \underline{v}_s + \underline{v}_s \underline{j}_o + \underline{j}_o \underline{v}_s) \cdot \underline{v}_n$$

$$- \underline{\nabla} \cdot \left[(\tfrac{1}{2} \rho v_s^2 + \underline{v}_s \cdot \underline{j}_o) \underline{v}_s \right] \qquad (4.24)$$

$$- \underline{\nabla} \cdot (\tfrac{1}{2} v_s^2 \underline{j}_o) - \underline{v}_s \cdot \underline{\nabla} \underline{j}_o \cdot (\underline{v}_n - \underline{v}_s)$$

$$- E_o \underline{\nabla} \cdot \underline{v}_s + \underline{\nabla} \cdot \pi_o \cdot \underline{v}_n - \nabla \cdot (\pi_o \cdot \underline{v}_s)$$

$$+ T \underline{\nabla} \cdot (\sigma \underline{v}_s + \underline{F}_o) - \Phi \underline{\nabla} \rho \cdot \underline{v}_s - T \underline{\nabla} \sigma \cdot \underline{v}_s .$$

Expanding and collecting terms, the result is

$$\underline{\nabla} \cdot \underline{Q}_o = \underline{\nabla} \cdot \pi_o \cdot \underline{v}_n - \underline{\nabla} \cdot (\pi_o \cdot \underline{v}_s)$$

$$- \left[E_o - \Phi \rho - T \sigma - (\underline{v}_n - \underline{v}_s) \cdot \underline{j}_o \right] \underline{\nabla} \cdot \underline{v}_s$$

$$+ \left[\underline{j}_o - \rho (\underline{v}_n - \underline{v}_s) \right] \cdot \underline{\nabla} \psi + T \underline{\nabla} \cdot \underline{F}_o + \Phi \underline{\nabla} \cdot \underline{j}_o \qquad (4.25)$$

$$+ \underline{j}_o \cdot \underline{\nabla} \underline{v}_s \cdot \underline{v}_n - \underline{v}_s \cdot \underline{\nabla} \underline{v}_s \cdot \underline{j}_o .$$

We now define the pressure by

$$p = -\frac{\partial(E_o V)}{\partial V} = -E_o - V\frac{\partial E_o}{\partial V}$$

$$= -E_o - V\left[\Phi\frac{\partial\rho}{\partial V} + T\frac{\partial\sigma}{\partial V} + (\underset{\sim}{v}_n - \underset{\sim}{v}_s)\cdot\frac{\partial \underset{\sim}{j}_o}{\partial V}\right], \tag{4.26}$$

where the total mass ρV, total entropy σV, and total momentum $\underset{\sim}{j}_o V$ are to be held constant. Thus $\rho dV + Vd\rho = 0$, $\sigma dV = Vd\sigma = 0$, and $\underset{\sim}{j}_o dV + Vd\underset{\sim}{j}_o = 0$, and (4.26) becomes

$$p = -E_o + \Phi\rho + T\sigma + (\underset{\sim}{v}_n - \underset{\sim}{v}_s)\cdot\underset{\sim}{j}_o. \tag{4.27}$$

(We note that for a classical fluid the pressure can be defined as the force acting on a surface of unit area moving with the fluid. For He II, because of the existence of two motions, the pressure cannot be unambiguously defined in this manner.) We next note that since $\underset{\sim}{\nabla} \times \underset{\sim}{v}_s = 0$, the dyadic $\underset{\sim}{\nabla}\underset{\sim}{v}_s$ is symmetric, that is, $\frac{\partial v_{si}}{\partial x_k} - \frac{\partial v_{sk}}{\partial x_i} = 0$, so that $\underset{\sim}{j}_o \cdot \underset{\sim}{\nabla}\underset{\sim}{v}_s \cdot \underset{\sim}{v}_n = \underset{\sim}{v}_n \cdot \underset{\sim}{\nabla}\underset{\sim}{v}_s \cdot \underset{\sim}{j}_o$. Using this and (4.27), (4.25) becomes

$$\begin{aligned}\underset{\sim}{\nabla}\cdot\underset{\sim}{Q}_o &= \underset{\sim}{\nabla}\cdot\pi_o\cdot\underset{\sim}{v}_n - \underset{\sim}{\nabla}\cdot(\pi_o\cdot\underset{\sim}{v}_s) - p\underset{\sim}{\nabla}\cdot\underset{\sim}{v}_s \\ &+ \left[\underset{\sim}{j}_o - \rho(\underset{\sim}{v}_n - \underset{\sim}{v}_s)\right]\cdot\underset{\sim}{\nabla}\psi + T\underset{\sim}{\nabla}\cdot\underset{\sim}{F}_o + \Phi\underset{\sim}{\nabla}\cdot\underset{\sim}{j}_o \\ &+ (\underset{\sim}{v}_n - \underset{\sim}{v}_s)\cdot\underset{\sim}{\nabla}\underset{\sim}{v}_s\cdot\underset{\sim}{j}_o\,.\end{aligned} \tag{4.28}$$

We now define dyadic m by

$$\pi_o = p\delta + m = -\left[E_o - \Phi\rho - T\sigma - (\underset{\sim}{v}_n - \underset{\sim}{v}_s)\cdot\underset{\sim}{j}_o\right]\delta + m. \tag{4.29}$$

(m is the kinetic contribution to the momentum flux which for a classical fluid would simply be $\rho \underset{\sim}{v}_o \underset{\sim}{v}_o$ as seen in K_o.) Then

$$\underset{\sim}{\nabla} \cdot \pi_o \cdot \underset{\sim}{v}_n - \underset{\sim}{\nabla} \cdot (\pi_o \cdot \underset{\sim}{v}_s)$$

$$= \underset{\sim}{\nabla} \cdot m \cdot \underset{\sim}{v}_n - \underset{\sim}{\nabla} \cdot (m \cdot \underset{\sim}{v}_s) + (\underset{\sim}{v}_n - \underset{\sim}{v}_s) \cdot \underset{\sim}{\nabla} p - p \underset{\sim}{\nabla} \cdot \underset{\sim}{v}_s ,$$

and (4.29) becomes

$$\begin{aligned} \underset{\sim}{\nabla} \cdot \underset{\sim}{Q}_o = {} & \underset{\sim}{\nabla} \cdot m \cdot \underset{\sim}{v}_n - \underset{\sim}{\nabla} \cdot (m \cdot \underset{\sim}{v}_s) + (\underset{\sim}{v}_n - \underset{\sim}{v}_s) \cdot \underset{\sim}{\nabla} p \\ & + \left[\underset{\sim}{j}_o - \rho (\underset{\sim}{v}_n - \underset{\sim}{v}_s) \right] \cdot \underset{\sim}{\nabla} \psi + T \underset{\sim}{\nabla} \cdot \underset{\sim}{F}_o + \Phi \underset{\sim}{\nabla} \cdot \underset{\sim}{j}_o \\ & + (\underset{\sim}{v}_n - \underset{\sim}{v}_s) \cdot \underset{\sim}{\nabla} \underset{\sim}{v}_s \cdot \underset{\sim}{j}_o . \end{aligned} \tag{4.30}$$

Using (4.23) and (4.27), we find

$$\begin{aligned} \underset{\sim}{\nabla} p & = - \nabla \left[E_o - \Phi \rho - T \sigma - (\underset{\sim}{v}_n - \underset{\sim}{v}_s) \cdot \underset{\sim}{j}_o \right] \\ & = \rho \underset{\sim}{\nabla} \Phi + \sigma \underset{\sim}{\nabla} T + \underset{\sim}{\nabla} (\underset{\sim}{v}_n - \underset{\sim}{v}_s) \cdot \underset{\sim}{j}_o , \end{aligned} \tag{4.31}$$

and thus

$$\begin{aligned} \underset{\sim}{\nabla} \cdot \underset{\sim}{Q}_o = {} & \underset{\sim}{\nabla} \cdot m \cdot \underset{\sim}{v}_n - \underset{\sim}{\nabla} \cdot (m \cdot \underset{\sim}{v}_s) + (\underset{\sim}{v}_n - \underset{\sim}{v}_s) \cdot \underset{\sim}{\nabla} \underset{\sim}{v}_n \cdot \underset{\sim}{j}_o \\ & + \left[\underset{\sim}{j}_o - \rho (\underset{\sim}{v}_n - \underset{\sim}{v}_s) \right] \cdot \underset{\sim}{\nabla} (\psi - \Phi) \\ & - \left[\underset{\sim}{F}_o - \sigma (\underset{\sim}{v}_n - \underset{\sim}{v}_s) \right] \cdot \underset{\sim}{\nabla} T + \underset{\sim}{\nabla} \cdot (\Phi \underset{\sim}{j}_o + T \underset{\sim}{F}_o). \end{aligned} \tag{4.32}$$

Although in the derivation of this equation emphasis has been placed on identifying $\underset{\sim}{v}_n$ and $\underset{\sim}{v}_s$ as the normal and superfluid velocities, the equation is a consequence of the conservation laws and the Galilean transformations only. For a classical fluid with a velocity field $\underset{\sim}{v}_n$ as seen in K, (4.32) gives the divergence of the energy flux as seen in K_o

moving with velocity $\underset{\sim}{v}_s$ as defined through the arbitrary function ψ. Since dissipation is neglected, the fluxes $\underset{\sim}{Q}_o$, $\underset{\sim}{F}_o$, and m cannot depend on the space (or time) derivatives of velocity or thermodynamic variables. Thus the apparent dependence on these quantities must vanish in (4.32), and to this end for a classical fluid we would take

$$\underset{\sim}{j}_o = \rho(\underset{\sim}{v}_n - \underset{\sim}{v}_s), \tag{4.33}$$

$$\underset{\sim}{F}_o = \sigma(\underset{\sim}{v}_n - \underset{\sim}{v}_s), \tag{4.34}$$

and

$$m = (\underset{\sim}{v}_n - \underset{\sim}{v}_s)\underset{\sim}{j}_o . \tag{4.35}$$

The choice for m can be readily seen by noting that $\underset{\sim}{\nabla}\cdot m\cdot\underset{\sim}{v}_n - \underset{\sim}{\nabla}\cdot(m\cdot\underset{\sim}{v}_s) + (\underset{\sim}{v}_n - \underset{\sim}{v}_s)\cdot\underset{\sim}{\nabla}\underset{\sim}{v}_n\cdot\underset{\sim}{j}_o$ must be the divergence of some quantity. In component form this expression is just

$$\frac{\partial m_{ik}}{\partial x_i} v_{nk} - \frac{\partial}{\partial x_i}(m_{ik} v_{sk}) + (v_{ni} - v_{si}) j_{ok} \frac{\partial v_{nk}}{\partial x_i}$$

$$= \frac{\partial}{\partial x_i}\Big[m_{ik}(v_{nk} - v_{sk})\Big] - \Big[m_{ik} - (v_{ni} - v_{si}) j_{ok}\Big] \frac{\partial v_{nk}}{\partial x_i} .$$

Thus $m_{ik} = (v_{ni} - v_{si}) j_{ok}$, which is (4.35). For He II, however, the choice (4.33) for the momentum density would be at variance with the known dependence $\underset{\sim}{j}_o = \rho_n(\underset{\sim}{v}_n - \underset{\sim}{v}_s)$ given by (3.66). Thus the dependence of the fluxes on $\underset{\sim}{\nabla}\Phi$ in (4.32) is removed by the alternate choice

$$\psi = \Phi . \tag{4.36}$$

The choice allows $\underset{\sim}{j}_o = \rho_n(\underset{\sim}{v}_n - \underset{\sim}{v}_s)$ to be used later as a definition of ρ_n.

In addition, this choice uniquely specifies the function ψ, which determines the superfluid velocity field $\underset{\sim}{v}_s$. We retain, however, (4.34) and (4.35) so that substituting (4.34), (4.35), and (4.36) in (4.32), we get

$$\underset{\sim}{\nabla} \cdot \underset{\sim}{Q}_o = \underset{\sim}{\nabla} \cdot \left[m \cdot (\underset{\sim}{v}_n - \underset{\sim}{v}_s) \right] + \underset{\sim}{\nabla} \cdot (T\underset{\sim}{F}_o + \Phi \underset{\sim}{j}_o) \,, \tag{4.37}$$

and eliminating m by (4.35)

$$\underset{\sim}{Q}_o = T\underset{\sim}{F}_o + \Phi \underset{\sim}{j}_o + \left[(\underset{\sim}{v}_n - \underset{\sim}{v}_s) \cdot \underset{\sim}{j}_o \right] (\underset{\sim}{v}_n - \underset{\sim}{v}_s) \,. \tag{4.38}$$

(This is the same as the classical result if the fluid velocity is $\underset{\sim}{v}_n$, $\underset{\sim}{v}_s$ is taken as an arbitrary velocity, and $\underset{\sim}{j}_o$ defined according to [4.33].)

The fluxes $\underset{\sim}{F}$, π, and $\underset{\sim}{Q}$ can now be found from (4.6), (4.8), and (4.9). From (4.9) and (4.34)

$$\underset{\sim}{F} = \sigma \underset{\sim}{v}_n \,, \tag{4.39}$$

which, as expected, shows that entropy is carried only by the excitation gas or normal fluid. From (4.6), (4.29), and (4.35) we get

$$\pi = \rho \underset{\sim}{v}_s \underset{\sim}{v}_s + \underset{\sim}{j}_o \underset{\sim}{v}_s + \underset{\sim}{v}_n \underset{\sim}{j}_o + p\delta \,, \tag{4.40}$$

and finally from (4.8), (4.29), (4.34), (4.35), and (4.38)

$$\underset{\sim}{Q} = (\tfrac{1}{2} v_s^2 + \Phi)(\underset{\sim}{j}_o + \rho \underset{\sim}{v}_s) + \sigma T \underset{\sim}{v}_n + (\underset{\sim}{v}_n \cdot \underset{\sim}{j}_o) \underset{\sim}{v}_n \,. \tag{4.41}$$

The complete two-fluid hydrodynamics is then described by

$$\dot{\rho} + \underset{\sim}{\nabla} \cdot \underset{\sim}{j} = 0 \,, \tag{4.42}$$

$$\dot{\underset{\sim}{j}} + \underset{\sim}{\nabla} \cdot \pi = 0 \,, \tag{4.43}$$

$$\dot{\sigma} + \underset{\sim}{\nabla} \cdot (\sigma \underset{\sim}{v}_n) = 0 , \tag{4.44}$$

and

$$\dot{\underset{\sim}{v}}_s + \underset{\sim}{\nabla}(\tfrac{1}{2} \underset{\sim}{v}_s^2 + \Phi) = 0 . \tag{4.45}$$

We now make the explicit definitions of the normal fluid density through

$$\underset{\sim}{j}_o = \rho_n (\underset{\sim}{v}_n - \underset{\sim}{v}_s) , \tag{4.46}$$

and the superfluid density through

$$\rho_s = \rho - \rho_n . \tag{4.47}$$

Then (4.40) becomes

$$\pi = \rho_s \underset{\sim}{v}_s \underset{\sim}{v}_s + \rho_n \underset{\sim}{v}_n \underset{\sim}{v}_n + p\delta \tag{4.48}$$

and (4.6) becomes

$$\underset{\sim}{j} = \rho_s \underset{\sim}{v}_s + \rho_n \underset{\sim}{v}_n . \tag{4.49}$$

It should be noted that the quantities Φ, ρ, ρ_n, and σ are generally functions of the relative velocity $w = |\underset{\sim}{v}_n - \underset{\sim}{v}_s|$. Indeed, if in the derivation of ρ_n in §12 the distribution function had not been expanded, (3.71) and (3.73) would have read

$$\rho_{nph} = \frac{2\pi^4 (kT)}{45 u_1^2 \zeta(3)} N_{ph} \left(1 - \frac{w^2}{u_1^2}\right)^{-3} , \tag{4.50}$$

and

$$\rho_{nr} = \frac{kTN_r}{w^2} \left[\cosh\left(\frac{p_o w}{kt}\right) - \frac{kt}{p_o w} \sinh\left(\frac{p_o w}{kt}\right) \right] . \tag{4.51}$$

To second order, these become

$$\rho_{nph} = \frac{2\pi^4 (kT)}{45 u_1^2 \zeta(3)} N_{ph} \left(1 + \frac{3w^2}{u_1^2}\right), \tag{4.52}$$

and

$$\rho_{nr} = \frac{p_o^2 N_r}{3kT} \left[1 + \frac{1}{10}\left(\frac{p_o w}{kT}\right)^2\right]. \tag{4.53}$$

The hydrodynamic equations will now be expanded to second order in $\underset{\sim}{v}_n - \underset{\sim}{v}_s$. Note in this context that ρ_n and ρ_s enter the quations as coefficients of the velocities (4.48) and (4.49), which are assumed small. Thus to second order, the velocity dependence of the normal and superfluid densities may be neglected. The velocity dependence of the total density ρ, however, cannot be neglected since it appears alone in (4.42). From (4.18) and (4.27) we have

$$d\Phi = - SdT + \frac{1}{\rho} dp - \frac{1}{\rho} \underset{\sim}{j}_o \cdot d(\underset{\sim}{v}_n - \underset{\sim}{v}_s), \tag{4.54}$$

where we have reverted to the entropy per unit mass $S = \frac{\sigma}{\rho}$. Using (4.46), we get

$$\begin{aligned} d\Phi &= - SdT + \frac{1}{\rho} dp - \frac{\rho_n}{\rho} (\underset{\sim}{v}_n - \underset{\sim}{v}_s) \cdot d(\underset{\sim}{v}_n - \underset{\sim}{v}_s) \\ &= - SdT + \frac{1}{\rho} dp - \frac{\rho_n}{2\rho} d(w^2). \end{aligned} \tag{4.55}$$

To expand S, ρ, and Φ, it is first noted that they cannot depend on the direction of $\underset{\sim}{v}_n - \underset{\sim}{v}_s$ and thus the linear terms vanish. Thus

$$S(pTw) = S_o(pT) + w^2 \left(\frac{\partial S}{\partial w^2}\right)_{pT}, \tag{4.56}$$

$$\rho(pTw) = \rho_o(pT) + w^2 \left(\frac{\partial \rho}{\partial w^2}\right)_{pT}, \tag{4.57}$$

and

$$\Phi(pTw) = \Phi_o(pT) + w^2 \left(\frac{\partial \Phi}{\partial w^2}\right)_{pT} , \qquad (4.58)$$

where S_o, ρ_o, and Φ_o are the zero-velocity values. Then from (4.55) we find

$$\left(\frac{\partial S}{\partial w^2}\right)_{pT} = \tfrac{1}{2}\left[\frac{\partial}{\partial T}\left(\frac{\rho_n}{\rho}\right)\right]_{p, w^2 = 0} = aS_o , \qquad (4.59)$$

$$\left(\frac{\partial \rho}{\partial w^2}\right)_{pT} = -\rho^2\left[\frac{\partial}{\partial w^2}\left(\frac{1}{\rho}\right)\right]_{pT} = \tfrac{1}{2}\rho_o^2\left[\frac{\partial}{\partial p}\left(\frac{\rho_n}{\rho}\right)\right]_{T, w^2 = 0} = b\rho_o , \qquad (4.60)$$

and

$$\left(\frac{\partial \Phi}{\partial w^2}\right)_{pT} = -\frac{\rho_n}{2\rho_o} . \qquad (4.61)$$

Thus the expansion coefficient can be found from the pressure and temperature dependence of the densities at zero-relative velocity. Thus to second order we have

$$S(pTw) = S_o(1 + aw^2) , \qquad (4.62)$$

$$\rho(pTw) = \rho_o(1 + bw^2) , \qquad (4.63)$$

and

$$\Phi(pTw) = \Phi_o - \frac{\rho_n}{2\rho_o} w^2 , \qquad (4.64)$$

and the hydrodynamic equations, to second order in w, become (with $\sigma_o = \rho_o S_o$)

$$\frac{\partial}{\partial t}\left[\rho_o(1 + bw^2)\right] + \underset{\sim}{\nabla} \cdot \underset{\sim}{j} = 0 , \qquad (4.65)$$

$$\dot{\underset{\sim}{j}} + \underset{\sim}{\nabla} \cdot \pi = 0 , \qquad (4.66)$$

$$\frac{\partial}{\partial t}\left\{\sigma_o\left[1+(a+b)w^2\right]\right\} + \nabla\cdot(\sigma_o \mathbf{v}_n) = 0 , \qquad (4.67)$$

and

$$\dot{\mathbf{v}}_s + \nabla\left(\tfrac{1}{2}v_s^2 + \Phi_o - \frac{\rho_n}{2\rho} w^2\right) = 0 , \qquad (4.68)$$

with

$$\mathbf{j} = \rho_s \mathbf{v}_s + \rho_n \mathbf{v}_n \qquad (4.69)$$

and

$$\pi = \rho_s \mathbf{v}_s \mathbf{v}_s + \rho_n \mathbf{v}_n \mathbf{v}_n + p\delta . \qquad (4.70)$$

It should be noted that if critical velocities are exceeded, the equations just derived are insufficient to describe the flow. The expansion to the second order is needed, however, in a number of cases for small velocities for which the first-order terms cancel identically. Generally, if the first-order terms do not cancel, the linearized equations are sufficient.

§ 17. The Bekaravich-Khalatnikov Hydrodynamic Equations

Since superfluid vorticity is localized in vortex cores and not distributed in fluid, a complete hydrodynamical description must consider the motion of individual vortices. This would require the introduction of many coordinates to specify the positions of each elementary segment of each vortex. If we limit the description to averages over regions containing many vortices, however, the vorticity may be assumed distributed and the individual vortex motions may be neglected. Specifically, we are interested in describing He II under conditions (such as rotation) in which many vortex lines can be produced. Superfluid in a container rotating at angular velocity Ω appears to rotate as a solid body with uniform vorticity $\omega = 2\Omega$.

Let us pause in the derivation of the hydrodynamic equations to obtain the energy of N-line vortices located at points (r_1, θ_1), (r_2, θ_2), $\dots, (r_N, \theta_N)$ in a cylindrical container of radius R. In general, this system must be treated quantum-mechanically; however, if the vortices do not approach one another or the walls closer than a distance comparable to the core radius (or healing length, see §22), the flow may be treated classically (Fetter, 1965). We may simulate the boundary condition of vanishing normal velocity at the wall by introducing an image vortex, of opposite circulation, for each real vortex at points (r'_1, θ_1), $(r'_1, \theta_2) \cdots (r'_N, \theta_N)$, where $r_k r'_k = R^2$ (Milne-Thomson 1960), §13.50). The fluid velocity for $r < R$ is then the sum of the velocity fields induced by all real and image vortices. The energy per unit depth is taken as the total kinetic energy per unit depth given by

$$T = \tfrac{1}{2}\rho_s \int\int v^2 \, ds \, . \qquad (4.71)$$

Since the velocity fields are additive, the energy will contain cross terms giving the interaction energy of the vortices as well as the self-energy terms. The calculation of the energy is most readily performed in a system of coordinates formed by the streamlines and equipotentials (see Kaufmann 1963, §II.A.14). Assuming each vortex to be singly quantized (see §8), the energy per unit depth becomes

$$T_N = \frac{\rho_s \kappa^2}{4\pi} \left[\sum_{k=1}^{N} \log \left(\frac{R^2 - r_k^2}{aR} \right) + \sum_{i,k=1}^{N}{}' \log \left(\frac{R'_{ik}}{R_{ik}} \right) \right] + NT_C . \qquad (4.72)$$

T_c is the kinetic energy of the core, a is the radius of the core, and $\kappa = h/m$. R_{ik} is the distance between the ith real vortex and the kth real vortex, and R'_{ik} is the distance between the ith image vortex and the kth real vortex. The prime on the second summation indicates that the terms with i = k are deleted. For one vortex (4.72) gives

$$T_1 = \frac{\rho_s \kappa^2}{4\pi} \log \left(\frac{R^2 - r_1^2}{aR} \right) + T_c .$$

This includes both the vortex self-energy and the interaction energy of the vortex with its image. In the general equation (4.72), the first term is just the sum of the vortex self-energies plus the interaction energies of the vortices with their own images. The interaction energies of the real vortices with the other images and the interaction energies between real vortices are included in the second term.

Since there are many vortices, the number per unit area, n_o, is given by (2.105)

$$n_o = \frac{2\Omega}{\kappa} = \frac{\omega}{\kappa} . \qquad (4.73)$$

Thus N in (4.72) is taken as $N = \frac{\omega \pi R^2}{\kappa}$, and the total energy density E_V can be considered as a function of ω,

$$E_V(\omega) = \frac{TN(\omega)}{\pi R^2} . \qquad (4.74)$$

From (4.72) it is seen that this energy density is not uniquely specified by ω since the distances r_k, R_{ik}, and R'_{ik} must also be given. We assume, however, that for a given ω, there exists a unique steady state value for the energy, and we define the phenomenological function $\lambda(\omega)$ by

$$dE_v = \lambda(\omega) d\omega \ . \tag{4.75}$$

Since $d\omega$ is proportional to dn_o, this expression basically gives the increase in energy density resulting from an increase in the number of vortices. We further specify λ by requiring that dE_v is the energy change seen in a system moving with the superfluid.

We are now in a position to derive the hydrodynamic equations. In a frame of reference moving with the local average superfluid velocity, the total energy density is

$$dE_o = \Phi d\rho + T d\sigma + (v_n - v_s) \cdot d\underset{\sim}{j}_o + \lambda d\omega \ , \tag{4.76}$$

the first three terms coming from (4. 18) and the last from (4. 75). The three conservation laws are taken as

$$\dot{\rho} + \underset{\sim}{\nabla} \cdot \underset{\sim}{j} = 0 \ , \tag{4.77}$$

$$\dot{\underset{\sim}{j}} + \underset{\sim}{\nabla} \cdot (\pi + \pi') = 0 \ , \tag{4.78}$$

and

$$\dot{E} + \underset{\sim}{\nabla} \cdot (\underset{\sim}{Q} + \underset{\sim}{Q}') = 0 \ , \tag{4.79}$$

where π and $\underset{\sim}{Q}$ are the fluxes given by (4. 40) and (4. 41):

$$\pi = \rho \underset{\sim}{v}_s \underset{\sim}{v}_s + \underset{\sim}{j}_o \underset{\sim}{v}_s + \underset{\sim}{v}_n \underset{\sim}{j}_o + p\delta \tag{4.80}$$

and

$$\underset{\sim}{Q} = (\tfrac{1}{2} v_s^2 + \Phi) \underset{\sim}{j} + \sigma T \underset{\sim}{v}_n + (\underset{\sim}{v}_n \cdot \underset{\sim}{j}_o) \underset{\sim}{v}_n . \qquad (4.81)$$

π' and $\underset{\sim}{Q}'$ are the additional fluxes arising from viscosity, heat conduction, and superfluid vorticity. Since entropy is no longer conserved, we take

$$\dot{\sigma} + \underset{\sim}{\nabla} \cdot (\sigma v_n + \frac{q}{T}) = \frac{R}{T} , \qquad (4.82)$$

where $\underset{\sim}{q}/T$ is the additional entropy flux and R is the dissipation function. Also since superfluid vorticity is allowed, we write

$$\dot{\underset{\sim}{v}}_s + \underset{\sim}{v}_s \cdot \underset{\sim}{\nabla} \underset{\sim}{v}_s + \underset{\sim}{\nabla} \Phi = \underset{\sim}{f} , \qquad (4.83)$$

where $\underset{\sim}{f}$ would be the gradient of some scalar function if superfluid vorticity were neglected. It should be noted that (4.83) does not follow from (4.45) by the addition of $\underset{\sim}{f}$, since $\underset{\sim}{\nabla} \times \underset{\sim}{v}_s \neq 0$ and $\underset{\sim}{\nabla}(\tfrac{1}{2} v_s^2) = \underset{\sim}{\nabla} \underset{\sim}{v}_s \cdot \underset{\sim}{v}_s \neq \underset{\sim}{v}_s \cdot \underset{\sim}{\nabla} \underset{\sim}{v}_s$. Of course (4.45) could also be written as (4.83) with $\underset{\sim}{f} = 0$. In (4.83) the second term is properly written as the convective part of the total time derivative.

To find the additional fluxes, we form the expression $\dot{E} + \underset{\sim}{\nabla} \cdot \underset{\sim}{Q} = 0$. In doing so, we will get an equation for R, and the fact that R must be positive definite will lead to specific forms for the fluxes. Although some of the following expressions will involve $\underset{\sim}{j}_o$ for convenience, the calculations are assumed carried out in frame K of §16. We first calculate $\dot{E}$ from (4.7) using (4.76) and noting $\dot{\underset{\sim}{j}}_o = \dot{\underset{\sim}{j}} - \dot{\rho} \underset{\sim}{v}_s - \rho \dot{\underset{\sim}{v}}_s$:

$$\begin{aligned} \dot{E} &= (\tfrac{1}{2} v_s^2 + \Phi - \underset{\sim}{v}_n \cdot \underset{\sim}{v}_s) \dot{\rho} + (\underset{\sim}{j} - \rho \underset{\sim}{v}_n) \cdot \dot{\underset{\sim}{v}}_s \\ &+ \dot{\underset{\sim}{j}} \cdot \underset{\sim}{v}_n + T \dot{\sigma} + \lambda \dot{w} . \end{aligned} \qquad (4.84)$$

Eliminating the time derivatives by (4.77), (4.78), (4.82), and (4.83), we get

$$\dot{E} = -(\tfrac{1}{2}v_s^2 + \Phi - \underset{\sim}{v}_n \cdot \underset{\sim}{v}_s)\underset{\sim}{\nabla}\cdot \underset{\sim}{j} - (\underset{\sim}{v}_s \cdot \underset{\sim}{\nabla}\underset{\sim}{v}_s + \nabla\Phi)\cdot(\underset{\sim}{j} - \rho\underset{\sim}{v}_n) + (\underset{\sim}{j} - \rho\underset{\sim}{v}_n)\cdot\underset{\sim}{f} - \underset{\sim}{\nabla}\cdot(\pi + \pi')\cdot\underset{\sim}{v}_n - T\underset{\sim}{\nabla}\cdot(\sigma\underset{\sim}{v}_n) + R + \lambda\dot{\omega} - T\underset{\sim}{\nabla}\cdot\left(\frac{\underset{\sim}{q}}{T}\right), \tag{4.85}$$

which can be rearranged to yield

$$\begin{aligned}\dot{E} = & -\underset{\sim}{\nabla}\cdot\left[(\tfrac{1}{2}\underset{\sim}{v}_s^2 + \Phi)\underset{\sim}{j} + T\sigma\underset{\sim}{v}_n + (\underset{\sim}{v}_n\cdot\underset{\sim}{j}_o)\underset{\sim}{v}_n\right] \\ & + (\underset{\sim}{v}_s\cdot\underset{\sim}{v}_n)\underset{\sim}{\nabla}\cdot\underset{\sim}{j} + \underset{\sim}{v}_s\cdot\underset{\sim}{\nabla}\underset{\sim}{v}_s\cdot\rho\underset{\sim}{v}_n + \rho\underset{\sim}{v}_n\cdot\underset{\sim}{\nabla}\Phi \\ & + \underset{\sim}{\nabla}\cdot\left[(\underset{\sim}{v}_n\cdot\underset{\sim}{j}_o)\underset{\sim}{v}_n\right] + (\underset{\sim}{j} - \rho\underset{\sim}{v}_n)\cdot\underset{\sim}{f} - \underset{\sim}{\nabla}\cdot(\pi + \pi')\cdot\underset{\sim}{v}_n \\ & + \sigma\underset{\sim}{v}_n\cdot\underset{\sim}{\nabla}T + R + \lambda\dot{\omega} - T\underset{\sim}{\nabla}\cdot\left(\frac{\underset{\sim}{q}}{T}\right) \\ & + \underset{\sim}{j}\cdot\underset{\sim}{\nabla}\underset{\sim}{v}_s\cdot\underset{\sim}{v}_s - \underset{\sim}{v}_s\cdot\underset{\sim}{\nabla}\underset{\sim}{v}_s\cdot\underset{\sim}{j}\,.\end{aligned} \tag{4.86}$$

We see from (4.81) that the first term is just $-\underset{\sim}{\nabla}\cdot\underset{\sim}{Q}$, and replacing π from (4.80), we get

$$\begin{aligned}\dot{E} = & -\underset{\sim}{\nabla}\cdot Q - \underset{\sim}{\nabla}\cdot\pi'\cdot\underset{\sim}{v}_n + R + \lambda\dot{\omega} + \sigma\underset{\sim}{v}_n\cdot\underset{\sim}{\nabla}T - T\underset{\sim}{\nabla}\cdot\left(\frac{\underset{\sim}{q}}{T}\right) \\ & + (\underset{\sim}{j} - \rho\underset{\sim}{v}_n)\cdot\underset{\sim}{f} + (\underset{\sim}{v}_s\cdot\underset{\sim}{v}_n)\underset{\sim}{\nabla}\cdot\underset{\sim}{j} + \underset{\sim}{v}_s\cdot\underset{\sim}{\nabla}\underset{\sim}{v}_s\cdot\rho\underset{\sim}{v}_n \\ & + \underset{\sim}{\nabla}\cdot\left[(\underset{\sim}{v}_n\cdot\underset{\sim}{j}_o)\underset{\sim}{v}_n\right] + \underset{\sim}{j}\cdot\underset{\sim}{\nabla}\underset{\sim}{v}_s\cdot\underset{\sim}{v}_s - \underset{\sim}{v}_s\cdot\underset{\sim}{\nabla}\underset{\sim}{v}_s\cdot\underset{\sim}{j} \\ & - \underset{\sim}{\nabla}\cdot\left(\rho\underset{\sim}{v}_s\underset{\sim}{v}_s + \underset{\sim}{j}_o\underset{\sim}{v}_s + \underset{\sim}{v}_n\underset{\sim}{j}_o\right) - \underset{\sim}{\nabla}p\cdot\underset{\sim}{v}_n\,,\end{aligned} \tag{4.87}$$

which can be reduced to

$$\dot{E} = -\underset{\sim}{\nabla}\cdot\underset{\sim}{Q} - \underset{\sim}{\nabla}\cdot\underset{\sim}{\pi}'\cdot\underset{\sim}{v}_n + R + \lambda\dot{\omega} - T\underset{\sim}{\nabla}\cdot\left(\frac{\underset{\sim}{q}}{T}\right) + (\underset{\sim}{j} - \rho\underset{\sim}{v}_n)\cdot\underset{\sim}{f}$$

$$+ \sigma\underset{\sim}{v}_n\cdot\underset{\sim}{\nabla}T + \rho\underset{\sim}{v}_n\cdot\underset{\sim}{\nabla}\Phi - \underset{\sim}{\nabla}p\cdot\underset{\sim}{v}_n \tag{4.88}$$

$$+ \underset{\sim}{v}_n\cdot\underset{\sim}{\nabla}\underset{\sim}{v}_n\cdot\underset{\sim}{j}_o - \underset{\sim}{j}_o\cdot\underset{\sim}{\nabla}\underset{\sim}{v}_s\cdot\underset{\sim}{v}_n$$

$$+ \underset{\sim}{j}\cdot\underset{\sim}{\nabla}\underset{\sim}{v}_s\cdot\underset{\sim}{v}_s - \underset{\sim}{v}_s\cdot\underset{\sim}{\nabla}\underset{\sim}{v}_s\cdot\underset{\sim}{j} \,.$$

The pressure p has been defined in (4.27), and using (4.76), the result is

$$\underset{\sim}{\nabla}p = \rho\underset{\sim}{\nabla}\Phi + \sigma\underset{\sim}{\nabla}T + \underset{\sim}{\nabla}(\underset{\sim}{v}_n - \underset{\sim}{v}_s)\cdot\underset{\sim}{j}_o - \lambda\underset{\sim}{\nabla}\omega \,. \tag{4.89}$$

Substituting this in (4.88) and using $\underset{\sim}{j}_o = \underset{\sim}{j} - \rho\underset{\sim}{v}_s$, we get

$$\dot{E} = -\underset{\sim}{\nabla}\cdot\underset{\sim}{Q} - \underset{\sim}{\nabla}\cdot\underset{\sim}{\pi}'\cdot\underset{\sim}{v}_n + R + \lambda\dot{\omega} - T\underset{\sim}{\nabla}\cdot\left(\frac{\underset{\sim}{q}}{T}\right) + \lambda\underset{\sim}{\nabla}\omega\cdot\underset{\sim}{v}_n$$

$$+ (\underset{\sim}{v}_n - \underset{\sim}{v}_s)\cdot\underset{\sim}{\nabla}\underset{\sim}{v}_s\cdot(\underset{\sim}{j} - \rho\underset{\sim}{v}_s) - (\underset{\sim}{j} - \rho\underset{\sim}{v}_s)\cdot\underset{\sim}{\nabla}\underset{\sim}{v}_s\cdot(\underset{\sim}{v}_n - \underset{\sim}{v}_s) \tag{4.90}$$

$$+ (\underset{\sim}{j} - \rho\underset{\sim}{v}_s)\cdot\underset{\sim}{f} \,.$$

Noting that $\underset{\sim}{A} \times (\underset{\sim}{\nabla} \times \underset{\sim}{B}) = \underset{\sim}{\nabla}\underset{\sim}{B}\cdot\underset{\sim}{A} - \underset{\sim}{A}\cdot\underset{\sim}{\nabla}\underset{\sim}{B}$, the last equation can be written

$$\dot{E} = -\underset{\sim}{\nabla}\cdot\underset{\sim}{Q} - \underset{\sim}{\nabla}\cdot\underset{\sim}{\pi}'\cdot\underset{\sim}{v}_n + R + \lambda\dot{\omega} - T\underset{\sim}{\nabla}\cdot\left(\frac{\underset{\sim}{q}}{T}\right) + \lambda\underset{\sim}{\nabla}\omega\cdot\underset{\sim}{v}_n$$

$$+ (\underset{\sim}{j} - \rho\underset{\sim}{v}_n)\cdot\left[\underset{\sim}{f} + \underset{\sim}{\omega} \times (\underset{\sim}{v}_n - \underset{\sim}{v}_s)\right] , \tag{4.91}$$

where $\underset{\sim}{\omega} = \underset{\sim}{\nabla} \times \underset{\sim}{v}_s$. By definition $\omega^2 = \underset{\sim}{\omega}\cdot\underset{\sim}{\omega}$ so that $\omega\dot{\omega} = \underset{\sim}{\omega}\cdot\dot{\underset{\sim}{\omega}}$ and defining the unit vector $\hat{\omega} = \frac{\underset{\sim}{\omega}}{\omega}$, we get $\dot{\omega} = \hat{\omega}\cdot(\underset{\sim}{\nabla} \times \dot{\underset{\sim}{v}}_s)$. Using (4.83) we find

$$\dot{\omega} = \hat{\omega} \cdot \nabla \times \left[\underset{\sim}{f} + \underset{\sim}{\omega} \times (\underset{\sim}{v}_n - \underset{\sim}{v}_s) \right] - \hat{\omega} \cdot \nabla \times (\underset{\sim}{\omega} \times \underset{\sim}{v}_n) \,. \tag{4.92}$$

Substituting this in (4.91) and using $\underset{\sim}{j}_o = \underset{\sim}{j} - \rho \underset{\sim}{v}_s$, we get

$$\dot{E} = \nabla \cdot \left\{ \underset{\sim}{Q} + \pi' \cdot \underset{\sim}{v}_n + \lambda \hat{\omega} \times \left[\underset{\sim}{f} + \underset{\sim}{\omega} \times (\underset{\sim}{v}_n - \underset{\sim}{v}_s) \right] + \underset{\sim}{q} \right\}$$

$$= R + (\pi' + \lambda \frac{\underset{\sim}{\omega}\underset{\sim}{\omega}}{\omega} - \lambda \omega \delta) : \nabla \underset{\sim}{v}_n + \frac{1}{T} \underset{\sim}{q} \cdot \nabla T \tag{4.93}$$

$$+ \left[\underset{\sim}{f} + \underset{\sim}{\omega} \times (\underset{\sim}{v}_n - \underset{\sim}{v}_s) \right] \cdot \left[(\underset{\sim}{j} - \rho \underset{\sim}{v}_n) + \nabla \times (\lambda \underset{\sim}{\omega}) \right] .$$

Let us now write

$$\underset{\sim}{f} = \underset{\sim}{f}' - \nabla h \,, \tag{4.94}$$

where ∇h is the source term for the superfluid velocity if vorticity were absent and $\underset{\sim}{f}'$ is the source term resulting from vorticity. Putting this in (4.93), we finally obtain

$$\dot{E} + \nabla \cdot \left\{ \underset{\sim}{Q} + \pi' \cdot \underset{\sim}{v}_n + \underset{\sim}{q} + h(\underset{\sim}{j} - \rho \underset{\sim}{v}_n) + \lambda \hat{\omega} \times \left[\underset{\sim}{f}' + \underset{\sim}{\omega} \times (\underset{\sim}{v}_n - \underset{\sim}{v}_s) \right] \right\}$$

$$= R + (\pi' + \lambda \frac{\underset{\sim}{\omega}\underset{\sim}{\omega}}{\omega} - \lambda \omega \delta) : \nabla \underset{\sim}{v}_n + \frac{1}{T} \underset{\sim}{q} \cdot \nabla T + h \nabla \cdot (\underset{\sim}{j} - \rho \underset{\sim}{v}_n)$$

$$+ \left[\underset{\sim}{f}' + \underset{\sim}{\omega} \times (\underset{\sim}{v}_n - \underset{\sim}{v}_s) \right] \cdot \left[\underset{\sim}{j} - \rho \underset{\sim}{v}_n - \nabla \times \lambda \hat{\omega}) \right] . \tag{4.95}$$

Comparing this to (4.79), we find

$$\underset{\sim}{Q}' = \pi' \cdot \underset{\sim}{v}_n + \underset{\sim}{q} + h(\underset{\sim}{j} - \rho \underset{\sim}{v}_n) + \lambda \hat{\omega} \times \left[\underset{\sim}{f}' + \underset{\sim}{\omega} \times (\underset{\sim}{v}_n - \underset{\sim}{v}_s) \right] \tag{4.96}$$

and

$$R = -(\pi' + \lambda \frac{\underset{\sim}{\omega}\underset{\sim}{\omega}}{\omega} - \lambda\omega\delta) : \underset{\sim}{\nabla}\underset{\sim}{v}_n - \frac{1}{T}\underset{\sim}{q}\cdot\underset{\sim}{\nabla}T - h\underset{\sim}{\nabla}\cdot(\underset{\sim}{j} - \rho\underset{\sim}{v}_n)$$

$$- \left[\underset{\sim}{f}' + \underset{\sim}{\omega} \times (\underset{\sim}{v}_n - \underset{\sim}{v}_s)\right] \cdot \left[\underset{\sim}{j} - \rho\underset{\sim}{v}_n - \underset{\sim}{\nabla} \times (\lambda\hat{\underset{\sim}{\omega}})\right]. \tag{4.97}$$

Let us first assume that vorticity in the superfluid is absent, thus $\underset{\sim}{f}' = 0$, $\underset{\sim}{\omega} = 0$, and we take $\pi' = \tau$, the viscous contribution to the momentum flux. The last two equations become

$$Q' = \tau\cdot\underset{\sim}{v}_n + \underset{\sim}{q} + h(\underset{\sim}{j} - \rho\underset{\sim}{v}_n) \tag{4.98}$$

and

$$R = -\tau:\underset{\sim}{\nabla}\underset{\sim}{v}_n - \frac{1}{T}\underset{\sim}{q}\cdot\underset{\sim}{\nabla}T - h\underset{\sim}{\nabla}\cdot(\underset{\sim}{j} - \rho\underset{\sim}{v}_n). \tag{4.99}$$

We now consider the general forms for τ, $\underset{\sim}{q}$, and h consistent with the requirement that R must be positive definite. First we take

$$\underset{\sim}{q} = -K\underset{\sim}{\nabla}T, \tag{4.100}$$

where $\underset{\sim}{q}$ is the heat flux, K being the thermal conductivity (this is the true conductivity not to be confused with the "anomalous conductivity" associated with counterflow). We note that most generally $\underset{\sim}{q}$ can be the sum of terms involving all odd powers of $\underset{\sim}{\nabla}T$; however, we restrict ourselves to the linear term. (The same is generally accepted for classical fluids.) Let us now neglect the term containing h in (4.99), which is absent for a classical fluid. Then in the linear approximation, τ must be proportional to the normal fluid velocity gradients. For a uniform rotation of the system, however, no viscous forces act so that τ must vanish. Thus τ can only be a function of terms of the form $(\partial v_{ni}/\partial x_k) + (\partial v_{nk}/\partial x_i)$, which vanish for a uniform rotation. (Of course under rotation, vortices cannot be neglected; however, we would still assume that the viscous momentum flux vanishes.) Thus in the linear approximation we have most generally

$$\tau_{ik} = -\eta\left(\frac{\partial v_{ni}}{\partial x_k} + \frac{\partial v_{nk}}{\partial x_i} - \frac{2}{3}\delta_{ik}\frac{\partial v_{n\ell}}{\partial x_\ell}\right) - \zeta_2\delta_{ik}\nabla\cdot\underline{v}_n, \quad (4.101)$$

where η is the shear viscosity and ζ_2 is the second viscosity (the definition of ζ_2 follows that of Landau and Lifshitz [1959]: in many texts ζ_2 is termed the bulk viscosity and $\zeta_2 - \frac{2}{3}\eta$ the second viscosity). Thus, neglecting the term in h, we have

$$R = \eta\left(\frac{\partial v_{ni}}{\partial x_k} + \frac{\partial v_{nk}}{\partial x_i} - \frac{2}{3}\delta_{ik}\frac{\partial v_{n\ell}}{\partial x_\ell}\right)\frac{\partial v_{ni}}{\partial x_k} + \zeta_2(\underline{\nabla}\cdot\underline{v}_n)^2 + K\frac{(\underline{\nabla}T)^2}{T}, \quad (4.102)$$

which can be rewritten as

$$R = \tfrac{1}{2}\eta\left(\frac{\partial v_{ni}}{\partial x_k} + \frac{\partial v_{nk}}{\partial x_i} - \frac{2}{3}\delta_{ik}\frac{\partial v_{n\ell}}{\partial x_\ell}\right)^2 + \zeta_2(\underline{\nabla}\cdot\underline{v}_n)^2 + K\frac{(\underline{\nabla}T)^2}{T}, \quad (4.103)$$

where by definition $(A_{ik})^2 = A_{ik}A_{ki}$. Thus, for R to be positive definite, η, ζ_2, and K must all be positive. If the term with h is retained in (4.99), τ can have an additional term:

$$\tau_{ik} = -\eta\left(\frac{\partial v_{ni}}{\partial x_k} + \frac{\partial v_{nk}}{\partial x_i} - \frac{2}{3}\delta_{ik}\frac{\partial v_{n\ell}}{\partial x_\ell}\right) - \delta_{ik}\left[\zeta_1\underline{\nabla}\cdot(\underline{j} - \rho\underline{v}_n) + \zeta_2\underline{\nabla}\cdot\underline{v}_n\right], \quad (4.104)$$

and h can have the form

$$h = - \zeta_3 \underline{\nabla} \cdot (\underline{j} - \rho \underline{v}_n) - \zeta_4 \underline{\nabla} \cdot \underline{v}_n . \tag{4.105}$$

Thus there are four second viscosities for He II. From kinetic theory it can be shown that $\zeta_1 = \zeta_4$ (Khalatnikov 1965) so that R becomes

$$R = \zeta_2 \underline{\nabla} \cdot \underline{v}_n)^2 + 2\zeta_1 (\underline{\nabla} \cdot \underline{v}_n) \left[\underline{\nabla} \cdot (\underline{j} - \rho \underline{v}_n) \right] + \zeta_3 \left[\underline{\nabla} \cdot (\underline{j} - \rho \underline{v}_n) \right]^2$$

$$+ \tfrac{1}{2} \eta \left(\frac{\partial v_{ni}}{\partial x_k} + \frac{\partial v_{nk}}{\partial x_i} - \frac{2}{3} \delta_{ik} \frac{\partial v_{n\ell}}{\partial x_\ell} \right)^2 + K \frac{(\underline{\nabla}T)^2}{T} . \tag{4.106}$$

For R to be positive definite, ζ_2, ζ_3, η, and K must all be positive. To find the condition on ζ_1, we must consider the quadratic expression

$$z = \zeta_2 x^2 + 2\zeta_1 xy + \zeta_3 y^2 . \tag{4.107}$$

For z to be positive definite for all x and y implies that there are no real solutions for x (or y) for negative z. But

$$x = - \frac{\zeta_1 y}{\zeta_2} \pm \frac{1}{\zeta_2} \left[(\zeta_1^2 - \zeta_2 \zeta_3) y^2 + \zeta_2 z \right]^{\frac{1}{2}} . \tag{4.108}$$

For no real solutions to exist we require

$$(\zeta_1^2 - \zeta_2 \zeta_3) y^2 < - \zeta_2 z \tag{4.109}$$

for any y and any negative z, thus $\zeta_1^2 < \zeta_2 \zeta_3$. The complete hydrodynamic equations may now be written for flow not having superfluid vorticity:

$$\dot{\rho} + \underline{\nabla} \cdot \underline{j} = 0 , \tag{4.110}$$

$$\dot{\underset{\sim}{j}}_i + \frac{\partial \pi_{ki}}{\partial x_k} = \frac{\partial}{\partial x_k}\left\{\eta\left(\frac{\partial v_{ni}}{\partial x_k} + \frac{\partial v_{nk}}{\partial x_i} - \frac{2}{3}\delta_{ik}\underset{\sim}{\nabla}\cdot\underset{\sim}{v}_n\right) + \delta_{ik}\left[\zeta_1\underset{\sim}{\nabla}\cdot(\underset{\sim}{j} - \rho\underset{\sim}{v}_n) + \zeta_2(\underset{\sim}{\nabla}\cdot\underset{\sim}{v}_n)\right]\right\}, \tag{4.111}$$

$$\dot{\underset{\sim}{v}}_s + \underset{\sim}{\nabla}(\tfrac{1}{2}v_s^2 + \Phi) = \nabla\left[\zeta_3\underset{\sim}{\nabla}\cdot(\underset{\sim}{j} - \rho\underset{\sim}{v}_n) + \zeta_4\underset{\sim}{\nabla}\cdot\underset{\sim}{v}_n\right], \tag{4.112}$$

and

$$\dot{\sigma} + \nabla\cdot(\sigma\underset{\sim}{v}_n + \frac{1}{T}\underset{\sim}{q}) = \frac{1}{T}R, \tag{4.113}$$

where

$$\underset{\sim}{j} = \rho_n\underset{\sim}{v}_n + \rho_s\underset{\sim}{v}_s, \tag{4.114}$$

$$\pi_{ik} = \rho_s v_{si} v_{sk} + \rho_n v_{ni} v_{nk} + p\delta_{ik}, \tag{4.115}$$

and R is given by (4. 106). We now return to (4. 97) and take $\pi' = \tilde{\pi} + \tau$, where τ is the viscous contribution to the momentum flux, proportional to the gradients of $\underset{\sim}{j}$ and $\underset{\sim}{v}_n$ and $\tilde{\pi}$ is the additional contribution due to vortices. In general, since the direction $\hat{\omega}$ has been singled out, the fluid is anisotropic; however, the anisotropic contributions to τ and $\underset{\sim}{j}_o$ can be shown to be quite small and are neglected. From (4. 97), in order that R be positive definite, we take

$$\tilde{\pi} = \lambda\omega\delta - \lambda\frac{\underset{\sim}{\omega}\underset{\sim}{\omega}}{\omega}. \tag{4.116}$$

The first term gives an added contribution to the pressure, while the second term represents a tension along the vortex lines and is termed the "vortex filament tension." Also from (4.97), the most general linear form for $\underset{\sim}{f}'$ is seen to be

$$\underset{\sim}{f}' = -\underset{\sim}{\omega} \times (\underset{\sim}{v}_n - \underset{\sim}{v}_s) + \alpha\underset{\sim}{\omega} \times \underset{\sim}{A} + \beta\hat{\omega} \times (\underset{\sim}{\omega} \times \underset{\sim}{A}) - \gamma\hat{\omega}(\underset{\sim}{\omega} \cdot \underset{\sim}{A}), \tag{4.117}$$

where

$$\underset{\sim}{A} = \underset{\sim}{j} - \rho\underset{\sim}{v}_n + \underset{\sim}{\nabla} \times (\lambda\hat{\omega}). \tag{4.118}$$

Putting (4.116) and (4.117) in (4.97), neglecting the terms in h and $\underset{\sim}{q}$, and remembering that $\pi' = \tilde{\pi} + \tau$, we get

$$R = -\tau : \nabla\underset{\sim}{v}_n + \gamma\omega(\hat{\omega} \cdot \underset{\sim}{A})^2 + \beta\omega\left[A^2 - (\underset{\sim}{A} \cdot \hat{\omega})^2\right]. \tag{4.119}$$

Letting θ be the angle between $\mathbf{A}$ and $\underset{\sim}{\omega}$, this becomes

$$R = -\tau : \nabla\underset{\sim}{v}_n + \omega A^2\left(\gamma\cos^2\theta + \beta\sin^2\theta\right), \tag{4.120}$$

so that γ and $\beta > 0$. Now, neglecting the slight anisotropy, we take

$$\underset{\sim}{j}_o = \rho_n(\underset{\sim}{v}_n - \underset{\sim}{v}_s), \tag{4.121}$$

so that $\underset{\sim}{j} - \rho\underset{\sim}{v}_n = -\rho_s(\underset{\sim}{v}_n - \underset{\sim}{v}_s)$. Thus (4.117) can be written

$$\begin{aligned}\underset{\sim}{f}' = &-\frac{1}{\rho_s}\underset{\sim}{\omega} \times \underset{\sim}{\nabla} \times (\lambda\hat{\omega}) - B\frac{\rho_n}{2\rho}\hat{\omega} \times \left[\underset{\sim}{\omega} \times (\underset{\sim}{v}_n - \underset{\sim}{v}_s - \frac{1}{\rho_s}\underset{\sim}{\nabla} \times \lambda\hat{\omega})\right] \\ &- B'\frac{\rho_n}{2\rho}\underset{\sim}{\omega} \times (\underset{\sim}{v}_n - \underset{\sim}{v}_s - \frac{1}{\rho_s}\underset{\sim}{\nabla} \times \lambda\hat{\omega}) \\ &+ B''\frac{\rho_n}{2\rho}\hat{\omega}\left[\underset{\sim}{\omega} \cdot (\underset{\sim}{v}_n - \underset{\sim}{v}_s - \frac{1}{\rho_s}\underset{\sim}{\nabla} \times \lambda\hat{\omega}\right],\end{aligned} \tag{4.122}$$

where

$$B = \frac{2\rho\rho_s}{\rho_n}\beta, \quad B' = 2\frac{\rho}{\rho_n}(1+\alpha\rho_s), \quad B'' = \frac{2\rho\rho_s}{\rho_n}\gamma. \tag{4.123}$$

The equation of motion for the superfluid then becomes

$$\rho_s \dot{\underset{\sim}{v}}_s + \rho_s \underset{\sim}{v}_s \cdot \underset{\sim}{\nabla}\underset{\sim}{v}_s + \rho_s \underset{\sim}{\nabla}\Phi = -\underset{\sim}{\omega} \times (\underset{\sim}{\nabla} \times \lambda\hat{\omega}) + \underset{\sim}{G} - \underset{\sim}{\nabla}h, \tag{4.124}$$

where $\underset{\sim}{G}$ is the force of mutual friction:

$$\begin{aligned}\underset{\sim}{G} = {} & B\frac{\rho_n\rho_s}{2\rho}\hat{\omega} \times \left[\underset{\sim}{\omega} \times (\underset{\sim}{v}_n - \underset{\sim}{v}_s - \frac{1}{\rho_s}\underset{\sim}{\nabla} \times \lambda\hat{\omega})\right] \\ & - B'\frac{\rho_n\rho_s}{2\rho}\underset{\sim}{\omega} \times (\underset{\sim}{v}_n - \underset{\sim}{v}_s - \frac{1}{\rho_s}\underset{\sim}{\nabla} \times \lambda\hat{\omega}) \\ & + B''\frac{\rho_s\rho_n}{2\rho}\hat{\omega}\left[\underset{\sim}{\omega}\cdot(\underset{\sim}{v}_n - \underset{\sim}{v}_s - \frac{1}{\rho_s}\underset{\sim}{\nabla} \times \lambda\hat{\omega})\right].\end{aligned} \tag{4.125}$$

The hydrodynamic equations are then completed by

$$\dot{\rho} + \underset{\sim}{\nabla}\cdot\underset{\sim}{j} = 0, \tag{4.126}$$

$$\dot{j}_i + \frac{\partial}{\partial x_k}(\pi_{ki} + \tau_{ki}) = \frac{\partial}{\partial x_k}\left(\lambda\frac{\omega_k\omega_i}{\omega} - \lambda\omega\delta_{ik}\right), \tag{4.127}$$

and

$$\dot{\sigma} + \underset{\sim}{\nabla}\cdot(\sigma\underset{\sim}{v}_n + \frac{1}{T}\underset{\sim}{q}) = \frac{1}{T}R, \tag{4.128}$$

where π_{ik} is given by (4.115), τ_{ik} by (4.104), and

$$R = -\tau : \underset{\sim}{\nabla}\underset{\sim}{v}_n + \gamma\omega(\hat{\omega}\cdot\underset{\sim}{A})^2 + \beta\omega\left[A^2 - (\underset{\sim}{A}\cdot\hat{\omega})^2\right] + K\frac{(\nabla T)^2}{T} - h\underset{\sim}{\nabla}\cdot(\underset{\sim}{j} - \rho\underset{\sim}{v}_n), \tag{4.129}$$

with $\underset{\sim}{A} = \underset{\sim}{j} - \rho\underset{\sim}{v}_n + \underset{\sim}{\nabla} \times (\lambda\hat{\omega})$ and h given (4.105).

Let us assume that the vortex lines are all parallel and evenly distributed so that $\underset{\sim}{\nu} \times \lambda \hat{\omega}$ vanishes. For equilibrium rotation $\underset{\sim}{v}_s = \underset{\sim}{v}_n$ and the force of mutual friction G vanishes. Now, let the rotation of the normal fluid be increased so that $\underset{\sim}{v}_n - \underset{\sim}{v}_s$ is in the positive θ-direction, θ being the angle of rotation. From (4.125) we see that B' term produces a force radially outward on the superfluid, while the B term gives a force in the θ-direction tending to drag the superfluid along with the normal fluid. Under the conditions given above, the B'' term vanishes. The third term comes into play when the vortices are not straight, for example, if there are oscillations on the lines; however, this term has not been observed experimentally and it is assumed that it is quite small. Now assume that λ is essentially constant but that the vortex lines are curved. Then $\underset{\sim}{\nu} \times \hat{\omega}$ will not vanish. In (4.124) the force $-\underset{\sim}{\omega} \times (\underset{\sim}{\nu} \times \lambda \hat{\omega})$ then acts as a restoring force that tends to straighten the lines. There are then also additional frictional terms from $\underset{\sim}{G}$.

There have been other generalizations to Landau's equations to include superfluid vorticity. Notably, there is Hall and Vinen's (1956) derivation based on the kinetic theory and the interaction of rotons with vortices. Their results are not quite as general as Bekaravich and Khalatnikov's, but their derivation allows a greater insight into the source of the mutual friction term. This derivation will not be given here: the reader is referred to the original papers by Hall and Vinen (1956) and especially to Hall (1963).

Another generalization based on a variational principle has been given by Lin (1963). His derivation produces only the B' term and uniquely fixes B' = 2. As will be seen in § 18, the B' term causes splitting of degenerate second-sound modes in a rotating resonator only if B' ≠ 2. The splitting is, therefore, predicted by the BKHV equations but not by Lin's; furthermore, the splitting has been found experimentally.

§ 18. Second Sound in Rotating Helium. Determination of the B-Coefficients.

The parameters B, B', and B'' in the mutual friction can be determined from a study of second sound in rotating helium. It will be shown that B and B'' produce attenuation, while B' couples certain modes in a second-sound resonator. Before considering second sound, the effect of rotation on ordinary sound in an ideal fluid will be presented. Conservation of mass and momentum are expressed through the equations

$$\rho \frac{d\underset{\sim}{v}}{dt} = - \underset{\sim}{\nabla} p \tag{4.130}$$

and

$$\dot{\rho} + \underset{\sim}{\nabla} \cdot (\rho \underset{\sim}{v}) = 0 , \tag{4.131}$$

where $\frac{d}{dt} = \frac{\partial}{\partial t} + \underset{\sim}{v} \cdot \underset{\sim}{\nabla}$, p is the pressure and ρ the density. Generally speaking, the sound source and receiver will be fixed to the rotating system, and thus the boundary conditions will be time independent only in the rotating frame. It is therefore convenient to rewrite the hydrodynamic equations in terms of the variables seen in the rotating frame. The transformations to a system rotating with velocity $\underset{\sim}{\Omega}$ are just

$$\underset{\sim}{v} \rightarrow \underset{\sim}{v} + \underset{\sim}{\Omega} \times \underset{\sim}{r} \,, \qquad (4.132)$$

$$\frac{d\underset{\sim}{v}}{dt} \rightarrow \frac{d\underset{\sim}{v}}{dt} + 2\underset{\sim}{\Omega} \times \underset{\sim}{v} + \underset{\sim}{\Omega} \times (\underset{\sim}{\Omega} \times \underset{\sim}{r}) \,, \qquad (4.133)$$

and

$$\dot{\rho} \rightarrow \dot{\rho} - (\underset{\sim}{\Omega} \times \underset{\sim}{r}) \cdot \underset{\sim}{\nabla} \rho \,, \qquad (4.134)$$

where $\underset{\sim}{r}$ locates some fluid element (see Goldstein 1959, §4-8 and §4-9). In the rotating frame the hydrodynamic equations become

$$\rho \frac{d\underset{\sim}{v}}{dt} + 2\rho \underset{\sim}{\Omega} \times \underset{\sim}{v} + \rho \underset{\sim}{\Omega} \times (\underset{\sim}{\Omega} \times \underset{\sim}{r}) = -\underset{\sim}{\nabla} p \qquad (4.135)$$

and

$$\dot{\rho} - (\underset{\sim}{\Omega} \times \underset{\sim}{r}) \cdot \underset{\sim}{\nabla} \rho + (\underset{\sim}{v} + \underset{\sim}{\Omega} \times \underset{\sim}{r}) \cdot \underset{\sim}{\nabla} \rho + \rho \underset{\sim}{\nabla} \cdot (\underset{\sim}{v} + \underset{\sim}{\Omega} \times \underset{\sim}{r}) = 0 \,. \qquad (4.136)$$

Linearizing these two equations and assuming the rotational velocity $\underset{\sim}{\Omega} \times \underset{\sim}{r}$ to be small compared with $\underset{\sim}{v}$, we get

$$\dot{\underset{\sim}{v}} + 2\underset{\sim}{\Omega} \times \underset{\sim}{v} = -\frac{1}{\rho_o} \underset{\sim}{\nabla} p \qquad (4.137)$$

and

$$\dot{\rho} + \rho_o \underset{\sim}{\nabla} \cdot \underset{\sim}{v} = 0 \,, \qquad (4.138)$$

where ρ_o is the equilibrium density. The equation of state for sound propagation gives $\dot{p} = c^2 \dot{\rho}$, where c is the sound velocity, so that (4.137) and (4.138) can be combined into a wave equation for $\underset{\sim}{v}$:

$$c^2 \underset{\sim}{\nabla}(\underset{\sim}{\nabla} \cdot \underset{\sim}{v}) - \ddot{\underset{\sim}{v}} - 2\underset{\sim}{\Omega} \times \dot{\underset{\sim}{v}} = 0 \,. \qquad (4.139)$$

Letting the time dependence be $e^{i\sigma t}$, this becomes

$$c^2 \underline{\nabla}(\underline{\nabla} \cdot \underline{v}) + \sigma^2 \underline{v} - 2i\sigma \underline{\Omega} \times \underline{v} = 0 . \qquad (4.140)$$

Consider first a plane wave traveling in the x-direction, $\underline{v} \propto e^{-ikx}$, and take $\underline{\Omega} = \Omega \hat{1}_z$, then (4.140) gives the three equations:

$$(c^2 k^2 - \sigma^2)v_x - 2i\sigma \Omega v_y = 0 , \qquad (4.141)$$

$$2i\sigma \Omega v_x - \sigma^2 v_y = 0 , \qquad (4.142)$$

and

$$v_z = 0 . \qquad (4.143)$$

Equation (4.142) shows that rotation couples a transverse component v_y to the ordinary longitudinal component v_x:

$$v_y = 2i \frac{\Omega}{\sigma} v_x . \qquad (4.144)$$

Ω is assumed to be much smaller than σ so that the v_y component will be small. It should also be noted that there is no coupling of v_z to v_x or v_y.

Now consider a plane wave propagating along the z-axis, $\underline{v} \propto e^{-ikz}$, then (4.140) gives

$$\sigma^2 v_x + 2i\sigma \Omega v_y = 0 , \qquad (4.145)$$

$$2i\sigma \Omega v_x - \sigma^2 v_y = 0 , \qquad (4.146)$$

and

$$(\sigma^2 - c^2 k^2)v_z = 0 . \qquad (4.147)$$

Equations (4.145) and (4.146) are consistent only if $\Omega = \frac{1}{2}\sigma$ and then $v_y = iv_x$. Equation (4.147) requires $\sigma = ck$. Since $\Omega \ll \sigma$, the transverse components must be zero, and the rotation does not affect the wave propagating along the axis of rotation.

Finally, let us consider the normal mode solutions of (4.140) in a square cavity (we consider only modes for which $v_z = 0$, and there is no variation in v_x and v_y in the z-direction). Specifically we wish to find the effect of rotation on the eigenfrequencies. In (4.140) the term $\underset{\sim}{\Omega} \times \underset{\sim}{v}$ is assumed small, and a perturbation approach is used expanding $\underset{\sim}{v}$ and σ:

$$\underset{\sim}{v} = \sum \Omega^n \underset{\sim}{v}_n \tag{4.148}$$

and

$$\sigma = \sum \Omega^n \sigma_n \, . \tag{4.149}$$

Then (4.140) becomes

$$\underset{\sim}{\nabla}\left[\underset{\sim}{\nabla}\cdot(\underset{\sim}{v}_o + \Omega \underset{\sim}{v}_1)\right] + \frac{1}{c^2}(\sigma_o + \Omega \underset{\sim}{v}_1)^2 (\underset{\sim}{v}_o + \Omega \underset{\sim}{v}_1)$$

$$- \frac{2i}{c^2}(\sigma_o + \Omega\sigma_1)\underset{\sim}{\Omega} \times (\underset{\sim}{v}_o + \Omega \underset{\sim}{v}_1) \tag{4.150}$$

$$+ \text{higher order terms} = 0 \, .$$

The zero and first-order equations are then

$$\underset{\sim}{\nabla}(\underset{\sim}{\nabla}\cdot \underset{\sim}{v}_o) + \frac{\sigma_o^2}{c^2} \underset{\sim}{v}_o = 0 \tag{4.151}$$

and

$$\underset{\sim}{\nabla}(\underset{\sim}{\nabla}\cdot \underset{\sim}{v}_1) + \frac{\sigma_o^2}{c^2} \underset{\sim}{v}_1 + \frac{2\sigma_o\sigma_1}{c^2} \underset{\sim}{v}_o - \frac{2i\sigma_o}{c^2\Omega} \underset{\sim}{\Omega} \times \underset{\sim}{v}_o = 0. \tag{4.152}$$

Let $\underset{\sim}{u}_m$ be the vector eigenfunctions of (4.151) and σ_{om} the corresponding eigenfrequencies. Expanding

$$\underset{\sim}{v}_1 = \sum a_n \underset{\sim}{u}_n \tag{4.153}$$

and taking $\underset{\sim}{v}_o$ to be $\underset{\sim}{u}_m$ and σ_o to be σ_{om}, (4.152) becomes

$$\sum a_n \underset{\sim}{\nabla}(\underset{\sim}{\nabla}\cdot u_n) + \sum_n \frac{\sigma_{om}^2}{c^2} a_n \underset{\sim}{u}_n$$

$$+ \frac{2\sigma_{om}\sigma_1}{c^2} \underset{\sim}{u}_m - \frac{2i\sigma_{om}}{c^2\Omega} \underset{\sim}{\Omega} \times \underset{\sim}{u}_m = 0. \tag{4.154}$$

Using (4.151) and taking $\underset{\sim}{\Omega} = \Omega \hat{1}_z$, this equation reduces to

$$\sum_n (\sigma_{om}^2 - \sigma_{on}^2) a_n \underset{\sim}{u}_n$$

$$+ 2\sigma_{om}\sigma_1 - 2i\sigma_{om} \hat{1}_z \times \underset{\sim}{u}_m = 0. \tag{4.155}$$

Multiplying by $\underset{\sim}{u}_k^*\cdot$ and integrating over the square cross-section yields

$$(\sigma_{om}^2 - \sigma_{ok}^2)a_k + 2\sigma_{om}\sigma_1\delta_{mk}$$

$$- 2i\sigma_{om} \int \underset{\sim}{u}_k^* \cdot (\hat{1}_z \times \underset{\sim}{u}_m) dxdy = 0. \tag{4.156}$$

Finally, taking k = m,

$$\sigma_{1m} = i \int \underset{\sim}{u}_m^* \cdot (\hat{1}_z \times \underset{\sim}{u}_m) dxdy$$

$$= i \int (\underset{\sim}{u}_m \times \underset{\sim}{u}_m^*)_z \, dxdy. \tag{4.157}$$

Now consider solutions to the zero order equation (4.151):

$$\frac{\partial^2 u_{mx}}{\partial x^2} + \frac{\partial^2 u_{my}}{\partial x \partial y} + \frac{\sigma_{om}^2}{c^2} u_{mx} = 0 \tag{4.158}$$

$$\frac{\partial^2 u_{mx}}{\partial x \partial y} + \frac{\partial^2 u_{my}}{\partial y^2} + \frac{\sigma_{om}^2}{c^2} u_{my} = 0. \tag{4.159}$$

The corners of the cavity are taken at (0, 0), (b, 0), (0, b), and (b, b). Solutions to (4. 158) and (4. 159), which vanish at the boundaries, are then (of course there are solutions other than these)

$$u_{mx} = \sin\frac{q\pi x}{b} \tag{4.160}$$

and

$$u_{my} = \sin\frac{s\pi y}{b}, \tag{4.161}$$

where q and s are integers. Substituting, we readily find

$$\left(\frac{q\pi}{b}\right)^2 = \left(\frac{s\pi}{b}\right)^2 = \frac{\sigma_{om}^2}{c^2} \tag{4.162}$$

so that $q^2 = s^2 = m^2$. Since the sign is not specified, each value of m has two degenerate solutions so that

$$\underset{\sim}{u}_m^{\pm} = \hat{1}_x \frac{1}{b} \sin\frac{m\pi x}{b} \pm \hat{1}_y \frac{1}{b} \sin\frac{m\pi y}{b}, \tag{4.163}$$

where the factor $\frac{1}{b}$ normalizes the eigenfunctions (i. e., $\int \underset{\sim}{u}_m^+ \cdot \underset{\sim}{u}_m^+ \, dxdy = \underset{\sim}{u}_m^- \cdot \underset{\sim}{u}_m^- \, dxdy = 1$). Since the eigenfunctions are degenerate, (4. 157) cannot be used directly to find the eigenfrequencies, rather the matrix

$$\begin{pmatrix} \sigma_{lm}^{++} & \sigma_{lm}^{+-} \\ \sigma_{lm}^{-+} & \sigma_{lm}^{--} \end{pmatrix} \tag{4.164}$$

must be diagonalized. Now

$$\sigma_{lm}^{++} = \sigma_{lm}^{--} = i \int (\underset{\sim}{u}_m^+ \times \underset{\sim}{u}_m^+)_z \, dxdy = 0 \tag{4.165}$$

and

$$\begin{aligned} \sigma_{lm}^{+-} &= -\sigma_{lm}^{-+} = i \int (\underset{\sim}{u}_m^- \times \underset{\sim}{u}_m^+)_z \, dxdy \\ &= \frac{2i}{m^2 \pi^2} \left[(-1)^m - 1\right]^2 . \end{aligned} \tag{4.166}$$

Thus for m odd, we diagonalize

$$\frac{-8i}{m^2\pi^2}\begin{pmatrix} 0 & 1 \\ -1 & 0 \end{pmatrix}. \tag{4.167}$$

The eigenvalues of the matrix are ± i so that using (4. 149) to first order we get

$$\sigma_m^{\pm} = \sigma_{om} \pm \frac{8\Omega}{m^2\pi^2}. \tag{4.168}$$

Thus there is a splitting of the degenerate modes given by $\frac{16\Omega}{m^2\pi^2}$.

Having seen some of the effects of rotation on sound propagation in an ideal classical fluid, we turn to second sound in He II (Lucas 1965). Dissipation will be neglected so that from (4. 124), (4. 125), (4. 126), (4. 127), and (4. 128) we have after linearization

$$\rho_s \dot{\underset{\sim}{v}}_s + \rho_n \dot{\underset{\sim}{v}}_n = - \underset{\sim}{\nabla} p , \tag{4.169}$$

$$\rho_s \dot{\underset{\sim}{v}}_s = - \rho_s \underset{\sim}{\nabla} \Phi + \underset{\sim}{G} , \tag{4.170}$$

$$\dot{\rho} + \rho_s \underset{\sim}{\nabla} \cdot \underset{\sim}{v}_s + \rho_n \underset{\sim}{\nabla} \cdot \underset{\sim}{v}_n = 0 , \tag{4.171}$$

$$\rho_o \dot{S} + S_o \dot{\rho} + \rho_o S_o \underset{\sim}{\nabla} \cdot \underset{\sim}{v}_n = 0 , \tag{4.172}$$

and

$$\underset{\sim}{G} = - B \frac{\rho_s \rho_n}{2\rho_o} \hat{\omega} \times (\underset{\sim}{\omega} \times \underset{\sim}{q}) - B' \frac{\rho_s \rho_n}{2\rho_o} \underset{\sim}{\omega} \times \underset{\sim}{q} + B'' \frac{\rho_s \rho_n}{2\rho_o} \hat{\omega} (\underset{\sim}{\omega} \cdot \underset{\sim}{q}) , \tag{4.173}$$

where $\underset{\sim}{q} = \underset{\sim}{v}_n - \underset{\sim}{v}_s$ and $\sigma = \rho S$. In addition, it is assumed that the vorticity $\underset{\sim}{\omega}$ is uniform and $\underset{\sim}{\omega} = 2\Omega \hat{1}_z$. From (4. 54) to first order we have

$$\underset{\sim}{\nabla} \Phi = \frac{1}{\rho_o} \underset{\sim}{\nabla} p - S_o \underset{\sim}{\nabla} T. \tag{4.174}$$

Then (4.170) becomes

$$\dot{\underset{\sim}{v}}_s = -\frac{1}{\rho_o} \underset{\sim}{\nabla} p + S_o \underset{\sim}{\nabla} T + \frac{1}{\rho_s} \underset{\sim}{G}. \tag{4.175}$$

Eliminating $\dot{\underset{\sim}{v}}_s$ from (4.169) and using (4.175), we get

$$\dot{\underset{\sim}{v}}_n = -\frac{1}{\rho_o} \underset{\sim}{\nabla} p - \frac{\rho_s}{\rho_n} S_o \underset{\sim}{\nabla} T - \frac{1}{\rho_n} \underset{\sim}{G}. \tag{4.176}$$

Subtracting (4.175) from (4.176) yields

$$\dot{\underset{\sim}{q}} = -\frac{\rho_o S_o}{\rho_n} \underset{\sim}{\nabla} T - \frac{\rho_o}{\rho_s \rho_n} \underset{\sim}{G}. \tag{4.177}$$

Using $\rho_o = \rho_s + \rho_n$, (4.171) becomes

$$\dot{\rho} + \rho_o \underset{\sim}{\nabla} \cdot \underset{\sim}{v} - \rho_s \underset{\sim}{\nabla} \cdot \underset{\sim}{q} = 0, \tag{4.178}$$

and eliminating $\underset{\sim}{\nabla} \cdot \underset{\sim}{v}_n$ from this by (4.172), there results

$$\dot{S} = -\frac{\rho_s S_o}{\rho_o} \underset{\sim}{\nabla} \cdot \underset{\sim}{q}. \tag{4.179}$$

Letting C be the specific heat (remember that $C_p \approx C_v = C$) so that $\dot{S} = C\dot{T}$, (4.179) becomes

$$\dot{T} = -\frac{\rho_s S_o}{C\rho_o} \underset{\sim}{\nabla} \cdot \underset{\sim}{q}. \tag{4.180}$$

We now transform (4.177) and (4.180) to the rotating frame in the same approximation as for the classical fluid. Thus

$$\dot{\underset{\sim}{q}} + 2\Omega \times \underset{\sim}{q} = -\frac{\rho_o S_o}{\rho_n} \underset{\sim}{\nabla} T - \frac{\rho_o}{\rho_s \rho_n} \underset{\sim}{G}, \tag{4.181}$$

$$\dot{T} = -\frac{\rho_s S_o}{C\rho_o} \underset{\sim}{\nabla} \cdot \underset{\sim}{q}, \tag{4.182}$$

and

$$\underset{\sim}{G} = - B \frac{\rho_s \rho_n}{\rho_o} \hat{\Omega} \times (\underset{\sim}{\Omega} \times \underset{\sim}{q}) - B' \frac{\rho_s \rho_n}{\rho_o} \underset{\sim}{\Omega} \times \underset{\sim}{q}$$

$$+ B'' \frac{\rho_s \rho_n}{\rho_o} \hat{\Omega}(\underset{\sim}{\Omega} \cdot \underset{\sim}{q}) \, . \tag{4.183}$$

These three equations are now combined to form a wave equation for $\underset{\sim}{q}$:

$$\ddot{\underset{\sim}{q}} + (2-B')\underset{\sim}{\Omega} \times \dot{\underset{\sim}{q}} - B\hat{\Omega} \times (\underset{\sim}{\Omega} \times \dot{\underset{\sim}{q}})$$

$$+ B''\hat{\Omega}(\underset{\sim}{\Omega} \cdot \dot{\underset{\sim}{q}}) = u_2^2 \, \underset{\sim}{\nabla}(\underset{\sim}{\nabla} \cdot \underset{\sim}{q}) \, , \tag{4.184}$$

where $u_2^2 = \frac{\rho_s S_o^2}{\rho_n C}$ is the speed of second sound. Let $\underset{\sim}{q} \propto e^{i\sigma t}$ so that

$$u_2^2 \, \underset{\sim}{\nabla}(\underset{\sim}{\nabla} \cdot \underset{\sim}{q}) + \sigma^2 \underset{\sim}{q} - i\sigma(2-B')\underset{\sim}{\Omega} \times \underset{\sim}{q}$$

$$+ i\sigma B\hat{\Omega} \times (\underset{\sim}{\Omega} \times \underset{\sim}{q}) - i\sigma B''\hat{\Omega}(\underset{\sim}{\Omega} \cdot \underset{\sim}{q}) = 0 \, . \tag{4.185}$$

Consider a plane wave solution, $\underset{\sim}{q} \propto e^{-ikx}$ with $q_z = 0$ and $\underset{\sim}{\Omega} = \Omega \hat{1}_z$. Then (4.185) gives

$$(u_2^2 k^2 - \sigma^2 + i\sigma\Omega B)q_x - i\sigma\Omega(2-B')q_y = 0 \tag{4.186}$$

and

$$i\sigma\Omega(2-B')q_x + (i\sigma\Omega B - \sigma^2)q_y = 0. \tag{4.187}$$

From (4.187) we have a transverse component q_y coupled to the longitudinal component

$$q_y = \frac{\frac{i\Omega}{\sigma}(2-B')}{\left(1 - \frac{i\Omega B}{\sigma}\right)} q_x \approx \frac{i\Omega}{\sigma}(2-B')q_x \tag{4.188}$$

to first order in $\frac{\Omega}{\sigma}$. For (4.186) and (4.187) to be consistent, we must also have

$$(u_2^2 k^2 - \sigma^2 + i\sigma\Omega B)(i\sigma\Omega B - \sigma^2) - \sigma^2\Omega^2(2-B')^2 = 0, \tag{4.189}$$

or to first order in Ω

$$k = \frac{\sigma}{u_2} - i\frac{B\Omega}{2u_2}. \tag{4.190}$$

Thus, for these waves, the B term gives rise to an absorption coefficient

$$\alpha = \frac{B\Omega}{2u_2}, \tag{4.191}$$

and the B' term couples the x- and y-velocity components. Now consider a wave along the rotation axis, $q_z \propto e^{-ikz}$, $q_x = q_z = 0$. Then

$$(u_2^2 k^2 - \sigma^2 + i\sigma\Omega B'')q_z = 0 \tag{4.192}$$

and

$$k = \frac{\sigma}{u_2}\left(1 - \frac{i\Omega B''}{\sigma}\right)^{\frac{1}{2}} \approx \frac{\sigma}{u_2} - \frac{iB''\Omega}{2u_2}, \tag{4.193}$$

and there is an absorption coefficient

$$\alpha'' = \frac{B''\Omega}{2u_2}. \tag{4.194}$$

If in (4.185) the terms in B and B'', which cause absorption, are neglected, the mode splitting in a square cavity is readily found by comparison with the classical case. The factor 2 in (4.140) is simply replaced with the factor 2-B'. Then the degenerate modes (4.163) are split in frequency by an amount

$$\Delta\sigma_m = \frac{8(2-B')\Omega}{m^2\pi^2}. \tag{4.195}$$

(In Lin's equations, considered briefly at the end of §17, B' has the value of 2, and no splitting is predicted.)

Snyder (1963) and Snyder and Linekin (1966) have measured B' by observing the mode splitting in a square second-sound resonator under rotation. The cavity is shown in Figure 4. 1.

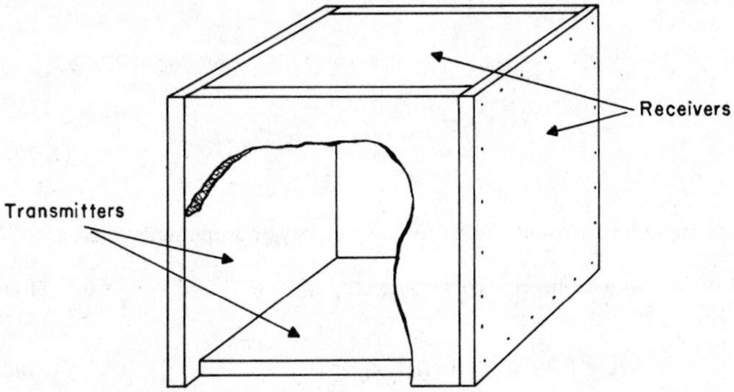

Fig. 4. 1.

The dimensions of one cavity used are 3.70 × 3.70 × 3.65 cm. The length of the cavity in the z-direction is made different from the other dimensions to prevent a coupling to a mode along the z-axis (axis of rotation). The walls of the cavity are made from a ceramic known as Lava Stone, which can be machined while soft and then fired. This material is porous to both the normal fluid and the superfluid, allowing the heat generated by the electrical apparatus to pass through the walls easily, while second sound, having a wavelength much greater than the pores in the ceramic, is reflected efficiently. The opposite faces were coated with aquadag serving as transmitters and receivers of second sound. A typical response curve for the cavity is shown in Figure 4. 2a, and a plot of the peak separation versus Ω is given in Figure 4. 2b.

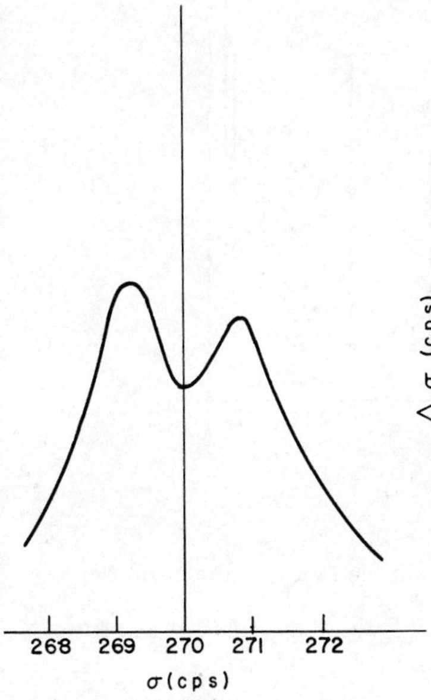

Fig. 4.2a.

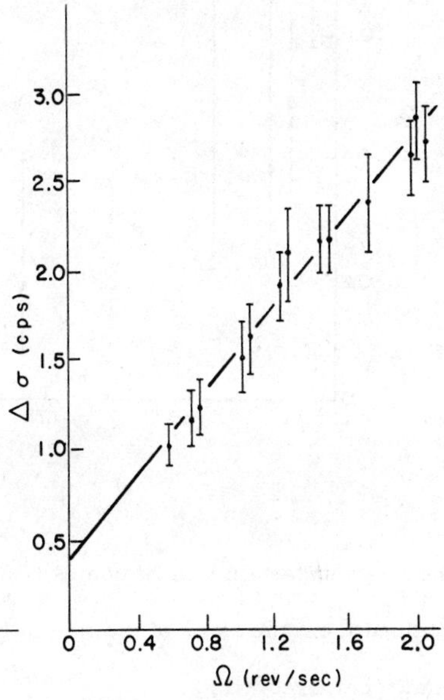

Fig. 4.2b.

No explanation has yet been given for the residual splitting shown in Figure 4.2b for $\Omega = 0$. The values of B' versus temperature are given in Figure 4.3.

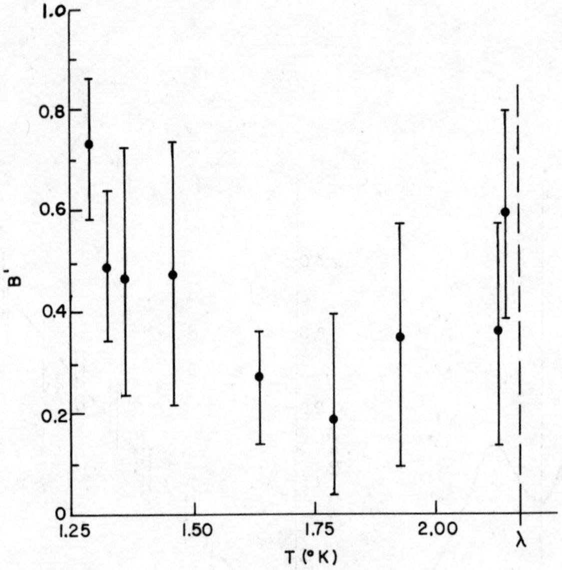

Fig. 4.3.

The large uncertainty in B' comes from the fact that the quantity obtained from the slope of the line in Figure 4.2b is (2-B') and B' is small compared with 2.

Attempts to measure B'' by Snyder and Linekin (1966) show that B'' is quite small. B/B'' is found to be larger than 120 at low temperature and larger than 560 near the λ-point. B and B'' can be found from (4.191) and (4.194) in terms of the absorption coefficients α and

α''. The total absorption coefficient α_T is related to the Q of a cavity by

$$\alpha_T = \frac{2\pi}{\lambda Q} . \qquad (4.196)$$

Letting $\alpha_T = \alpha_o + \alpha(\Omega)$, where α_o is the absorption coefficient with the resonator at rest (resulting from viscosity and heat conduction), we get

$$\alpha_o = \frac{2\pi}{\lambda Q_o} , \qquad (4.197)$$

where Q_o is measured for $\Omega = 0$. Then we find

$$\alpha(\Omega) = \frac{2\pi}{\lambda Q_o} \left(\frac{Q_o}{Q(\Omega)} - 1 \right), \qquad (4.198)$$

where α represents either α or α'', depending on the excited mode, and $Q(\Omega)$ is the total Q under rotation. Hall and Vinen (1956) have found B by measuring Q_o and $\frac{Q_o}{Q(\Omega)}$. The ratio $\frac{Q(\Omega)}{Q_o}$ is given by the ratio of the resonant peak height under rotation to the peak height for $\Omega = 0$. Q_o was determined from the shape of the resonance curves and also from the decay time of a second-sound mode. The two methods agree within 3 per cent. The resulting values for B as a function of temperature are given in Figure 4.4.

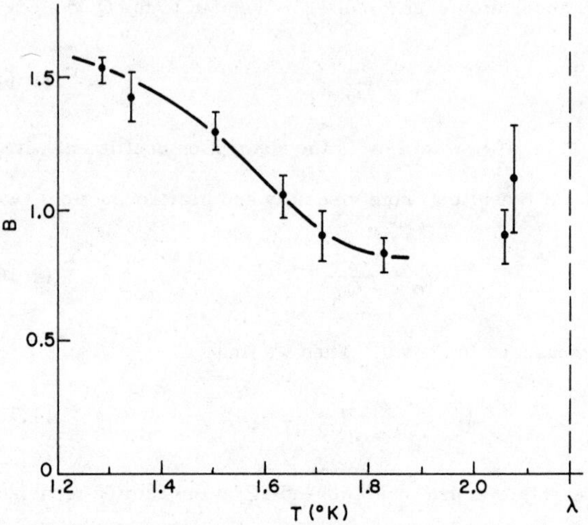

Fig. 4.4.

§19. Hydrodynamic Stability of He II

Consider the steady flow velocity $\underset{\sim}{v}$ for a classical fluid between two concentric cylinders of radii R_1 and R_2 ($R_1 < R_2$) rotating with angular velocities Ω_1 and Ω_2. Taking the fluid to be incompressible, one steady-state solution of the Navier-Stokes equation assuming only a θ component of velocity is

$$v_o = \frac{\Omega_2 R_2^2 - \Omega_1 R_1^2}{R_2^2 - R_1^2}\, r + \frac{(\Omega_1 - \Omega_2)}{R_2^2 - R_1^2}\, \frac{1}{r} \qquad (4.199)$$

(Landau and Lifshitz 1959, §18). It is known experimentally that this flow does exist if certain conditions are met by the parameters Ω_1, Ω_2, R_1, and R_2. Other stationary flows exist that also satisfy the

Navier-Stokes equations, and one is led to consider the conditions for a transition from one state to the other. A simpler problem is to determine the conditions for which the flow (4. 199) becomes unstable to a small disturbance and to determine the wave number of the disturbance that causes the instability. The stability of a given stationary flow can be studied through perturbation theory taking the flow velocity as $\underset{\sim}{v} + \underset{\sim}{v}'$, where $\underset{\sim}{v}$ is the steady-state value and $\underset{\sim}{v}'$ is the time-dependent perturbation. Substituting $\underset{\sim}{v} + \underset{\sim}{v}'$ into the Navier-Stokes equation, we get an equation for $\underset{\sim}{v}'$. If only the conditions for the onset of instability are desired, the equation is linearized and solutions of the form $\underset{\sim}{v}' \propto e^{-i\omega t}$ are investigated. In general, the frequency ω is complex and the flow $\underset{\sim}{v}$ is stable if Im $\omega > 0$, that is, if the perturbation $\underset{\sim}{v}'$ decays with time. On the other hand, if, for some value of ω, Im $\omega < 0$, the perturbation will grow with time and the flow $\underset{\sim}{v}$ is unstable. Thus the conditions for which Im $\omega = 0$ are sought, that separate the stable and unstable regions. In the case of an <u>inviscid</u> fluid between rotating cylinders, the flow (4. 199) is stable if the cylinders rotate in the same direction and if $\Omega_2 R_2^2 > \Omega_1 R_1^2$. The flow is unstable if $\Omega_2 R_2^2 < \Omega_1 R_1^2$ of if the cylinders rotate in opposite directions (Rayleigh's criterion). Experiments by R. J. Donnelly (1959) and theoretical calculations of S. Chandrasekhar and R. J. Donnelly (1957) and S. Chandrasekhar (1957) indicate that there are two stability criteria for He II, one associated with the superfluid and the other associated with the normal fluid. Torque measurements made with a rotating Viscometer (§4) show these regions of flow. The point Ω_s (Fig. 2.4) is associated with an instability in the superfluid, and the point Ω_n results from an instability in the normal fluid. The equations used by Chandrasekhar and Donnelly were incomplete as they antedated the Bekarevich-Khalatnikov equations. The problem is presently receiving renewed experimental attention and should prove to be of fundamental interest in fluid mechanics.

REFERENCES

Chandrasekhar, S. 1957, Proc. Roy. Soc. (London), A241, 29.

Chandrasekhar, S., and Donnelly, R. J. 1957, Proc. Roy. Soc. (London), A241, 9.

Chester, G. V. 1963, Proceedings of the International School of Physics, Course XXI, edited by G. Careri (New York: Academic Press).

Donnelly, R. J. 1959, Phys. Rev. Letters, 3, 507.

Fetter, A. L. 1965, Phys. Rev., A429, 138.

Goldstein, H. 1959, Classical Mechanics (Reading, Mass.: Addison-Wesley).

Hall, H. E. 1963, Proceedings of the International School of Physics, Course XXI, edited by G. Careri (New York: Academic Press).

Hall, H. E., and Vinen, W. F. 1956, Proc. Roy. Soc. (London), A238, 204, 215.

Kaufmann, Walther 1963, Fluid Mechanics (New York: McGrow-Hill).

Khalatnikov, I. M. 1965, An Introduction to the Theory of Superfluidity (New York: Benjamin).

Landau, L. D., and Lifshitz, E. M. 1959, Fluid Mechanics (Reading, Mass.: Addison-Wesley).

Lin, C. C. 1963, Proceedings of the International School of Physics, Course XXI, edited by G. Careri (New York: Academic Press).

Lucas, P. 1965, Phys. Rev. Letters, 15, 750.

Milne-Thomson, L. M. 1960, Theoretical Hydrodynamics (New York: Macmillan).

Snyder, H. A. 1963, Phys. Fluids, 6, 755.

Snyder, H. A., and Linekin, D. M. 1966, Phys. Rev., 147, 131.

CHAPTER 5

MICROSCOPIC THEORY OF HELIUM II

§20. Ideal Bose-Einstein Gas

In a first crude attempt at developing a microscopic theory of liquid helium, we consider the behavior of a dilute Bose-Einstein gas. This model, which at first sight might seem a poor approximation to liquid helium, is supported by two observations. First, the zero point energy of liquid helium has an unusually large effect on the structure, making it only about one-third as dense as would be expected classically. In addition, above 1.5°K the viscosity behaves gaslike, increasing with increasing temperature.

It is well known that as the temperature is lowered, the particles of an ideal Bose gas condense into the state of zero momentum (Landau and Lifshitz 1958). This condensation begins to occur at the temperature

$$T_c = \frac{h^2}{2\pi mk}\left(\frac{N/V}{2.612}\right)^{2/3}, \tag{5.1}$$

where N is the total number of particles and V is the volume. Below this temperature the number of particles N_o in the ground state is

$$N_o = N\left[1 - \left(\frac{T}{T_c}\right)^{3/2}\right] \tag{5.2}$$

and is of order N. Above T_c, the number of condensed particles N_o is only of order one. At $T = T_c$ a phase transition is said to occur, although the phase separation is in momentum space rather than configuration space. One phase, the condensed phase, consists of the N_o particles in the zero-momentum state while the other phase consists of the $N - N_o = N\left(\frac{T}{T_c}\right)^{2/3}$ uncondensed particles distributed over the excited states. The superfluid can now be associated with the particles in the ground state and the normal fluid identified with the excited particles. The entropy of a system is proportional to the logarithm of the number of available states, and since there is only one available state for the particles in the superfluid as defined above, the entropy of the superfluid is zero in agreement with the observations in §5 on liquid helium. Also, for a fluid to exhibit a viscosity, it must be able to exchange momentum with other objects, such as ions or walls. In an ideal Bose gas, the superfluid cannot lose momentum since all the superfluid particles are in the zero-momentum state. The particles in the ground state can, on the other hand, gain momentum and become excited particles. In §14 it was shown that excited states cannot be produced from the superfluid until certain critical velocities are reached and that this requirement results from the particular shape of the energy momentum curve in Figure 3.3. For the ideal Bose gas, the single particle energy-momentum relation is just $\epsilon = \frac{p^2}{2m}$, and Landau's criterion will hold for vanishing velocities (§14). Thus the ideal Bose gas does not possess the property of superfluidity, and the interparticle interactions will have to be considered if the spectrum $\varepsilon = \frac{p^2}{2m}$ is to be modified to predict superfluidity.

The specific heat for the ideal Bose gas can also be calculated, and using the helium parameters, we get the curve in Figure 5.1.

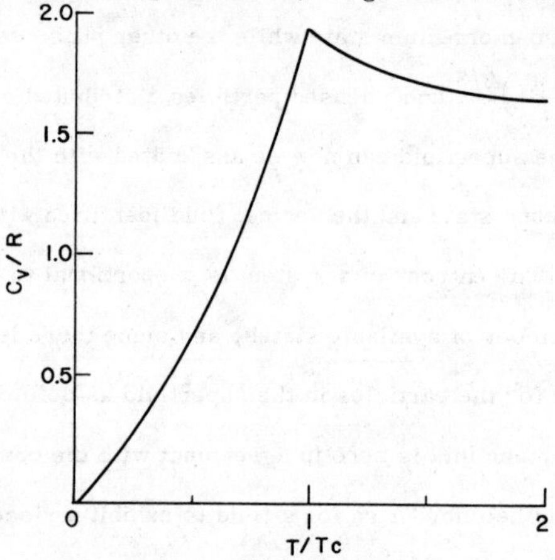

Fig. 5.1.

The temperature T_c using the helium parameters is 3.13° K and is close to the λ temperature (2.17° K). The specific heat in Figure 5.1 is continuous at T_c but its slope is discontinuous. In liquid helium the specific heat itself has a logarithmic discontinuity at the λ-point (Fig. 1.3), and we see again that the interparticle interactions will have to be included if a realistic picture is to result.

It should be noted, however, that the ideal Bose gas does have the convenient feature that the superfluid can be identified with the particles in the zero-momentum state. The momentum states referred to here are the eigenstates of the single particle momentum that for an ideal gas commutes with the total Hamiltonian of the system. When interactions are included, the single particle momentum no longer commutes with the total Hamiltonian and it is more difficult to define what is meant by the Bose condensation (Penrose and Onsager 1956). Of more immediate importance is the effect of interactions on the energy spectrum, and this is considered in the following section.

§21. Bogoliubov's Theory— the Weakly Interacting Bose Gas

The Landau model assumes that the normal fluid can be treated as a gas of particles, each particle having the energy spectrum shown in Figure 3.3. From these assumptions all of the thermodynamic functions can be calculated quite accurately (except in the vicinity of the λ-point, §12). Thus any microscopic theory must predict this energy spectrum, and since the ideal Bose gas has for a single particle energy spectrum $\epsilon = \frac{p^2}{2m}$, it is obvious that the interactions between the particles must be included. Bogoliubov (1947) has obtained an approximatate energy spectrum for a weakly interacting Bose system that predicts the linear phonon region of the spectrum. His approach is based on the formalism of second quantization, and we shall discuss this first.

If a set of functions $\{\varphi_i(\underset{\sim}{x})\}$ is complete in three space dimensions, then the set of all product functions $\{\varphi_{i_1}(\underset{\sim}{x}_1)\,\varphi_{i_2}(\underset{\sim}{x}_2)\cdots \varphi_{i_N}(\underset{\sim}{x}_N)\}$ will be complete in 3N dimensions, the same boundary conditions being assumed in the N-subspaces. The stationary solutions to Schroedinger's equation for N-particles can, therefore, be written as a linear combination of these product functions; however, since the wave function must be symmetric (only Bose systems are considered), it is convenient to use a symmetrized set of base functions. Thus we take as elements for our complete set

$$\Phi_{N_1, N_2 \cdots}(\underset{\sim}{x}_1, \underset{\sim}{x}_2, \cdots \underset{\sim}{x}_N)$$
$$= \left(\frac{N_1! N_2! \cdots}{N!}\right)^{\frac{1}{2}} \sum_P \varphi_{Pi_1}(\underset{\sim}{x}_1) \varphi_{Pi_2}(\underset{\sim}{x}_2) \cdots \varphi_{Pi_N}(\underset{\sim}{x}_N), \tag{5.3}$$

where the numbers $N_1, N_2, \cdots$ give the number of times the functions $\varphi_1, \varphi_2, \cdots$ appear in the products, and the summation extends over all <u>distinct</u> permutations of the numbers $i_1, i_2 \cdots i_N$. The functions $\varphi_i(\underset{\sim}{x})$ are assumed to be orthonormal, and with the definition (5.3), it can be shown that the functions $\Phi_{N_1, N_2 \cdots}$ are also orthonormal, that is,

$$\int \Phi^*_{N_1, N_2 \cdots}(\underset{\sim}{x}_1, \underset{\sim}{x}_2, \cdots \underset{\sim}{x}_N) \Phi_{N_1', N_2' \cdots}(\underset{\sim}{x}_1, \underset{\sim}{x}_2, \cdots \underset{\sim}{x}_N)$$
$$d^3x_1 \cdots d^3x_N = \delta_{N_1, N_1'} \delta_{N_2, N_2'} \cdots \quad . \tag{5.4}$$

The functions $\varphi_i(\underset{\sim}{x})$ can be chosen as eigenfunctions of any single particle operator, and choosing the momentum operator, we would have

$$\varphi_{\underset{\sim}{p}}(\underset{\sim}{x}) = \frac{1}{\sqrt{\Omega}} e^{i\underset{\sim}{p} \cdot \underset{\sim}{x}}, \tag{5.5}$$

where Ω is the volume of the system and $\underset{\sim}{p}$ is the single particle momentum in units of $\hbar$. For this reason the functions $\varphi_i(\underset{\sim}{x})$ are referred to as single particle states and the numbers $N_1, N_2 \cdots$ as the occupation numbers for these states. If there were no interactions and if the momentum states (5.5) were chosen for the single particle states, (5.3) would be an exact eigenfunction of the N-body Hamiltonian, and the occupation numbers would give the exact number of particles in the various momentum states. When interactions are included, the exact eigenfunctions of the Hamiltonians will be a linear combination of the states (5.3), and one can then only ask for the probability of finding a certain occupation $N_1, N_2 \cdots$ of the single particle states.

We will be interested in the expectation values of operators, in particular the Hamiltonian, taken with respect to the exact solutions of the N-body Schroedinger equation. Let us first consider single particle operators of the form

$$\mathfrak{F}^{(1)}(\underset{\sim}{x}_1 \cdots \underset{\sim}{x}_N) = \sum_{i=1}^{N} f^{(1)}(\underset{\sim}{x}_i) \ . \tag{5.6}$$

If the exact wave function is expanded in a series of the functions (5.3), the expectation value of $\mathfrak{F}^{(1)}$ will include terms of the form

$$\left(\Phi_{N_1, N_2, \cdots} ; \mathfrak{F}^{(1)} \Phi_{N_1', N_2' \cdots} \right) . \tag{5.7}$$

From (5.3) and (5.6) it can be seen that (5.7) can be written as the sum

$$\sum_{ik} A_{ik} f_{ik}^{(1)} , \tag{5.8}$$

where

$$f_{ik}^{(1)} = \int \varphi_i^*(\underset{\sim}{x}) f^{(1)}(\underset{\sim}{x}) \varphi_k(\underset{\sim}{x}) d^3x . \qquad (5.9)$$

If the algebra is carried out, it is found that the coefficients A_{ik} depend in a simple way on the numbers $N_1, N_2, \cdots N_1', N_2' \cdots$. This dependence can be formally indicated by

$$\langle N_1, N_2, \cdots | F^{(1)} | N_1', N_2' \cdots \rangle = \sum_{ik} A_{ik} f_{ik}^{(1)} . \qquad (5.10)$$

The formalism can be carried further by defining a state vector $| \cdots N_i \cdots \rangle$, and the operators a_i and a_i^+ through

$$a_i | N_1 \cdots N_i \cdots \rangle = \sqrt{N_i}\, | N_1 \cdots N_i - 1 \cdots \rangle , \qquad (5.11)$$

$$a_i^+ | N_1 \cdots N_i \cdots \rangle = \sqrt{N_i + 1}\, | N_1 \cdots N_i + 1 \cdots \rangle , \qquad (5.12)$$

and

$$\langle N_1 \cdots N_i \cdots | N_1' \cdots N_i' \cdots \rangle = \delta_{N_1, N_2'} \delta_{N_2, N_2'} \cdots . \qquad (5.13)$$

Thus a_i decreases the number of particles in state φ_i by one, and its hermitian conjugate a_i^+ increases the number of particles in state φ_i by one. Taking the hermitian conjugate of (5.11) and (5.12), we also have

$$\langle N_1 \cdots N_i \cdots | a_i^+ = \sqrt{N_i}\, \langle N_1 \cdots N_i - 1 \cdots | \qquad (5.14)$$

and

$$\langle N_1 \cdots N_i \cdots | a_i = \sqrt{N_i + 1}\, \langle N_1 \cdots N_i + 1 \cdots | , \qquad (5.15)$$

so that

$$\langle N_1 \cdots N_i \cdots | a_i | N_1' \cdots N_i' \cdots \rangle$$

$$= \sqrt{N_i'}\, \delta_{N_1, N_1'} \cdots \delta_{N_i, N_i'-1} \cdots \qquad (5.16)$$

or

$$= \sqrt{N_i + 1}\, \delta_{N_1, N_1'} \cdots \delta_{N_i + 1, N_i'} \cdots ,$$

and similarly for a_i^+. From (5.11) and (5.12) the following commutation relations are readily found:

$$\left[a_i , a_k \right] = \left[a_i^+ , a_k^+ \right] = 0 \qquad (5.17)$$

and

$$\left[a_i , a_k^+ \right] = \delta_{ik} . \qquad (5.18)$$

It should be noted that the commutation relations imply equations (5.11) and (5.12) (Roman 1965). With these definitions it is just an algebraic problem (a tedious one perhaps) to show that (5.10) can be written

$$\langle N_1 , N_2 , \cdots | F^{(1)} | N_1' , N_2' \cdots \rangle$$

$$= \sum_{ik} f_{ik}^{(1)} \langle N_1 , N_2 \cdots | a_i^+ a_k | N_1' , N_2' \cdots \rangle , \qquad (5.19)$$

and

$$F^{(1)} = \sum_{ik} f_{ik}^{(1)} a_i^+ a_k \qquad (5.20)$$

can be defined as the single particle operator in this number representation. For example, the particle density operator in configuration space is

$$\rho(\underset{\sim}{x}') = \sum_{i=1}^{N} \delta(\underset{\sim}{x}' - \underset{\sim}{x}_i) , \tag{5.21}$$

and the operator for the total number of particles is

$$\mathfrak{n} = \int d^3x' \sum_{i=1}^{N} \delta(\underset{\sim}{x}' - \underset{\sim}{x}_i) = N . \tag{5.22}$$

Thus the single particle operator is just n = 1 and from (5.9)

$$n_{ik}^{(1)} = \int \varphi_i^* (\underset{\sim}{x}) n \varphi_k(\underset{\sim}{x}) d^3x = \delta_{ik} . \tag{5.23}$$

In the number representation, the operator for the total number of particles is then

$$N = \sum a_i^+ a_i \tag{5.24}$$

and should be obvious from the definitions (5.11) and (5.12). From (5.11) and (5.12) we also find that $N_i = a_i^+ a_i$ is the operator for the number of particles in the individual states φ_i. For a two particle operator

$$\mathfrak{F}^{(2)}(\underset{\sim}{x}_1 \cdots \underset{\sim}{x}_N) = \sum_{ik}{}' f^{(2)}(\underset{\sim}{x}_i, \underset{\sim}{x}_k) , \tag{5.25}$$

we get after more algebra

$$F^{(2)} = \sum_{ik\ell m} f_{\ell m}^{(2)ik} a_i^+ a_k^+ a_\ell a_m \tag{5.26}$$

with

$$f_{\ell m}^{(2)ik} = \int \varphi_i^* (\underset{\sim}{x}) \varphi_k^* (\underset{\sim}{x}') f^{(2)} (\underset{\sim}{x}, \underset{\sim}{x}') \varphi_\ell(\underset{\sim}{x}) \varphi_m(\underset{\sim}{x}') d^3x d^3x' . \tag{5.27}$$

The number representation does not give us anything new. Its advantage lies in the fact that the many algebraic manipulations resulting from the symmetrization of the base function have been suppressed.

We now turn to the weakly interacting Bose gas whose Hamiltonian is

$$\mathcal{H} = \sum_k \frac{p_k^2}{2m} + \tfrac{1}{2}\sum_{ik}{}' V(|\underset{\sim}{x}_i - \underset{\sim}{x}_k|) = \mathcal{H}_o + \mathcal{H}' . \qquad (5.28)$$

In the number representation we have

$$H_o = \sum_{ik} H_{ik}\, a_i^+ a_k \qquad (5.29)$$

and

$$H' = \sum_{ik\ell m} V(i,k;\ell,m) a_i^+ a_k^+ a_\ell a_m . \qquad (5.30)$$

If the single particle states φ_i are taken as the momentum states (5.5), we find

$$H_{\underset{\sim}{p}\underset{\sim}{p}'} = \frac{1}{\Omega}\int e^{-i\underset{\sim}{p}\cdot\underset{\sim}{x}}\left(\frac{\nabla^2}{2m}\right) e^{i\underset{\sim}{p}'\cdot\underset{\sim}{x}} d^3x$$

$$= \frac{p^2}{2m}\,\delta_{\underset{\sim}{p}\underset{\sim}{p}'} . \qquad (5.31)$$

Thus

$$H_o = \sum_{\underset{\sim}{p}} \frac{p^2}{2m}\, a_{\underset{\sim}{p}}^+ a_{\underset{\sim}{p}} . \qquad (5.32)$$

Also

$$V(\underset{\sim}{p}_1,\underset{\sim}{p}_2;\underset{\sim}{p}_3,\underset{\sim}{p}_4)$$

$$= \frac{1}{\Omega^2}\int V(|\underset{\sim}{x}-\underset{\sim}{x}'|)\, e^{-i(\underset{\sim}{p}_1-\underset{\sim}{p}_3)\cdot\underset{\sim}{x}}\, e^{-i(\underset{\sim}{p}_2-\underset{\sim}{p}_4)\cdot\underset{\sim}{x}'}\, d^3x\, d^3x' \tag{5.33}$$

$$= \delta(\underset{\sim}{p}_1+\underset{\sim}{p}_2-\underset{\sim}{p}_3-\underset{\sim}{p}_4)\, V(|\underset{\sim}{p}_2-\underset{\sim}{p}_4|),$$

where

$$V(|\underset{\sim}{p}|) = \frac{1}{\Omega}\int v(|\underset{\sim}{x}|)\, e^{-i\underset{\sim}{p}\cdot\underset{\sim}{x}}\, d^3x . \tag{5.34}$$

Thus

$$H' = \tfrac{1}{2}\sum_{\underset{\sim}{p}_1\underset{\sim}{p}_2\underset{\sim}{p}_3\underset{\sim}{p}_4} V(|\underset{\sim}{p}_2-\underset{\sim}{p}_4|)\,\delta(\underset{\sim}{p}_1+\underset{\sim}{p}_2-\underset{\sim}{p}_3-\underset{\sim}{p}_4)\, a^+_{\underset{\sim}{p}_1} a^+_{\underset{\sim}{p}_2} a_{\underset{\sim}{p}_3} a_{\underset{\sim}{p}_4} . \tag{5.35}$$

The momentum conservation required by the delta function can be taken into account by letting $\underset{\sim}{k} = \underset{\sim}{p}_1-\underset{\sim}{p}_3 = \underset{\sim}{p}_4-\underset{\sim}{p}_2$ and replacing $\underset{\sim}{p}_3 \to \underset{\sim}{p}$ and $\underset{\sim}{p}_4 \to q$. Then

$$H' = \tfrac{1}{2}\sum_{\underset{\sim}{k}\underset{\sim}{p}\underset{\sim}{q}} V_{\underset{\sim}{k}}\, a^+_{\underset{\sim}{p}+\underset{\sim}{k}}\, a^+_{\underset{\sim}{q}-\underset{\sim}{k}}\, a_{\underset{\sim}{p}}\, a_{\underset{\sim}{q}} , \tag{5.36}$$

where $V_{\underset{\sim}{k}} = V(|\underset{\sim}{k}|)$ is the Fourier transform of the potential defined in (5.34). Expanding this, we get

$$H' = \tfrac{1}{2}V_o a^+_o a^+_o a_o a_o$$

$$+ \tfrac{1}{2}V_o {\sum}' a^+_o a^+_{\underset{\sim}{p}} a_o a_{\underset{\sim}{p}} + \tfrac{1}{2}V_o {\sum}' a^+_{\underset{\sim}{p}} a^+_o a_{\underset{\sim}{p}} a_o$$

$$+\tfrac{1}{2}\sum{}' V_{\underset{\sim}{p}} a_o^+ a_{-\underset{\sim}{p}}^+ a_{-\underset{\sim}{p}} a_o + \tfrac{1}{2}\sum{}' V_{\underset{\sim}{p}} a_{\underset{\sim}{p}}^+ a_o^+ a_o a_{\underset{\sim}{p}}$$

$$+\tfrac{1}{2}\sum{}' V_{\underset{\sim}{p}} a_{\underset{\sim}{p}}^+ a_{-\underset{\sim}{p}}^+ a_o a_o + \tfrac{1}{2}\sum{}' V_{\underset{\sim}{p}} a_o^+ a_o^+ a_{-\underset{\sim}{p}} a_{\underset{\sim}{p}} \tag{5.37}$$

$$+ \text{higher order terms ,}$$

in which the primed summation sign indicates that the terms with $\underset{\sim}{p} = 0$ are excluded.

The higher order terms involve $a_i^+ a_k^+ a_\ell a_m$ with no subscript zero. In (5.37) the first term represents the interaction of two particles both in the ground state, while the other terms represent interactions between a particle in the ground state with one in an excited state. The higher order terms included all interactions between pairs of excited particles. At very low temperatures there will be few excited particles and $N_o >> N_{\underset{\sim}{p}}$, $\underset{\sim}{p} \neq 0$ and Bogoliubov (1947) assumed that the higher order terms in (5.37) could be neglected. He also assumed that since $N_o >> N_{\underset{\sim}{p}}$, $\underset{\sim}{p} \neq 0$, the operators a_o and a_o^+ could be replaced with $\sqrt{N_o}$ with little error. Then (5.37) becomes

$$H' = \tfrac{1}{2} V_o N_o^2 + N_o V_o \sum{}' a_{\underset{\sim}{p}}^+ a_{\underset{\sim}{p}}$$
$$+ \tfrac{1}{2} N_o \sum{}' V_{\underset{\sim}{p}} \left(a_{-\underset{\sim}{p}}^+ a_{-\underset{\sim}{p}} + a_{\underset{\sim}{p}}^+ a_{\underset{\sim}{p}} \right) \tag{5.38}$$
$$+ \tfrac{1}{2} N_o \sum{}' V_{\underset{\sim}{p}} \left(a_{\underset{\sim}{p}}^+ a_{-\underset{\sim}{p}}^+ + a_{-\underset{\sim}{p}} a_{\underset{\sim}{p}} \right),$$

and since $V_{\underset{\sim}{p}} = V_{-\underset{\sim}{p}}$,

$$H' = \tfrac{1}{2}V_o N_o^2 + N_o V_o \sum{}' a^+_{\underset{\sim}{p}} a_{\underset{\sim}{p}}$$

$$+ N_o \sum{}' V_{\underset{\sim}{p}} a^+_{\underset{\sim}{p}} a_{\underset{\sim}{p}} + \tfrac{1}{2} N_o \sum{}' V_{\underset{\sim}{p}} \left(a^+_{\underset{\sim}{p}} a^+_{-\underset{\sim}{p}} + a_{\underset{\sim}{p}} a_{-\underset{\sim}{p}} \right). \tag{5.39}$$

Next, N_o is replaced by $N - \sum{}' a^+_{\underset{\sim}{p}} a_{\underset{\sim}{p}}$, retaining only the quadratic terms in the operators $a_{\underset{\sim}{p}}$, $a^+_{\underset{\sim}{p}}$,

$$H' = \tfrac{1}{2}V_o N^2 + N \sum{}' V_{\underset{\sim}{p}} a^+_{\underset{\sim}{p}} a_{\underset{\sim}{p}} + \tfrac{1}{2} N \sum{}' V_{\underset{\sim}{p}} \left(a^+_{\underset{\sim}{p}} a^+_{-\underset{\sim}{p}} + a_{\underset{\sim}{p}} a_{-\underset{\sim}{p}} \right) \tag{5.40}$$

and

$$H = \tfrac{1}{2}V_o N^2 + \sum{}' \left(\frac{p^2}{2m} + N V_{\underset{\sim}{p}} \right) a^+_{\underset{\sim}{p}} a_{\underset{\sim}{p}}$$

$$+ \tfrac{1}{2} N \sum{}' V_{\underset{\sim}{p}} \left(a^+_{\underset{\sim}{p}} a^+_{-\underset{\sim}{p}} + a_{\underset{\sim}{p}} a_{-\underset{\sim}{p}} \right). \tag{5.41}$$

Bogoliubov then introduced the transformations

$$a_{\underset{\sim}{p}} = A_{\underset{\sim}{p}} \alpha_{\underset{\sim}{p}} + B_{\underset{\sim}{p}} \alpha^+_{-\underset{\sim}{p}} \tag{5.42}$$

$$a^+_{\underset{\sim}{p}} = A_{\underset{\sim}{p}} \alpha^+_{\underset{\sim}{p}} + B_{\underset{\sim}{p}} \alpha_{-\underset{\sim}{p}}, \tag{5.43}$$

where $A_{\underset{\sim}{p}} = A_{-\underset{\sim}{p}}$ and $B_{\underset{\sim}{p}} = B_{-\underset{\sim}{p}}$ and demanded that the new operators satisfy the commutation relations

$$\left[\alpha_{\underset{\sim}{p}}, \alpha_{\underset{\sim}{p}'} \right] = \left[\alpha^+_{\underset{\sim}{p}}, \alpha^+_{\underset{\sim}{p}'} \right] = 0 \tag{5.44}$$

$$\left[\alpha_{\underset{\sim}{p}}, \alpha^+_{\underset{\sim}{p}'} \right] = \delta_{\underset{\sim}{pp}'}, \tag{5.45}$$

so that

$$A^2_{\underset{\sim}{p}} - B^2_{\underset{\sim}{p}} = 1 . \tag{5.46}$$

Substituting (5.42) and (5.43) into (5.41), we find

$$\begin{aligned} H = {} & \tfrac{1}{2}V_o N^2 \\ & + \sum{}' \left(\lambda_{\underset{\sim}{p}} A^2_{\underset{\sim}{p}} + NV_{\underset{\sim}{p}} A_{\underset{\sim}{p}} B_{\underset{\sim}{p}}\right) \alpha^+_{\underset{\sim}{p}} \alpha_{\underset{\sim}{p}} \\ & + \sum{}' \left(\lambda_{\underset{\sim}{p}} A^2_{\underset{\sim}{p}} + NV_{\underset{\sim}{p}} A_{\underset{\sim}{p}} B_{\underset{\sim}{p}}\right) \alpha_{\underset{\sim}{p}} \alpha^+_{\underset{\sim}{p}} \\ & + \sum{}' \left[\lambda_{\underset{\sim}{p}} A_{\underset{\sim}{p}} B_{\underset{\sim}{p}} + \tfrac{1}{2} NV_{\underset{\sim}{p}} \left(A^2_{\underset{\sim}{p}} + B^2_{\underset{\sim}{p}}\right)\right] \left[\alpha^+_{\underset{\sim}{p}} \alpha^+_{-\underset{\sim}{p}} + \alpha_{\underset{\sim}{p}} \alpha_{-\underset{\sim}{p}}\right] , \end{aligned} \tag{5.47}$$

where

$$\lambda_{\underset{\sim}{p}} = \frac{p^2}{2m} + NV_{\underset{\sim}{p}} , \tag{5.48}$$

and summations like $\sum' V_{\underset{\sim}{p}} A_{\underset{\sim}{p}} B_{\underset{\sim}{p}} \alpha_{-\underset{\sim}{p}} \alpha^+_{-\underset{\sim}{p}}$ have been replaced by $\sum' V_{\underset{\sim}{p}} A_{\underset{\sim}{p}} B_{\underset{\sim}{p}} \alpha_{\underset{\sim}{p}} \alpha^+_{\underset{\sim}{p}}$. Requiring

$$\lambda_{\underset{\sim}{p}} A_{\underset{\sim}{p}} B_{\underset{\sim}{p}} + \tfrac{1}{2} NV_{\underset{\sim}{p}} \left(A^2_{\underset{\sim}{p}} + B^2_{\underset{\sim}{p}}\right) = 0 \tag{5.49}$$

and using (5.45), (5.47) becomes

$$\begin{aligned} H = {} & \tfrac{1}{2}V_o N^2 + \sum{}' \left(\lambda_{\underset{\sim}{p}} B^2_{\underset{\sim}{p}} + NV_{\underset{\sim}{p}} A_{\underset{\sim}{p}} B_{\underset{\sim}{p}}\right) \\ & + \sum{}' \left[\lambda_{\underset{\sim}{p}} \left(A^2_{\underset{\sim}{p}} + B^2_{\underset{\sim}{p}}\right) + 2NV_{\underset{\sim}{p}} A_{\underset{\sim}{p}} B_{\underset{\sim}{p}}\right] \alpha^+_{\underset{\sim}{p}} \alpha_{\underset{\sim}{p}} . \end{aligned} \tag{5.50}$$

As mentioned above, the commutation relations (5.44) and (5.45) imply

$$\alpha_{\underset{\sim}{p}} \left| \cdots n_{\underset{\sim}{p}} \cdots \right\rangle = \sqrt{n_{\underset{\sim}{p}}} \left| \cdots n_{\underset{\sim}{p}} - 1 \cdots \right\rangle \tag{5.51}$$

$$\alpha^+_{\underset{\sim}{p}} |\cdots n_{\underset{\sim}{p}} \cdots\rangle = \sqrt{n_{\underset{\sim}{p}}+1}\, |\cdots n_{\underset{\sim}{p}}+1 \cdots\rangle, \qquad (5.52)$$

where the $n_{\underset{\sim}{p}}$'s are integers. The lower case n's are used here in order to emphasize the fact that the states $|\cdots n_{\underset{\sim}{p}} \cdots\rangle$ and $|\cdots N_{\underset{\sim}{p}} \cdots\rangle$ are not the same. Thus in (5.50), $\alpha^+_{\underset{\sim}{p}}\alpha_{\underset{\sim}{p}}$ is just the number operator for the state $\underset{\sim}{p}$, and the coefficient would be the energy of that state. Thus the excitation spectrum is simply

$$\epsilon_{\underset{\sim}{p}} = \lambda_{\underset{\sim}{p}}\left(A^2_{\underset{\sim}{p}} + B^2_{\underset{\sim}{p}}\right) + 2NV_{\underset{\sim}{p}}A_{\underset{\sim}{p}}B_{\underset{\sim}{p}}. \qquad (5.53)$$

Using the two conditions (5.46) and (5.49), $A_{\underset{\sim}{p}}$ and $B_{\underset{\sim}{p}}$ can be found, and replacing $\lambda_{\underset{\sim}{p}}$ with its value from (5.48), we finally get

$$\epsilon_{\underset{\sim}{p}} = \left[\left(\frac{p^2}{2m}\right)^2 + \frac{p^2}{2m} NV_p\right]^{\frac{1}{2}}. \qquad (5.54)$$

For small momenta, ϵ_p reduces to

$$\epsilon_p = \left(\frac{NV_o}{m}\right)^{\frac{1}{2}} p, \qquad (5.55)$$

which is the phonon dispersion relation. For large momenta, we find

$$\epsilon_p \approx \frac{p^2}{2m} \qquad (5.56)$$

and is just the free particle dispersion relation. Using the Born approximation and assuming only S-wave scattering, it can be shown that

$$V_{\underset{\sim}{p}} = \frac{2\pi\hbar f}{m\Omega}, \qquad (5.57)$$

where f is the scattering amplitude. Thus (5.54) becomes

$$\epsilon_p = \left[\left(\frac{p^2}{2m}\right)^2 + \frac{2\pi\hbar^2 fN}{m^2\Omega} p^2\right]^{\frac{1}{2}} \tag{5.58}$$

and does not possess the roton minimum. Nevertheless, the Bogoliubov method does show how the phonon spectrum can be obtained by including interactions and thus predicts superfluidity.

§ 22. Hartree Self-Consistent Field Approach

The Bogoliubov approach was useful for discussing the excitation spectrum of a weakly interacting Bose gas. The normal fluid is associated with these excitations, while the superfluid is associated with the ground state, and, in considering the ground state, it is also necessary to include the interparticle interactions. Consider a non-interacting Bose gas of N-particles confined between two walls at $x = 0$ and $x = L$. The ground-state wave function is simply

$$\Psi(x_1 \cdots x_N) = \left(\frac{2}{L}\right)^{N/2} \prod_{i=1}^{N} \sin\left(\frac{\pi x_i}{L}\right). \tag{5.59}$$

The particle number density is the expectation value of

$$\rho(x) = \sum_{i=1}^{N} \delta(x - x_i), \tag{5.60}$$

and we get

$$\rho(x) = \frac{2N}{L} \sin^2\left(\frac{\pi x}{L}\right), \tag{5.61}$$

which exhibits a large density hump at the center of the system. On physical grounds, we would expect that the inclusion of a repulsive interparticle potential would smooth the density out to a uniform value except at the walls where the density must still vanish. We take the Hamiltonian of the system to be

$$H = \sum_{i=1}^{N} \frac{p_i^2}{2m} + \frac{1}{2} \sum_{ik}{}' V(|\underset{\sim}{x}_i - \underset{\sim}{x}_k|) \tag{5.62}$$

and assume a product solution to Schroedinger's equation (Hartree approximation),

$$\Psi(\underset{\sim}{x}_1 \cdots \underset{\sim}{x}_N) = \prod_{i=1}^{N} \psi(\underset{\sim}{x}_i), \tag{5.63}$$

where the normalization is taken as

$$\int \psi^*(\underset{\sim}{x})\psi(\underset{\sim}{x})d^3x = N, \tag{5.64}$$

so that $\rho(\underset{\sim}{x}) = |\psi(\underset{\sim}{x})|^2$ is the particle number density. The Hartree self-consistent field equation is then

$$E\psi(\underset{\sim}{x}) = -\frac{\hbar^2}{2m} \nabla^2 \psi(\underset{\sim}{x}) + \psi(\underset{\sim}{x}) \int |\psi(\underset{\sim}{x}')|^2 V(|\underset{\sim}{x} - \underset{\sim}{x}'|)d^3x', \tag{5.65}$$

and the total energy of the system is

$$\begin{aligned} \mathcal{E} = & -\frac{\hbar^2}{2m} \int \psi^*(\underset{\sim}{x})\nabla^2\psi(\underset{\sim}{x})d^3x \\ & + \frac{1}{2} \int |\psi(\underset{\sim}{x})|^2 V(|\underset{\sim}{x} - \underset{\sim}{x}'|)|\psi(\underset{\sim}{x}')|^2 d^3x d^3x'. \end{aligned} \tag{5.66}$$

Our main interest is to remove the unphysical behavior of the ideal gas, and the simplest thing to do, from the standpoint of solving (5.65), is to set

$$V(|\underset{\sim}{x} - \underset{\sim}{x}'|) = V_o \delta(\underset{\sim}{x} - \underset{\sim}{x}'). \tag{5.67}$$

Thus (5.66) and (5.67) become

$$a^2\nabla^2\psi = -\left(1 - \frac{V_o}{E}|\psi|^2\right)\psi \tag{5.68}$$

and

$$\mathcal{E} = a^2 E\int |\nabla\psi|^2 d^3x + \tfrac{1}{2}V_o\int |\psi|^4 d^3x\,, \tag{5.69}$$

where Gauss's law and the vanishing of the wave function at the boundary has been used to obtain (5.69) and the "healing length" a is defined by

$$a^2 = \frac{\hbar^2}{2mE}\,. \tag{5.70}$$

Exact solutions to (5.68) have been found for a one-dimensional system confined by two walls and a semi-infinite system with one wall (Ginsburg and Pitaevski 1958). For the semi-infinite case, $x \geq 0$, we find

$$\psi(x) = \rho_o^{\frac{1}{2}}\tanh\left(\frac{x}{\sqrt{2}\,a}\right), \tag{5.71}$$

where

$$\rho_o = E/V_o\,. \tag{5.72}$$

Except for a small region $x \approx a$ near the wall, the wave function is constant and the asymptotic value of the particle density is ρ_o given in (5.72). For the system bounded by two walls, the solution is essentially the same; the wave function is uniform over the region except within a distance of order a from either wall. We conclude that the ground-state wave function for a system confined to a three-dimension region will be constant except in the small healing layer at the boundaries. Then the kinetic energy term in (5.69) will have contributions only from the boundaries and should be much smaller than the potential energy term. Thus, taking the ground-state wave function to be

$$\psi(\underset{\sim}{x}) = \rho_o^{\frac{1}{2}} \tag{5.73}$$

everywhere, (5.69) yields

$$\mathcal{E} = \tfrac{1}{2}N\rho_o V_o \; ; \tag{5.74}$$

or using (5.72),

$$\mathcal{E} = \tfrac{1}{2}NE \, . \tag{5.75}$$

The Hartree approximation outlined above and in extended versions including excited states and time dependence has been used with success in interpreting some of the qualitative features of He II. We will limit ourselves to the consideration of vortices only (Fetter 1965; Gross 1961, 1963). The single-line vortex is the simplest case and we look for cylindrically symmetric solutions of (5.68). Taking

$$\psi(r, \theta, z) = f(r)e^{in\theta} \, , \tag{5.76}$$

we find for the particle number density

$$\rho(r) = |f(r)|^2 \, . \tag{5.77}$$

We assume f(r) to be real so that there is only a θ-component to the particle current density

$$J_\theta = \frac{\hbar}{2mi}\left(\frac{1}{r}\psi^* \frac{\partial\psi}{\partial\theta} - \frac{1}{r}\psi\frac{\partial\psi^*}{\partial\theta}\right), \tag{5.78}$$

and using (5.76), we obtain

$$J_\theta = \frac{n\hbar}{2\pi mr}|f(r)|^2 . \qquad (5.79)$$

Thus the particle velocity $V_\theta = J_\theta/\rho$ becomes

$$V_\theta = \frac{n\hbar}{2\pi mr} \qquad (5.80)$$

and is the typical vortex flow pattern with circulation

$$\int_0^{2\pi} V_\theta \, r d\theta = \frac{nh}{m} . \qquad (5.81)$$

Substituting (5.76) in (5.68), we get

$$a^2 \left(\frac{1}{r}\frac{d}{dr}\left(r\frac{df}{dr}\right) - \frac{n^2}{r^2} f\right) = -\left(1 - \frac{f^2}{\rho_o}\right) f . \qquad (5.82)$$

Far from the vortex we have

$$f(r) \to \rho_o^{\frac{1}{2}} \text{ as } r \to \infty , \qquad (5.83)$$

so that ρ_o is the asymptotic value of the density. As $r \to 0$, however, the centrifugal term $\frac{n^2}{r^2} f \to \infty$ unless $f \to 0$, and if $f \to 0$ the wave function exhibits healing behavior at $r \approx 0$ as it would near a boundary. For small r we can neglect the non-linear term in f^3, and the solution to (5.82) are just the free particle solutions

$$f(r) \to AJ_n(r/a), \quad r \to 0 . \qquad (5.84)$$

(In the case $n = 0$, the centrifugal term will vanish and the solution to [5.82] would simply be $f(r) = \rho_o^{\frac{1}{2}}$ everywhere, that is, the uniform state with no vortex.) Fetter (1965) has obtained an approximate analytical solution to (5.83) for $n = 1$

$$f(r) = \frac{\rho_o^{\frac{1}{2}}}{\sqrt{a^2+r^2}} \tag{5.85}$$

and is shown in Figure 5.2 along with the solution obtained numerically (Ginsburg and Pitaevski 1958).

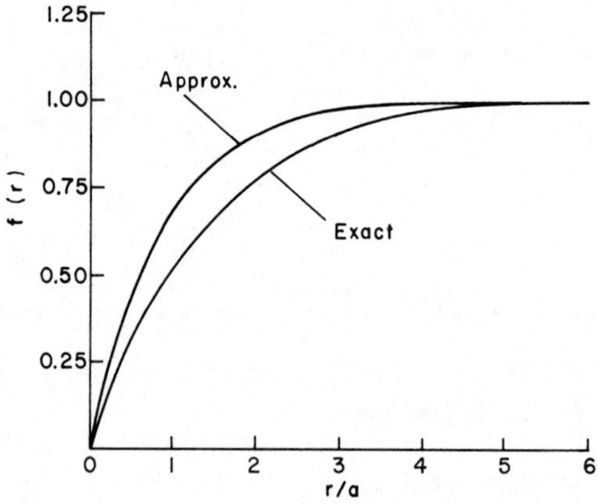

Fig. 5.2.

The energy per unit length of the vortex at the center of a cylinder of radius R has also been obtained numerically (Pitaevski 1961) and is

$$E_v = \frac{\pi\hbar^2\rho_o}{m}\log\left(\frac{1.46R}{a}\right). \tag{5.86}$$

As opposed to classical vortex theory, the quantum approach in the Hartree approximation shows that the circulation is quantized in units of h/m and that the behavior at the core of the vortex is completely determined.

We now examine the weakly interacting Bose gas at absolute zero in a circular cylinder of radius R rotating the angular velocity

Ω. The stationary states in the rotating frame are then given by the eigenstates of the Hamiltonian $H' = H - \Omega J_z$. In the Hartree approximation, the problem is to find solutions of

$$E\psi = -\frac{\hbar^2}{2m}\nabla^2\psi + v\psi|\psi|^2 - \Omega\left(-i\hbar\frac{\partial}{\partial\theta}\right)\psi. \tag{5.87}$$

If we assume a solution of the form (5.76), we indeed find that this is a solution except in the healing layers. It corresponds to an approximate value of E

$$E = \left(\frac{\hbar^2}{2m}\right)\rho_o \ln\left(\frac{R}{a}\right) + V_o\rho_o - \hbar\Omega\,. \tag{5.88}$$

We thus see that if $\Omega > \Omega_c = \frac{\hbar}{2m\rho_o}\ln\left(\frac{R}{a}\right)$, the value of E is lower for the state (5.75) with a line vortex than for the state where the superfluid is at rest (where $E = \rho_o V_o$, also a solution of [5.87]). Note that this does not say that a vortex line will form, but that at $\Omega > \Omega_c$ it is energetically favorable.

Fetter (1965) has developed an approximation scheme to be used with the Hartree self-consistent field approximation for use in calculating complex vortex problems. First,we use the simple analytic approximation of f(r) (5.85). This is shown for comparison with the exact solution in Figure 5.2.

Second, we assumed that the wave function for more than one vortex can be approximated by the product of solutions for independent vortices

$$\psi(r) = \rho_o^{\frac{1}{2}}\, e^{i\varphi_1} f(r_1)\cdot e^{i\varphi_2} f(r_2)\,.\;.\;.\;\;. \tag{5.89}$$

Using these approximations and considering the vortex distribution in a rotating body of fluid that minimizes the energy for a given total angular momentum, Fetter found that a uniform distribution of vortices with density

$$n_o = 2m\Omega/\hbar \text{ lines/cm}^2 \tag{5.90}$$

resulted. For a cylindrical body of fluid of radius R, the total angular momentum per unit length is then

$$L = \tfrac{1}{2}\pi R^4 \rho_o m\Omega = \tfrac{1}{2}MR^2\Omega , \tag{5.91}$$

as would be expected for a solid body rotation. The angular momentum per particle is

$$\frac{L}{M} = \tfrac{1}{2}m\hbar , \tag{5.92}$$

where m is the number of vortices. In general, it is found that far from the core the vortex behaves classically except for its quantization of circulation.

REFERENCES

Bogoliubov, N. 1947, J. Phys. USSR, 11, 23.

Fetter, A. L. 1965, Phys. Rev., 138, A429.

Ginsburg, V. L., and Pitaevski, L. P. 1958, Soviet Physics JETP, 34, 1240.

Gross, E. P. 1961, Nuovo Cimento, 20, 454.

———— 1963, J. Math. Phys., 4, 195.

Landau, L. D., and Lifshitz, E. M. 1958, Statistical Physics (Reading, Mass.: Addison-Wesley).

Penrose, O., and Onsager, L. 1956, Phys. Rev., 104, 576.

Pitaevski, L. P. 1961, Soviet Physics JETP, 13, 451.

Roman, P. 1965, Advanced Quantum Theory (Reading, Mass.: Addison-Wesley), § 1.7.

CHAPTER 6

IONS IN HELIUM II

§23. Structure of Ions

In §8 the energy spectrum of ions at low temperatures was shown to correspond to vortex rings with one quantum of circulation. In that section the ion was simply assumed to be bound to a ring and no explanation for the binding was given. Also, in rotating He II it is found that above 1°K negative ions are trapped by vortex lines while the positive ions are not (see §26). Before investigating these effects, it is necessary to have some idea of the structure of the ions themselves.

At present there are two convenient methods for producing ions in liquid helium. Electrons can be injected through photoelectric emission, while both positive and negative ions can be obtained from alpha tracks in the fluid. Po^{210} is a frequently used source producing α's with a range of about 0.3 mm in liquid helium. (β-radiation and field emission have also been used, though less frequently.) The radioactive source is usually plated onto an electrode so that electric fields can be used to draw out either the positive or negative ion, the undesired ion species being driven back to the electrode. The positive ion obtained in this way is assumed to be a molecular ion of the form He_n^+, where n is a small integer. He_2^+, for example, has a binding energy of 2.5 eV (Pauling 1933) and should be quite stable. He_2^+ ions are also found to be more numerous than He^+ ions in dense helium gas (Phelps and Brown 1952). This basic structure is probably not too important, however, since the polarization of the fluid in the vicinity of the molecule ion increases the effective size and mass of the ion. The interaction of an ion and helium has been considered from first principles, starting with the Hamiltonian for N bosons and one ion (Girardeau 1961 and Gross 1962). Although appealing, this approach is fraught with the usual difficulties associated with the many body problem. In order to obtain a picture in simple fashion we follow an approach given by Atkins (1963). It is assumed that helium can be treated as a continuum down to almost microscopic size and that macroscopically determined relations, such as the equation of state, remain valid on this level. Classical thermodynamics then allows the fluid density near a point charge to be found as a function of the distance from the charge (Landau and Lifshitz 1960 and Panofsky and Phillips 1962). The result for helium at 1.25°K is shown in Figure 6.1.

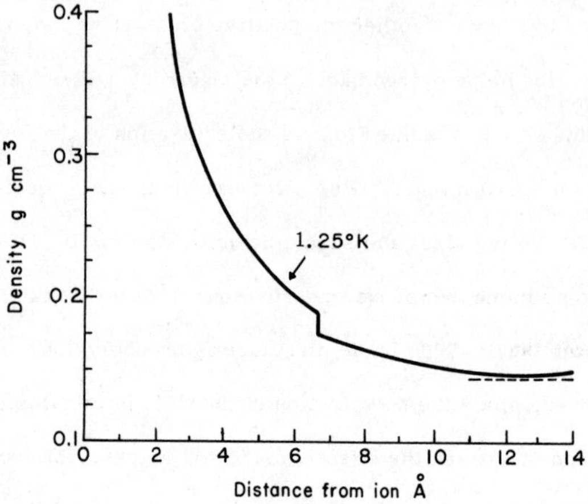

Fig. 6. 1.

Kuper (1963) has shown that this approach is valid at large distances from the charge but that it should break down close to the charge. If it is accepted as being qualitatively accurate, however, the interesting fact appears that there is a solid core to the ion, the melting point being about 6.3Å (at 1.25° K). The effective mass for this model can also be found. This would consist of (1) the mass in the core since the core must move rigidly, (2) the excess mass outside of the core, that is, the integral of the density minus the uniform density (polarization mass), and (3) the hydrodynamic mass associated with the motion of a rigid sphere through a liquid (Landau and Lifshitz 1959a). The sum of these three contributions turns out to be about 100 helium masses.

We now turn to the negative ion, which has been studied in much more detail. If the negative ion were basically a molecule ion of the type He_n^- (which is unlikely to be stable), the resulting picture for the negative ion would be identical with that of the positive ion. It is obvious from the mobility measurements in § 15 that the two ions are not the same. A more striking difference is observed in the capture of ions by vortex lines; negative ions are readily captured above 1° K while positive ions are not (§ 26). It is therefore assumed that the negative ion is basically an electron whose properties are modified by the surrounding fluid. Two possibilities have been considered: the electron is essentially a free particle being scattered by individual helium atoms, or the electron is localized to a small region from which the helium atoms have been excluded. The latter, the "bubble model," adequately accounts for the binding of negative ions to vortices (§ 24). In addition, Jortner, Kestner, Rice, and Cohen (1965) have shown theoretically that the bubble model is probably the more stable of the two possibilities for the electron in He II. It would be expected that if the fluid density were lowered, the localized electron would go over to the delocalized state. Mobility measurements by Levine and Sanders (1962) indicate that this transition does occur, but in helium vapor. Assuming the bubble model, its radius (i. e., the region from which helium atoms are excluded) can be found by minimizing the energy with respect to the radius. Roughly speaking, to make a large bubble requires a large energy to displace the helium atoms. On the other hand, a small bubble also requires a large energy resulting from the high kinetic energy needed to localize the electron. Somewhere in between, a radius exists for which the energy is a minimum. Assuming the bubble model to be correct, the total ion energy can be written as

$$E_t = \frac{\hbar^2 k^2}{2m_e} + 4\pi\gamma R^2 + \frac{4\pi p R^3}{3} .$$

The terms on the right-hand side are, respectively: (1) the kinetic energy of the electron in a spherical square well, where k is the solution of

$$k \cot kR = -(k_o^2 - k^2)^{\frac{1}{2}} ,$$

with $\frac{\hbar^2 k_o^2}{2m_e}$ being the well depth; (2) the surface energy of the bubble, where γ is a surface tension; and (3) the volume work required to create the cavity.

Minimizing E_t with respect to R, we can solve for the ion radius, R^-. The surface tension γ has been estimated by Hiroike, Kestner, Rice, and Jortner (1965) to be $\approx$ 0.53 dynes/cm; thus only the well depth is needed to find R^-. Sommer (1964) and Woolf and Rayfield (1965) have measured the energy necessary to inject an excess electron into the undisturbed fluid to be $\approx$ 1.1 eV, in good agreement with the calculated value of Burdick (1965). If this value is taken as the well depth, then R^- is found to be approximately 16Å. Hiroike, Kestner, Rice, and Jortner (1965), using a fuzzy bubble, find $R_i^- = 12.4$Å.

Clark (1965) has also considered the negative ion starting with a semiclassical approach to the many-body problem (Gross 1958, 1962). He finds the radial parts of the electron R_e and helium R_{He} wave functions as shown in Figure 6.2.

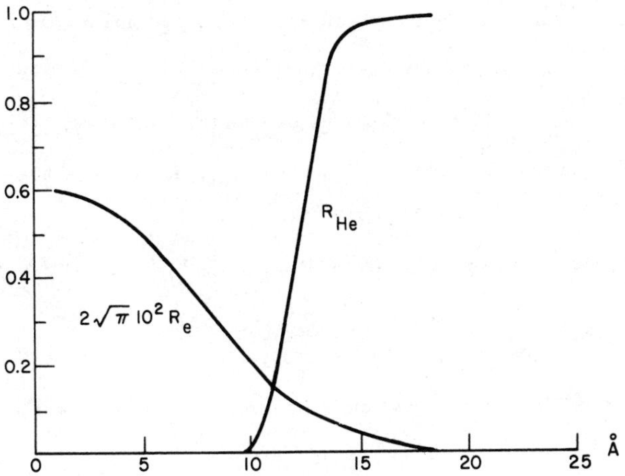

Fig. 6.2.

The inflection point for the helium wave function lies at 12.5Å in agreement with the work cited above. It should be noted that this model implies a decreasing radius with increasing pressure.

An effective mass for the negative ion can be obtained by taking the negative ion to be a rigid sphere of radius 12.4Å. The mass is the sum of the polarization mass ($\approx$ 17 helium masses) and the hydrodynamic mass ($\approx$ 82 helium masses), giving a total of about 100 helium masses.

§24. Interaction between Ions and Quantized Vortices

As mentioned in the last section, positive and negative ions are bound to vortex rings at low temperatures, and negative ions can be easily trapped by vortex lines. We now investigate this binding mechanism (Parks and Donnelly 1966). Consider an isolated vortex line in helium with the normal fluid at rest ($\underset{\sim}{v}_n = 0$). The flow is steady and all partial derivatives with respect to time vanish. We assume the fluid to be incompressible so that ρ, ρ_n, and ρ_s are uniform. Thus, from (4.42) and taking $\underset{\sim}{j} = \rho_s \underset{\sim}{v}_s + \rho_n \underset{\sim}{v}_n$, we have $\underset{\sim}{\nabla} \cdot \underset{\sim}{v}_s = 0$. We consider the flow only outside the core where $\underset{\sim}{\nabla} \times \underset{\sim}{v}_s = 0$, then the equation of motion for the superflow (4.45) using (4.55) becomes

$$\tfrac{1}{2}\rho \underset{\sim}{\nabla}(v_s^2) = -\rho \underset{\sim}{\nabla} \Phi = -\underset{\sim}{\nabla} p + \sigma \underset{\sim}{\nabla} T + \tfrac{1}{2}\rho_n \nabla(v_s^2) \tag{6.1}$$

or

$$\tfrac{1}{2}\rho_s \underset{\sim}{\nabla}(v_s^2) = -\underset{\sim}{\nabla} p + \sigma \underset{\sim}{\nabla} T . \tag{6.2}$$

On the other hand, the momentum conservation equation (4.43) becomes

$$\underset{\sim}{\nabla} \cdot (\rho_s \underset{\sim}{v}_s \underset{\sim}{v}_s + p\delta) = 0 \tag{6.3}$$

or

$$\tfrac{1}{2}\rho_s \underset{\sim}{\nabla}(v_s^2) = -\nabla p , \tag{6.4}$$

where we have used $\underset{\sim}{\nabla} \cdot \underset{\sim}{v}_s = 0$ and $\underset{\sim}{v}_s \cdot \underset{\sim}{\nabla} \underset{\sim}{v}_s = \tfrac{1}{2} \underset{\sim}{\nabla}(\underset{\sim}{v}_s^2)$. From (6.2) and (6.4), we see that $\underset{\sim}{\nabla} T = 0$ so that there is no temperature gradient in the vortex flow. Now let a rigid spherical body be introduced into the flow. The net force on the object is given by the surface integral

$$\underset{\sim}{F} = \oint p d\underset{\sim}{s} . \tag{6.5}$$

In general, the object modifies the flow so that the pressure p in (6.5) is not the same as in the absence of the body. We assume, however, that the flow is unaltered, the error introduced by this assumption being considered at the end of this section. Using Gauss's law and (6.4), (6.5) becomes

$$\underset{\sim}{F} = \int \underset{\sim}{\nabla} p \, d^3 r = \tfrac{1}{2}\rho_s \int \underset{\sim}{\nabla}(v_s^2) d^3 r \, , \tag{6.6}$$

where the integral is over the volume of the sphere and $\underset{\sim}{v}_s$ is the flow velocity in the absence of the sphere. Let $\underset{\sim}{r}$ locate the point of integration from an arbitrary origin and $\underset{\sim}{x}$ locate the center of the sphere. Then $\underset{\sim}{\xi} = \underset{\sim}{r} - \underset{\sim}{x}$ locates the point of integration relative to the center of the sphere. Thus

$$\underset{\sim}{\nabla}_r (v_s^2) = \underset{\sim}{\nabla}_x (v_s^2) \tag{6.7}$$

and

$$\underset{\sim}{F} = \underset{\sim}{\nabla}_x \int \tfrac{1}{2} \rho_s v_s^2 d^3 \xi \, . \tag{6.8}$$

The potential of the force $\underset{\sim}{F}$ is then

$$u(\underset{\sim}{x}) = \int \tfrac{1}{2} \rho_s v_s^2 d^3 \xi \tag{6.9}$$

and is just the kinetic energy of the fluid removed by the presence of the body. We have assumed in this derivation that the densities are uniform; however, in §22 it was shown that near a vortex the superfluid density behaves approximately like

$$\rho_s' = \rho_s r'^2 (r'^2 + a^2)^{-1} \, , \tag{6.10}$$

where a is the healing length, r' the perpendicular distance from the line, and ρ_s the superfluid density far from the vortex. We make the assumption that (6.9) is still valid in this case if the superfluid density is allowed to vary as in (6.10). In other words, we assume that the energy change when the ion moves is essentially accounted for by the kinetic energy difference in the fluid. Let an ion be located a distance r from the line as shown in Figure 6.3.

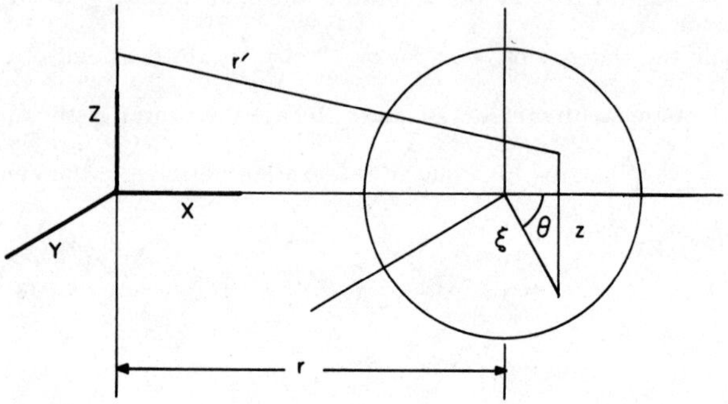

Fig. 6.3.

Thus

$$r'^2 = \xi^2 + r^2 + 2r\xi\cos\theta \qquad (6.11)$$

and, using $v_s = \frac{\hbar}{mr}$ and (6.10) and integrating over θ and z, (6.9) becomes

$$u(r) = -2\pi\rho_s\left(\frac{\hbar}{m}\right)^2 \int_o^R \frac{(R^2-\xi^2)^{\frac{1}{2}}\xi d\xi}{\left[(\xi^2+r^2+a^2)^2 - 4r^2\xi^2\right]^{\frac{1}{2}}}, \qquad (6.12)$$

where R is the ion radius. This elliptic integral can be simplified for certain values of r. For r = 0

$$u(o) = 2\pi\rho_s\left(\frac{\hbar}{m}\right)^2 R\left[1-\left(1+\frac{a^2}{R^2}\right)^{\frac{1}{2}}\sinh^{-1}\left(\frac{R}{a}\right)\right], \qquad (6.13)$$

for r >> a

$$u(r) = -2\pi\rho_s\left(\frac{\hbar}{m}\right)^2 R\left[1-\left(\frac{r^2}{R^2}-1\right)^{\frac{1}{2}}\sin^{-1}\left(\frac{R}{r}\right)\right] \qquad (6.14)$$

and for r >> R

$$u(r) = -\frac{2\pi\rho_s}{3}\left(\frac{\hbar}{m}\right)^2\left(\frac{R}{r}\right)^2. \tag{6.15}$$

The integral in (6.12) has been integrated numerically, and the potential for an ion of 15.96Å radius at 1.64° K is shown in Figure 6.4. (The choice of the ion size is explained in the following section.)

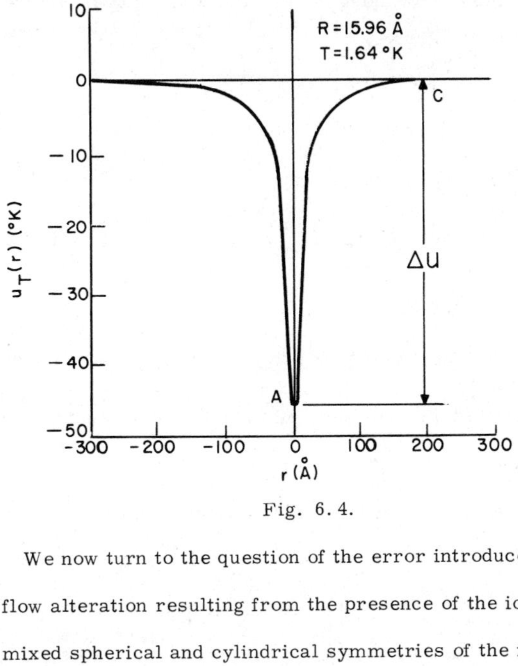

Fig. 6.4.

We now turn to the question of the error introduced by neglecting the flow alteration resulting from the presence of the ion. Because of the mixed spherical and cylindrical symmetries of the ion-line system, an exact expression in closed form is difficult to obtain. Let us simply consider a flow with uniform velocity $\underset{\sim}{v}_\infty$. If a sphere of radius R is introduced, the flow velocity outside the sphere is given by

$$\underset{\sim}{v} = \underset{\sim}{v}_\infty - \frac{R^3}{2r^3}\left[3\,\hat{1}_r\left(\underset{\sim}{v}_\infty\cdot\hat{1}_r\right) - \underset{\sim}{v}_\infty\right], \quad r \geq R, \tag{6.16}$$

where r is the distance measured from the center of the sphere and

$\hat{1}_r$ is a unit vector in the direction of r (Landau and Lifshitz 1959b). If the flow alteration is neglected, the change in kinetic energy on placing the sphere in the flow is simply

$$\Delta u = \frac{2}{3}\pi\rho R^3 v_\infty^2 . \tag{6.17}$$

The correction to the energy using the exact flow velocity (6. 16) is just

$$\Delta u' = \tfrac{1}{2}\rho \int_{r\geq R} (v^2 - v_\infty^2)d^3 r . \tag{6.18}$$

The integral is easily evaluated, yielding

$$\Delta u' = \frac{1}{3}\pi\rho R^3 v_\infty^2 . \tag{6.19}$$

Thus the actual energy change is

$$\Delta u + \Delta u' = \pi\rho R^3 v_\infty^2 . \tag{6.20}$$

The approximation (6. 17) is $33\frac{1}{3}$ per cent too small in absolute value. From this it is seen that the potential for an ion near a vortex actually lies below that given in (6. 4) and at large distances, where the flow becomes essentially uniform over a distance comparable to the ion size, the error will be about $33\frac{1}{3}$ per cent. At $r = 0$, on the other hand, the correction vanishes. In the next section the potential is needed to analyze the escape of ions from vortices. There it is shown that the error described above is not too important for this process.

The potential (6. 12) has been derived for a vortex line but will also be valid for an ion close enough to a vortex ring so that the ring may be approximated as a line.

§25. Escape of Ions from Vortex Lines and Rings

Positive and negative ions are bound to vortex rings, and negative ions can be readily trapped by vortex lines. If an electric field is applied, it is found that there is finite probability for the ion to escape. The lifetime for positive ions in rings (Cade 1965) and negative ions in lines (Douglass 1964) have both been measured. Let an electric field $\mathcal{E}$ be applied along the x-axis so that the total potential energy of a trapped ion is

$$u_T = u(r) - e\mathcal{E}x, \qquad (6.21)$$

where u(r) is the ion-vortex potential and e is the charge ($e\mathcal{E}$ is chosen positive regardless of the sign of the ionic charge). If the potential well u(r) is deep and the field $\mathcal{E}$ not too large, u_T will possess a minimum near the minimum of u(r). Because of the electric field u_T will also have a saddle point along the positive x-axis at x_c. Thus, if the ion can acquire sufficient energy, it can escape over the saddle point and be carried to $x = +\infty$. It is assumed that this energy is obtained through collisions with the excitations. Let us consider the ion as a Brownian particle in the potential field u_T. The Brownian particle can be described by a distribution function $W(\underset{\sim}{r}, \underset{\sim}{p}, t)$, which gives the probability $W(\underset{\sim}{r}, \underset{\sim}{p}, t)d^3rd^3p$ of finding the particle at $\underset{\sim}{r}$ with momentum $\underset{\sim}{p}$ at time t. (The following analysis essentially follows that of Chandrasekhar [1943] and Donnelly and Roberts [1967, to be published]). If the particle undergoes sufficiently frequent collisions, the momentum distribution will be Maxwellian and we need only find $w(\underset{\sim}{r}, t)$. The equation governing $w(\underset{\sim}{r}, t)$ is Smoluchowski's equation

$$\frac{\partial w}{\partial t} = \underset{\sim}{\nabla} \cdot \left(D \underset{\sim}{\nabla} w + \frac{w}{\beta m_i} \underset{\sim}{\nabla} u_T \right), \tag{6.22}$$

where D is the diffusion coefficient, β the friction constant, and m_i the ionic mass. This equation is just a continuity equation with a particle flux

$$\underset{\sim}{f} = - \left(D \underset{\sim}{\nabla} w + \frac{w}{\beta m_i} \underset{\sim}{\nabla} u_T \right). \tag{6.23}$$

The first term describes a flux of particles to regions of lower concentration, while the second shows a flux to regions of lower potential. The equilibrium distribution $\left(\frac{\partial w}{\partial t} = 0 \right)$ would put all the particles at $x = +\infty$ since the potential is $-\infty$ there. (If w is interpreted as a probability density, its integral over all space is unity; if it is taken as a concentration, its integral gives the total number of particles. The two views correspond to considering one ion in a vortex or many ions in an equal number of vortices. No confusion should arise, and the two views are used interchangeably.)

If the ion is $\approx 16\,\text{Å}$ and the electric field is small, the well depth will be approximately that shown in Figure 6.4 and is much deeper than kT for temperatures below 2°K. If the well is deep, the flux will be quite small and $\frac{\partial w}{\partial t} \approx 0$. Thus, for a deep well, we need only solve the time-independent equation

$$\nabla^2 w + g^2 \underset{\sim}{\nabla} \cdot (w \underset{\sim}{\nabla} u_T) = 0, \tag{6.24}$$

with $g^2 = \frac{1}{\beta D m_i}$. We will apply the non-equilibrium initial condition that all the particles are in the well at $t = 0$. This will result in a net flux of particles from the well given by

$$F = \oint \underset{\sim}{f} \cdot \hat{n} d\ell , \tag{6.25}$$

where the line integral goes around the vortex in a positive sense and $\hat{n}$ is an outwardly directed unit vector normal to the path. In this approximation the number of particles in the well is given by

$$N = \int w ds , \tag{6.26}$$

where the surface integration extends only over the vicinity of the minimum of u_T. It should be noted that by solving (6.24), we actually find a distribution in local equilibrium with the bottom of the well. Since this is not the true equilibrium, a small number of particles dN escape in a time dt, given by

$$dN = Fdt = N\left(\frac{F}{N}\right)dt . \tag{6.27}$$

In this deep well approximation, F is proportional to N and the time dependence of F enters only through N. Then $\frac{F}{N} = P$ is time independent and (6.27) is readily integrated to give

$$N = N_o e^{-Pt} , \tag{6.28}$$

the number of particles in the well at time t.

The problem is now to find F and N. Since N involves an integration only near $r \approx 0$, we need solve (6.24) only for small r. We expand the potential u_T about its minimum and obtain

$$u_T = u_o + \tfrac{1}{2}\omega_A{}^2 x^2 + \tfrac{1}{2} S_A{}^2 y^2 . \tag{6.29}$$

Then (6.24) becomes

$$\frac{\partial^2 w}{\partial x^2} + \frac{\partial^2 w}{\partial y^2} + g^2 \omega_A^2 x \frac{\partial w}{\partial x} + g^2 S_A^2 y \frac{\partial w}{\partial y} + g^2 \left(\omega_A^2 + S_A^2\right) w = 0. \tag{6.30}$$

Separating variables $w = X(x)Y(y)$, we get

$$X'' + g^2 \omega_A^2 x X' + g^2 (\omega_A^2 - nS_A^2) X = 0 \tag{6.31}$$

and

$$Y'' + g^2 S_A^2 y Y' + g^2 S_A^2 (1 + n) Y = 0 , \tag{6.32}$$

where $g^2 S_A^2 n$ is the separation constant. Letting $Y = \exp(-\frac{1}{2} g^2 S_A^2 y^2) H(y)$, we get

$$H'' - g^2 S_A^2 y H' + n g^2 S_A^2 H = 0 , \tag{6.33}$$

which is Hermite's equation. Now Y must vanish at $y = \pm\infty$ so that n must be an integer. Then

$$Y = \exp(-\tfrac{1}{2} g^2 S_A^2 y^2) H_n\left(\frac{1}{\sqrt{2}} g S_A y\right). \tag{6.34}$$

Obviously, $X \exp\left(\frac{1}{2} g^2 \omega_A^2 x^2\right)$ also satisfies Hermite's equation, and since X must vanish at $x = \pm\infty$, we require

$$g^2 \left(\omega_A^2 - nS_A^2\right) = g^2 \omega_A^2 (1 + m) , \tag{6.35}$$

where m and n are both integers. This condition is met only for $m = n = 0$. Thus the solution near $r \approx 0$ is simply

$$w = w' \exp\left[-\tfrac{1}{2} g^2 \left(\omega_A^2 x^2 + S_A^2 y^2\right)\right], \tag{6.36}$$

where w' is a normalization constant. The number of particles in the well is then

$$N = w' \int_{-\infty}^{\infty} \exp\left(-\tfrac{1}{2} g^2 \omega_A{}^2 x^2\right) dx \int_{-\infty}^{\infty} \exp\left(-\tfrac{1}{2} g^2 S_A{}^2 y^2\right) dy$$

$$= \frac{2\pi w'}{g^2 \omega_A S_A} . \qquad (6.37)$$

To find F, we note from the shape of the well that the only net flux can be in positive x-direction and that the particle must leave the well close to the saddle point. Thus we expand the potential about the saddle point $(x_c, 0)$

$$u_T = u_c - \tfrac{1}{2}\omega_c{}^2 \xi^2 + \tfrac{1}{2} S_c{}^2 y^2 , \qquad (6.38)$$

where $\xi = x - x_c$. Except for signs and the change of variable $x \rightarrow \xi$, (6.24) again separates as in (6.31) and (6.32):

$$X'' - g^2 \omega_c{}^2 \xi X' - g^2 \left(\omega_c{}^2 + n S_c{}^2\right) X = 0 . \qquad (6.39)$$

$$Y'' + g^2 S_c{}^2 y Y' + g^2 S_c{}^2 (1 + n) Y = 0. \qquad (6.40)$$

Again, Y must vanish for $y = \pm \infty$ so that

$$Y = \exp\left(-\tfrac{1}{2} g^2 S_c{}^2 y^2\right) H_n\left(\frac{1}{\sqrt{2}} g S_c y\right), \qquad (6.41)$$

where n is an integer. Letting $X = \exp\left(\tfrac{1}{4} g^2 \omega_c{}^2 \xi^2\right) U$ and $\zeta = g \omega_c \xi$ and $m = \left(\frac{S_c}{\omega_c}\right)^2 n$, we find from (6.39)

$$U'' - \left(\tfrac{1}{4}\zeta^2 + \tfrac{1}{2} + m\right) U = 0 , \qquad (6.42)$$

which is the equation for the parabolic cylinder functions in standard form (see Miller 1965 and Whittaker and Watson 1950). For large ζ the two solutions to (6.42) tend to $\zeta^{-m-1} e^{-\frac{1}{4}\zeta^2}$ and $\zeta^{-m} e^{-\frac{1}{4}\zeta^2}$.

Since X must vanish for large positive ζ, only one solution is appropriate and is designated by $D_{-m-1}(\zeta)$. Then

$$w = w_o e^{-\frac{1}{2}g^2 S_c^2 y^2} H_n\left(\frac{1}{\sqrt{2}} gS_c y\right) e^{\frac{1}{4}g^2 \omega_c^2 \xi^2} D_{-m-1}\left(g\omega_c \xi\right), \qquad (6.43)$$

where w_o is a normalization constant. At $(x_c, 0)$ the net flux in the x-direction

$$\int_{-\infty}^{\infty} f_x dy = -D \int_{-\infty}^{\infty} \left(\frac{\partial w}{\partial x} + g^2 w \frac{\partial u_T}{\partial x}\right) dy \qquad (6.44)$$

will involve integrals of the form

$$\int_{-\infty}^{\infty} \exp\left(-\tfrac{1}{2}g^2 S_c^2 y^2\right) H_n\left(\frac{1}{\sqrt{2}} gS_c y\right) dy, \qquad (6.45)$$

which vanish from the orthogonality of the Hermite polynomials if $n \neq 0$. Thus only the $n = 0$ term contributes. Also,the flux in the y-direction involves the terms

$$f_y = -D\left(\frac{\partial w}{\partial y} + g^2 w \frac{\partial u_T}{\partial y}\right)$$

$$= -\sqrt{2}\, nDgS_c \exp\left(-\tfrac{1}{2}g^2 S_c^2 y^2\right) H_n\left(\frac{1}{\sqrt{2}} gS_c y\right) X(\xi), \qquad (6.46)$$

which must vanish. Thus we take only the $n = 0$ term and find

$$w = w_o \exp\left(-\tfrac{1}{2}g^2 S_c^2 y^2\right) \exp\left(\tfrac{1}{4}g^2 \omega_c^2 \xi^2\right) D_{-1}\left(g\omega_c \xi\right). \qquad (6.47)$$

To calculate the net flux F from the well, we note that we need consider only the flux in the positive x-direction so that

$$f_x = -Dg\omega_c w_o e^{-\frac{1}{2}g^2 S_c^2 y^2} e^{\frac{1}{4}g^2 \omega_c^2 \xi^2} \left(D'_{-1} - \tfrac{1}{2}g\omega_c \xi D_{-1}\right). \qquad (6.48)$$

Using the recursion relation for D_n,

$$D'_{-n}(x) - \tfrac{1}{2}xD_{-n}(x) = -D_{1-n}(x)\,, \tag{6.49}$$

(6.48) becomes

$$f_x = Dg\omega_c w_o e^{-\frac{1}{2}g^2 S_c^2 y^2}\, e^{\frac{1}{4}g^2\omega_c^2\xi^2}\, D_o(g\omega_c\xi). \tag{6.50}$$

The integral from $y = \pm\infty$ gives $\dfrac{\sqrt{2\pi}}{gS_c}$, and taking $\xi = 0(D_o(o) = 1)$, we find

$$F = \sqrt{2\pi}\, w_o D \frac{\omega_c}{S_c}. \tag{6.51}$$

The escape probability per unit time $P = F/N$ is found from (6.51) and (6.37). But we must first relate the two normalization constants w_o and w'. For large negative ξ, D_{-1} becomes

$$D_{-1}(g\omega_c\xi) \approx \sqrt{2\pi}\,\exp\left(\tfrac{1}{4}g^2\omega_c^2\xi^2\right), \tag{6.52}$$

so that

$$\begin{aligned} w &\approx \sqrt{2\pi}\, w_o \exp\left(\tfrac{1}{2}g^2\omega_c^2\xi^2 - \tfrac{1}{2}g^2 S_c^2 y^2\right) \\ &= \sqrt{2\pi}\, w_o e^{-g^2(u_T - u_c)} \end{aligned} \tag{6.53}$$

deep into the well. From (6.36) we have

$$w \approx w' e^{-g^2(u_T - u_o)}. \tag{6.54}$$

Thus

$$\frac{w_o}{w'} = \frac{1}{\sqrt{2\pi}}\, e^{-g^2\Delta u}, \tag{6.55}$$

where $\Delta u = u_c - u_o$ is the well depth. Using (6.37), (6.51), and (6.55), we get

$$P = g^2 D \frac{\omega_A \omega_c}{2\pi} \left(\frac{S_A}{S_c}\right) e^{-g^2 \Delta u}. \qquad (6.56)$$

Now $g^2 = \frac{1}{m_i \beta D}$. β is related to the mobility μ by $\beta = e/\mu m_i$, and using Einstein's relation $D = kT\mu/e$, we have $\beta D = \frac{kT}{m_i}$ and

$$P = \frac{\omega_A \omega_c}{2\pi \beta m_i} \left(\frac{S_A}{S_c}\right) e^{-\frac{\Delta u}{kT}}. \qquad (6.57)$$

At sufficiently low temperatures, where the Fokker-Plank equation must be used rather than Smoluchowski's equation, we get in a fashion similar to the above (Donnelly and Roberts [1967]).

$$P = \frac{1}{2\pi} \left(\frac{\omega_A S_A}{\omega_c S_c}\right) \left[\left(\frac{\omega_c^2}{m_i} + \tfrac{1}{4}\beta^2\right)^{\frac{1}{2}} - \tfrac{1}{2}\beta\right] e^{-\frac{\Delta u}{kT}}. \qquad (6.58)$$

Using (6.12) for the well potential, we find for r = 0:

$$u_o = 2\pi \rho_s \left(\frac{\hbar}{m}\right)^2 R \left[1 - \left(1 + \frac{a^2}{R^2}\right)^{\frac{1}{2}} \sinh^{-1}\left(\frac{R}{a}\right)\right] \qquad (6.59)$$

and

$$\omega_A^2 = S_A^2 = \frac{\pi \rho_s \left(\frac{\hbar}{m}\right)^2}{R\left(1 + \frac{a^2}{R^2}\right)} \left[-1 + \frac{\left(2 + \frac{a^2}{R^2}\right)}{\sqrt{1 + \frac{a^2}{R^2}}} \sinh^{-1}\left(\frac{R}{a}\right)\right], \qquad (6.60)$$

and if the saddle point $x_c >> R$

$$u(x_c) \approx -\frac{2\pi \rho_s}{3} \left(\frac{\hbar}{m}\right)^2 \frac{R^3}{x_c^2} - e\mathcal{E} x_c, \qquad (6.61)$$

and

$$\omega_c^2 \approx 3S_c^2 \approx 4\pi \rho_s \left(\frac{\hbar}{m}\right)^2 \frac{R^3}{x_c^4}, \qquad (6.62)$$

where

$$x_c \approx R\left(\frac{4\pi\rho_s\hbar^2}{3e\mathcal{E}m^2}\right)^{\frac{1}{3}}. \qquad (6.63)$$

Douglass (1964) has measured the lifetime of negative ions trapped in vortex lines. A cross section of his experimental cell (cylindrical) is shown in Figure 6.5.

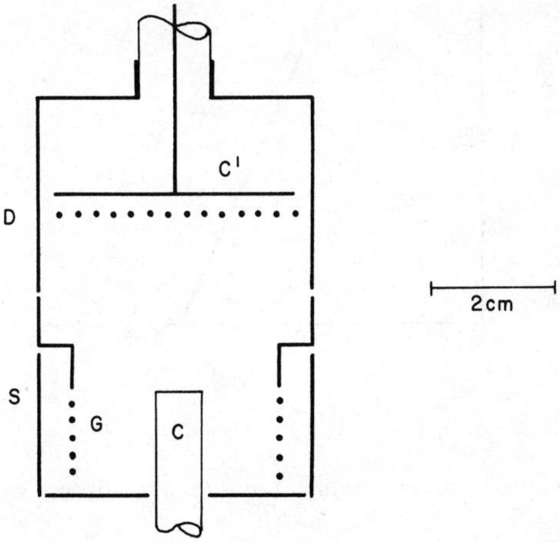

Fig. 6.5.

Negative ions are drawn from the source S(Po^{210}) through the grid G to collector C. Under rotation, some of the ions are trapped in vortex lines between G and C. The current source is then turned off and any free ions between C and G collected at C. After a given time t, the fields are switched and the ions remaining in the lines are drawn to collector C'. During the clearing time t, a certain fraction $1 - e^{-Pt}$ of the trapped ions escape and are collected by C. Thus the total charge reaching C' is proportional to e^{-Pt}. From this the escape probability per unit time P is found and is shown in Figure 6.6.

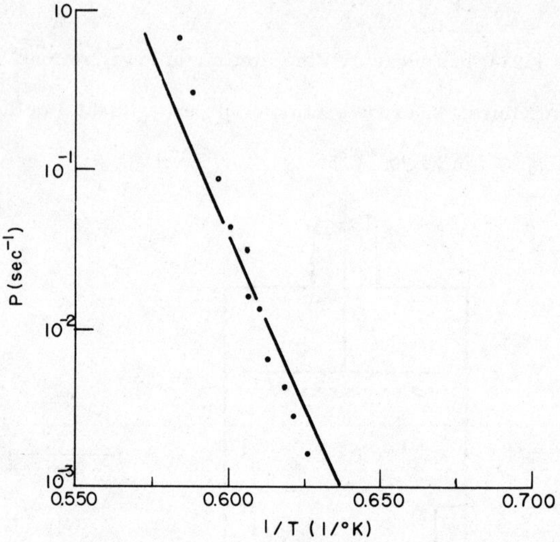

Fig. 6.6.

The solid curve is obtained from (6.58) with the well parameters ω_A, ω_c, S_A, S_c, u_o, and u_c obtained from numerical integration of (6.12). The radius is taken as $R^- = 15.96\,Å$, the mass 100 helium masses, and the field 25 v/cm. It should be noted that since the cavity is cylindrical, the field is not uniform and thus this 25 v/cm is taken as an average. A change in the field of $\pm$ 15 v/cm changes R^- by about 0.1Å (at low field strengths, P becomes independent of $\mathcal{E}$). The theoretical curve can be made to go through the end points of the experimental data by changing $R^- \pm 0.4\,Å$. Also at these temperatures $\beta >> \omega_c/\sqrt{m_i}$, which is the condition for (6.58) to go into (6.57). The latter is independent of the ion mass since $\beta = \frac{e}{\mu m_i}$

(of course the ion mass enters into the mobility but the mobility is known). The ion mass does enter in the second-order terms of (6.58) but is quite a small effect. Figure 6.7 shows a cross section (y = 0 plane) of the total potential energy u_T with $\mathcal{E}$ = 25 v/cm, and R^- = 15.96 at T = 1.64° K.

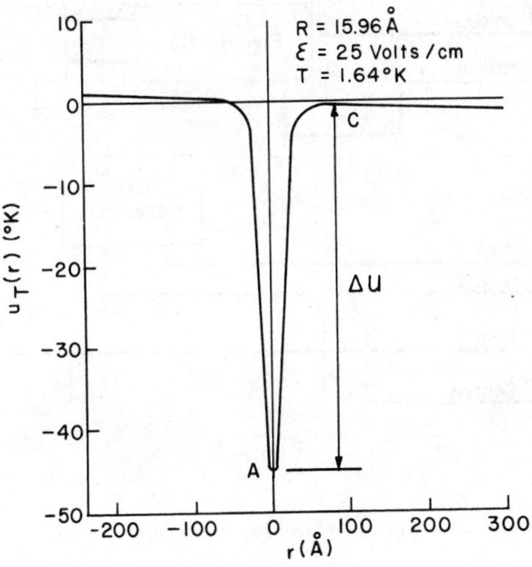

Fig. 6.7.

As seen, the condition for a deep well, $\Delta u >> kT$, is easily met. It is seen that the minimum is on the axis of the vortex and that the saddle point energy u_c is quite small when compared with u_o. The ion radius influences P primarily through the depth Δu and only in a secondary way through the second derivatives ω_A, ω_c, S_A, and S_c. In other words, if the four second derivatives are only roughly known, the ion radius is still closely determined owing to the rapid variation of P through Δu. Thus the discussion at the end of §24 concerning the neglect of the flow about the ion is justified for this case.

We now consider the lifetime of positive ions trapped by vortex rings as measured by Cade (1965). His experimental system is shown in Figure 6.8.

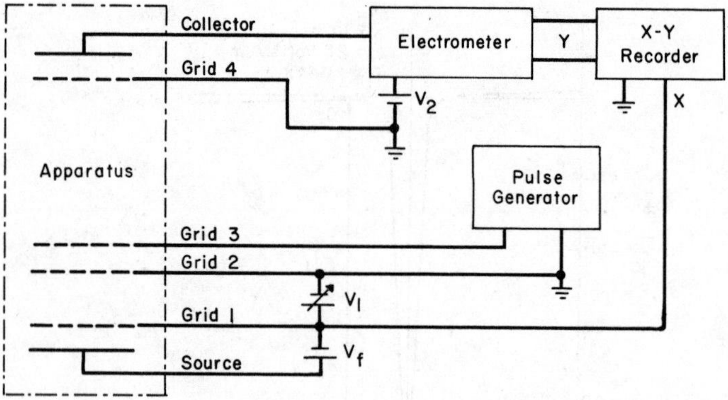

Fig. 6.8.

Vortex rings are produced between the source S and grid G_1. The rings then acquire a given energy in falling through the potential from G_1 to G_2 and then drift to the collector C. A potential about equal to that applied to $G_1 - G_2$ is applied with reversed polarity between G_4 - C. Assuming the rings lose no energy through collisions with excitations, the rings are just able to reach the collector. A high voltage pulse is then applied to $G_2 - G_3$. During the pulse width τ, a certain number of ions will escape from the rings. Since the energy acquired by the ring in passing between $G_1 - G_2$ is in the hydrodynamic flow connected with the ring, the ion, if it escapes, will not have sufficient energy to overcome the potential barrier at G_4 - C. Thus the current at C is a function of the pulse duration. For a given temperature and pulse height, the escape probability per unit time may be found. This data is shown in Figure 6.9.

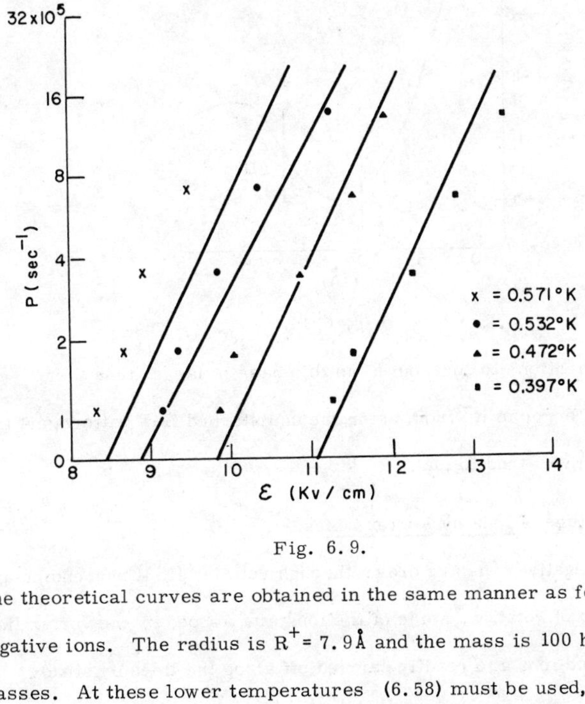

Fig. 6.9.

The theoretical curves are obtained in the same manner as for the negative ions. The radius is $R^+ = 7.9 Å$ and the mass is 100 helium masses. At these lower temperatures (6.58) must be used, and P is essentially inversely proportional to the square root of the mass. If the mass is taken as 40 helium masses, R^+ would increase to only 8.0Å. The potential for a 7.9Å ion and a mass of 100 helium masses is shown in Figure 6.10 for $\mathcal{E}$ = 7,000 v/cm.

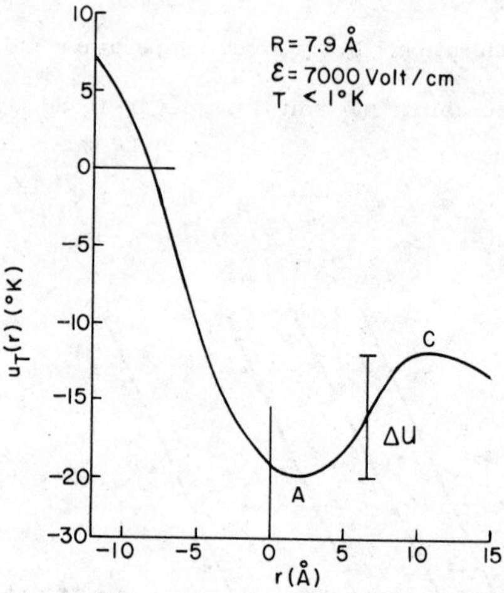

Fig. 6.10.

The contribution to Δu from u_c in this case is large, thus there will be an error in R^+ from using the undisturbed flow pattern, and the correction will tend to make R^+ larger.

§26. Capture of Ions by Vortex Lines

If negative ions are drawn through rotating He II perpendicular to the axis of rotation, some of the ions are trapped by the vortex lines. The trapped ions are readily carried off along the lines by steady electric fields and are collected at the end of the lines. The probability of escape must be small, however, for the time it takes for the captured ions to be collected. This collection time will depend on the field along the lines, the ion mobility in the line, and the distance the ion must travel. If the temperature is high, the ions will readily escape and no net decrease in the perpendicular current will be seen. Figure 6.6 shows that below 1.6° K the lifetime is greater than eight minutes, and it is assumed that escape can be neglected for negative ions. For positive ions above 1° K, however, the escape probability is large even for small electric fields (≈ 20 v/cm) so that positive ion capture is not expected to be observed. Under rotation, the density of lines is given by (2.105)

$$n_o = \frac{2\Omega}{\kappa}, \tag{6.64}$$

where Ω is the angular velocity and $\kappa = h/m$. If each line has a capture cross section σ (diameter), the fractional current lost in a distance dx is just

$$\frac{dI}{I} = -n_o \sigma dx \tag{6.65}$$

so that

$$I = I_o e^{-\frac{2\Omega\sigma x}{\kappa}}, \tag{6.66}$$

where I_o is the current in the ion beam for $\Omega = 0$. Then log I versus Ω is a straight line with slope $2\Omega\sigma/\kappa$ from which σ can be found. Tanner (to be published) has measured the capture cross section for negative ions as a function of temperature and field. His experimental cell is shown in Figure 6.11.

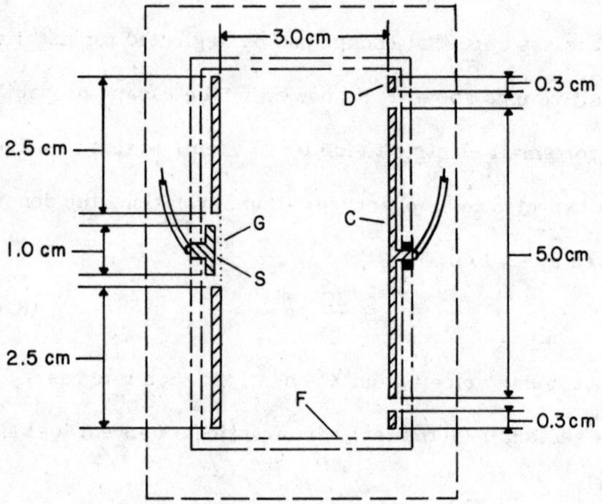

Fig. 6.11.

The ions are drawn out by the field between the sources S and grid G. They then traverse a distance x = 3.0 cm in a uniform field $\mathcal{E}$. The current is detected by a vibrating reed electrometer connected to the collector C. His cross sections are shown in Figure 6.12 (solid lines are from theory to be discussed).

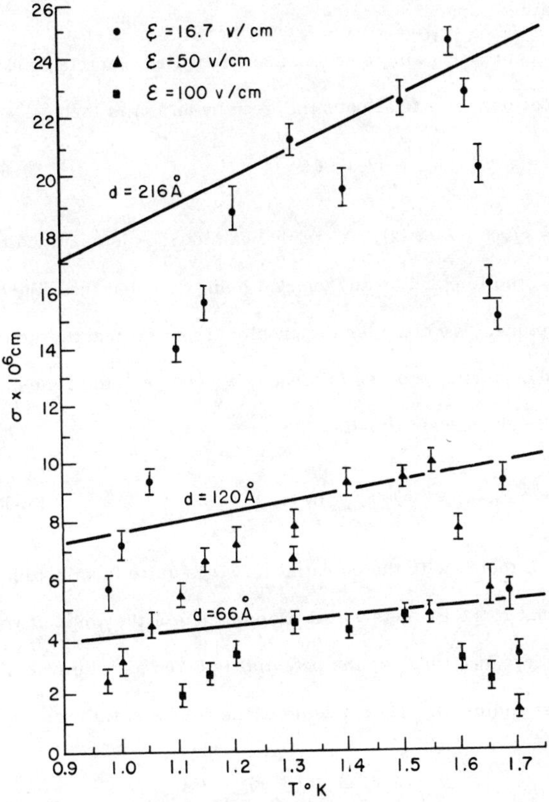

Fig. 6.12.

It should be noted that the cross sections drop rapidly between 1.6 and 1.7° K as expected from the large escape probabilities (Figure 6.6) in this temperature range.

Let us consider a single vortex and an applied electric field $\mathcal{E}$ in the x-direction. The total potential seen by an ion is then

$$u_T = u(r) - e\mathcal{E}x , \tag{6.67}$$

where u(r) is given by (6. 12). A steady beam of ions is assumed to be incident on the line and steady current being diverted from the beam by vortex capture. We consider the problem from stochastic theory, and since the capturing process is steady, we consider the time-independent Smoluchowski equation

$$\nabla^2 w + g^2 \underset{\sim}{\nabla} \cdot (w \underset{\sim}{\nabla} u_T) = 0. \tag{6.68}$$

The solution of (6. 68) with the potential (6. 67) is quite formidable. We assume that if the ion gets within a distance d of the core, it will definitely be captured (that is, the potential is taken as a infinite square well of radius d). Thus outside of the well w satisfies

$$\nabla^2 w - g^2 e\mathcal{E} \underset{\sim}{\nabla} \cdot (\hat{1}_x w) = 0 , \tag{6.69}$$

or defining

$$r_E = \frac{2}{g^2 e\mathcal{E}} = \frac{2\beta D}{m_i e\mathcal{E}} = \frac{2kT}{e\mathcal{E}} , \tag{6.70}$$

where $\beta = \frac{e}{\mu m_i}$ and $D = \frac{kT\mu}{e}$, we have

$$\nabla^2 w - \frac{2}{r_E} \underset{\sim}{\nabla} \cdot (\hat{1}_x w) = 0 . \tag{6.71}$$

Let us neglect the vortex altogether so that the problem is one dimensional

$$\frac{d^2 w}{dx^2} - \frac{2}{r_E} \frac{dw}{dx} = 0 . \qquad (6.72)$$

We assume that there is a uniform flux of particles f_∞ coming from $x = -\infty$ and being collected at $x = 0$ ($w = 0$ at points where particles are collected). Thus the solution to (6.72) is readily found to be

$$w = \frac{f_\infty r_E}{2D} \left(1 - e^{\frac{2x}{r_E}}\right) . \qquad (6.73)$$

The particle density is uniform except in the region of the collector, where it falls to zero. If we force w to vanish at a small distance d from the vortex, it will still take a distance of order $\frac{r_E}{2}$ for w to reach its uniform far field value. For a field of 50 v/cm and T = 1.3° K, we find $r_E \approx 4 \times 10^{-6}$ cm, which is of the same order as the corresponding cross section (diameter) of $\approx 7 \times 10^{-6}$ cm from Figure 6.12.

To include the vortex, we neglect the region close to the collector so that, far from the vortex, w should approach the uniform value in (6.73)

$$w \approx \frac{f_\infty r_E}{2D} , \qquad (6.74)$$

and the flux should go to $\underset{\sim}{f} \approx \hat{1}_x f_\infty$. In (6.71), we let

$$w = e^{\lambda x} \Omega , \qquad (6.75)$$

where

$$\lambda = \frac{1}{r_E} . \tag{6.76}$$

We then get

$$\nabla^2 \Omega = \lambda^2 \Omega . \tag{6.77}$$

The solutions to this are the products of the functions $\cos n\theta$ and $\sin n\theta$ with the modified Bessel function $I_n(\lambda r)$ and $K_n(\lambda r)$. Far from the vortex, however, we require from (6.74) and (6.75) that

$$\Omega \approx \frac{f_\infty}{2\lambda D} e^{-\lambda x} = \frac{f_\infty}{2\lambda D} e^{-\lambda r \cos \theta} , \tag{6.78}$$

which can be expanded in terms of $I_n(\lambda r) \cos n\theta$ as

$$\Omega \approx \frac{f_\infty}{2\lambda D} \sum_{n=0}^{\infty} (-1)^n \epsilon_n I_n(\lambda r) \cos n\theta , \quad r \to \infty , \tag{6.79}$$

where $\epsilon_o = 1$ and $\epsilon_n = 2$ for $n \neq 0$. Since the functions $K_n(\lambda r)$ vanish for large r and since the problem is symmetric in θ, we can add to (6.79) a series in $K_n(\lambda r) \cos n\theta$. Since we require w and thus Ω to vanish at $r = d$, Ω must take the form

$$\Omega = \frac{f_\infty}{2\lambda D} \sum_{n=0}^{\infty} (-1)^n \epsilon_n \left[I_n(\lambda r) - \frac{I_n(\lambda d)}{K_n(\lambda d)} K_n(\lambda r) \right] \cos n\theta . \tag{6.80}$$

Thus

$$w = \frac{f_\infty}{2\lambda D} \left[1 - e^{\lambda r \cos \theta} \sum_{n=0}^{\infty} (-1)^n \epsilon_n \frac{I_n(\lambda d)}{K_n(\lambda d)} K_n(\lambda r) \cos n\theta \right] . \tag{6.81}$$

The inward flux at $r = d$ is given by

$$-\hat{1}_r \cdot \underset{\sim}{f} = \left(D \frac{\partial w}{\partial r} - \frac{2D}{r_c} w\right)_{r=d}$$

$$= D \frac{\partial w}{\partial r}\bigg|_{r=d} \tag{6.82}$$

$$= D e^{\lambda d \cos\theta} \left(\frac{\partial \Omega}{\partial r}\right)_{r=d}$$

$$= \frac{f_\infty}{2} e^{\lambda d \cos\theta} \sum_{n=0}^{\infty} (-1)^n \epsilon_n \left[\frac{-I'_n(\lambda d) K_n(\lambda d) - I_n(\lambda d) K'_n(\lambda d)}{K_n(\lambda d)}\right] \cos n\theta \, .$$

Using the Wronskian relation,

$$K_n(z) I'_n(z) - I_n(z) K'_n(z) = \frac{1}{z} \, , \tag{6.83}$$

we get

$$-\hat{1}_r \cdot \underset{\sim}{f} = \frac{f_\infty}{2\lambda d} e^{\lambda d \cos\theta} \sum_{n=0}^{\infty} \frac{(-1)^n \epsilon_n \cos n\theta}{K_n(\lambda d)} \, . \tag{6.84}$$

The net inward flux is then the integral of (6.84) about the vortex.

$$F = -d \int_0^{2\pi} \hat{1}_r \cdot \underset{\sim}{f} \, d\theta \, . \tag{6.85}$$

Since

$$I_n(\lambda d) = \frac{1}{2\pi} \int_0^{2\pi} e^{\lambda d \cos\theta} \cos n\theta \, d\theta \, , \tag{6.86}$$

we have

$$F = \frac{\pi f_\infty}{\lambda} \sum_{n=0}^{\infty} (-1)^n \epsilon_n \frac{I_n(\lambda d)}{K_n(\lambda d)} \, . \tag{6.87}$$

The cross section is defined as the ratio of the flux into the vortex F to the incident flux f_∞, therefore

$$\sigma = \frac{\pi}{\lambda} \sum_{n=0}^{\infty} (-1)^n \epsilon_n \frac{I_n(\lambda d)}{K_n(\lambda d)} . \qquad (6.88)$$

The cross section is shown in Figure 6.12, d being chosen to best fit the experimental points between 1.3 and 1.6° K. At low temperatures, Smoluchowski's equation will no longer be valid since the ion mean-free path will become large compared to the potential well. Starting with the equations of motion for an ion, Donnelly and Roberts (1967) estimate that for low temperatures, the cross sections should approach 100 Å. The low-temperature points are all still above 100 Å, but experimental points at even lower temperatures are needed to check this limit. Between 1.6 and 1.7° K, the cross sections fall rapidly owing to a large escape probability. In §25 the escape probability was shown to be sensitive to the ion radius. As the fluid pressure is increased, it is expected that the negative ion bubble should become smaller, thereby increasing the escape probability. Thus, under pressure, the "lifetime edge" of the cross sections should shift to lower temperatures. Figure 6.13 shows that this shift does indeed occur (Springett and Donnelly 1966).

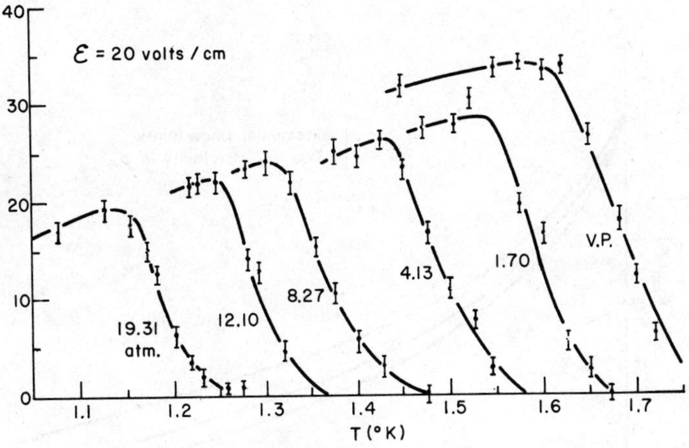

Fig. 6. 13.

In the vicinity of the lifetime edge, the cross section is written as

$$\sigma = \sigma_o e^{-P\tau} , \tag{6.89}$$

where P is the escape probability and τ is the average time the ions spend in the line before going beyond the range of the collector. The pressures and temperatures for which $\sigma = \frac{1}{2}\sigma_o$, $P\tau = 0.6932$, are taken from Figure 6. 13. At the vapor pressure R^- is taken as 15. 96Å as given in § 25, and thus τ is known at the vapor pressure. To find R^- for increased pressure, the pressure and temperature dependence of τ must be known. Figure 6. 14 gives R^- based on three different assumptions concerning τ.

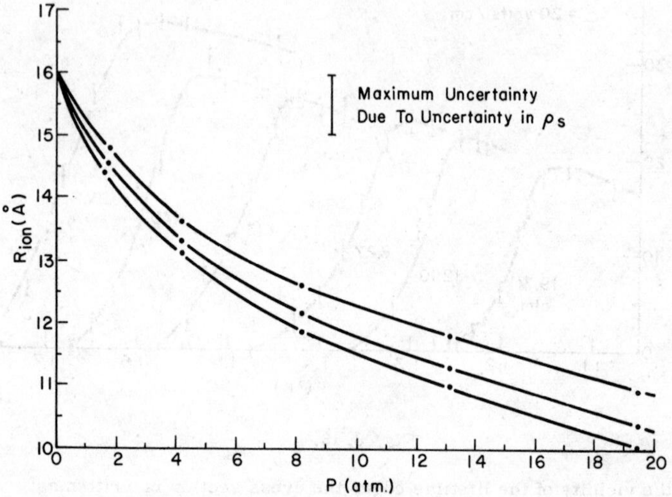

Fig. 6.14.

The upper curve assumes τ is constant and the middle curve allows τ to vary inversely as the free ion mobility, μ_F. The lower curve allows $\tau \propto \frac{1}{\mu_F}$ but also lets the vortex core radius vary as the square root of the superfluid density. Mobility measurements of ions trapped in lines (Domingo 1966) show that the line mobility is smaller than the free ion mobility so that the upper and lower curves in Figure 6.14 are upper and lower limits to the negative ion radius. Using the middle curve of Figure 6.14, Springett and Donnelly (1966) have also been able to explain qualitatively the pressure dependence of the free negative ion mobility of Figure 3.7. The agreement is good if the ion mass is assumed constant. This, however, would not be the case if the ion mass is calculated as at the end of §23.

§27. Further Aspects of Ion Motion

In §8 it was shown that at low temperatures, ions create vortex rings and thus Landau's criterion based on roton production (§13) does not apply. For pressures above 12 atm and temperature between 0.3 and 0.5°K, however, Rayfield (1966) has shown that the Landau critical velocity is reached for the negative ion. Thus, above 12 atm roton production appears to be favored over ring production with increasing pressure, and this is assumed to be associated with the decreasing ion radius. No effect, however, has been seen for the positive ion.

At higher temperature (≈ 1° K) Careri, Cunsolo, Mazzoldi, and Santini (1965) obtained the mobility curves in Figure 6.15 for negative ions (a very similar curve results for positive ions).

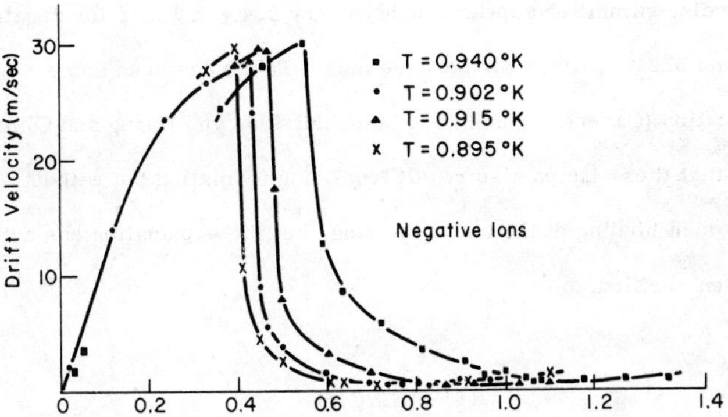

Fig. 6.15.

The rapid falloff near 400 kv/cm is assumed to result from ring formation, the creation of rings at lower fields being hindered by collisions with rotons. In the lower field region, however, closer inspection reveals a number of smaller jumps shown in Figure 6.16 for positive ions (Careri, Cunsolo, and Mazzoldi 1964).

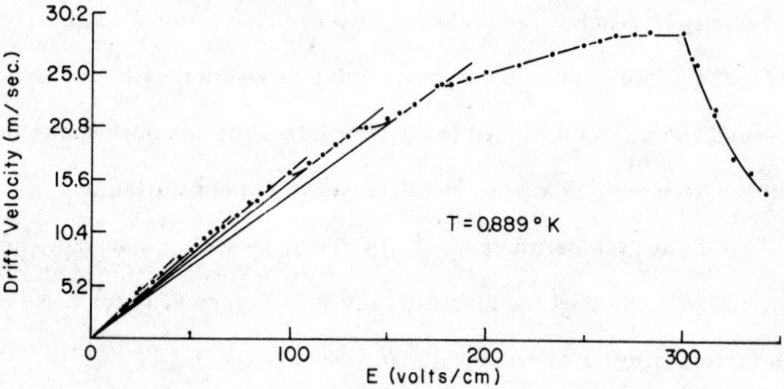

Fig. 6.16.

These discontinuities appear roughly every 2.4 ± 0.1 m/s for negative ions and 5.2 ± 0.1 m/s for positive ions. There has been some speculation (Careri, Cunsolo, and Mazzoldi 1964 and Huang and Olinto 1965) that these jumps also result from ring formation but without subsequent binding of the ion to the ring, but the explanation has not yet been verified.

REFERENCES

Atkins, K. R. 1963, Proceedings of the International School of Physics, Course XXI, edited by Careri (New York: Academic Press).

Burdick, B. 1965, Phys. Rev. Letters, 14, 11.

Cade, A. G. 1965, Phys. Rev. Letters, 15, 238.

Careri, G., Cunsolo, S., and Mazzoldi, P. 1964, Phys. Rev., 136, A303.

Careri, G., Cunsolo, S., Mazzoldi, P., and Santini, M. 1965, Proceedings of the Ninth International Conference on Low Temperature Physics, edited by J. G. Daunt, D. O. Edwards, F. J. Milford, and M. Yaqub (New York: Plenum), p. 335.

Chandrasekhar, S. 1943, Rev. Mod. Phys., 15, 1.

Clark, R. C. 1965, Phys. Letters, 16, 42.

Domingo, J. J. 1966, private communication.

Donnelly, R. J., and Roberts, P. H., 1967 (to be published).

Douglass, R. L. 1964, Phys. Rev. Letters, 13, 791.

Girardeau, M. 1961, Phys. of Fluids, 4, 279.

Gross, E. P. 1958, Ann. Phys. (N.Y.), 4, 57.

———— 1962, ibid., 19, 234.

Hiroike, K., Kestner, N. R., Rice, S. A., and Jortner, J. 1965, J. Chem. Phys., 43, 2625.

Huang, K., and Olinto, A. C. 1965, Phys. Rev., 139, A1441.

Jortner, J., Kestner, N. R., Rice, S. A., and Cohen, M. H. 1965, Phys. Rev., 43, 2614.

Kuper, C. G. 1963, Proceedings of the International School of Physics, Course XXI, edited by G. Careri (New York: Academic Press).

Landau, L. D. 1959a, Fluid Mechanics (Reading, Mass.: Addison-Wesley), sec. 11.

——————— 1959b, ibid., sec. 10.

Landau, L. D., and Lifshitz, E. M. 1960, Electrodynamics of Continuous Media (Reading, Mass.: Addison-Wesley), sec. 15.

Levine, J., and Sanders, T. M. 1962, Phys. Rev. Letters, 15, 159.

Miller, J. C. P. 1965, Handbook of Mathematical Functions, edited by Milton Abranowitz and Irene A. Stegun (New York:Dover).

Panofsky, W. K. H., and Phillips, M. 1962, Classical Electricity and Magnetism (Reading, Mass.:Addison-Wesley), sec. 6-7.

Parks, P. E., and Donnelly, R. J. 1966, Phys. Rev. Letters, 16, 45.

Pauling, L. 1933, J. Chem. Phys., 1, 56.

Phelps, A. V., and Brown, S. C. 1952, Phys. Rev., 86, 102.

Rayfield, G. W. 1966, Phys. Rev. Letters, 16, 934.

Sommer, W. T. 1964, Phys. Rev. Letters, 12, 271.

Springett, B. E., and Donnelly, R. J. 1966, Phys. Rev. Letters, 17, 364.

Tanner, D. J. (to be published in Phys. Rev.).

Whittaker, E. T., and Watson, G. N. 1927, A Course in Modern Analysis, 4th edition 1950 (Cambridge: Cambridge University Press).

Woolf, M. A., and Rayfield, G. W. 1965, Phys. Rev. Letters, 15, 235.

APPENDIX A

Vector and Dyadic Identities

Scalars: ψ, φ

Vectors: $\underset{\sim}{A} \to A_i$, $\underset{\sim}{B} \to B_i$, $\underset{\sim}{C} \to C_i$

Dyads: $\pi \to \pi_{ik}$, $\tau \to \tau_{ik}$

Definitions (Summation convention is followed)

$$\underset{\sim}{A} \cdot \underset{\sim}{B} = A_i B_i$$

$$\underset{\sim}{\nabla} \cdot \underset{\sim}{A} = \frac{\partial A_i}{\partial x_i}$$

$$\underset{\sim}{A}\,\underset{\sim}{B} \to (\underset{\sim}{A}\,\underset{\sim}{B})_{ik} = A_i B_k$$

$$\underset{\sim}{\nabla}\,\underset{\sim}{A} \to (\underset{\sim}{\nabla}\,\underset{\sim}{A})_{ik} = \frac{\partial A_k}{\partial x_i}$$

$$\underset{\sim}{A} \cdot \pi \to (\underset{\sim}{A} \cdot \pi)_i = A_k \pi_{ki}$$

$$\pi \cdot \underset{\sim}{A} \to (\pi \cdot \underset{\sim}{A})_i = \pi_{ik} A_k$$

$$\underset{\sim}{\nabla} \cdot \pi \to (\underset{\sim}{\nabla} \cdot \pi)_i = \frac{\partial \pi_{ki}}{\partial x_k}$$

$$\pi \cdot \tau \to (\pi \cdot \tau)_{ik} = \pi_{i\ell} \tau_{\ell k}$$

$$\pi : \tau = \pi_{ik} \tau_{ik}$$

$$\underset{\sim}{\nabla} \cdot \pi \cdot \underset{\sim}{A} = \frac{\partial \pi_{ik}}{\partial x_i} A_k$$

Identities

$$\underset{\sim}{A}\cdot(\underset{\sim}{B}\times\underset{\sim}{C}) = \underset{\sim}{B}\cdot(\underset{\sim}{C}\times\underset{\sim}{A}) = \underset{\sim}{C}\cdot(\underset{\sim}{A}\times\underset{\sim}{B})$$

$$\underset{\sim}{A}\times(\underset{\sim}{B}\times\underset{\sim}{C}) = \underset{\sim}{B}(\underset{\sim}{A}\cdot\underset{\sim}{C}) - \underset{\sim}{C}(\underset{\sim}{A}\cdot\underset{\sim}{B})$$

$$\nabla(\psi\varphi) = \psi\underset{\sim}{\nabla}\varphi + \varphi\underset{\sim}{\nabla}\psi$$

$$\underset{\sim}{\nabla}(\underset{\sim}{A}\cdot\underset{\sim}{B}) = \underset{\sim}{A}\times(\underset{\sim}{\nabla}\times\underset{\sim}{B}) + \underset{\sim}{B}\times(\underset{\sim}{\nabla}\times\underset{\sim}{A}) + \underset{\sim}{B}\cdot\underset{\sim}{\nabla}\underset{\sim}{A} + \underset{\sim}{A}\cdot\underset{\sim}{\nabla}\underset{\sim}{B} = \underset{\sim}{\nabla}\underset{\sim}{A}\cdot\underset{\sim}{B} + \underset{\sim}{\nabla}\underset{\sim}{B}\cdot\underset{\sim}{A}$$

$$\underset{\sim}{\nabla}\cdot(\psi\underset{\sim}{A}) = \psi\underset{\sim}{\nabla}\cdot\underset{\sim}{A} + \underset{\sim}{A}\cdot\underset{\sim}{\nabla}\psi$$

$$\underset{\sim}{\nabla}\cdot(\underset{\sim}{A}\times\underset{\sim}{B}) = \underset{\sim}{B}\cdot(\underset{\sim}{\nabla}\times\underset{\sim}{A}) - \underset{\sim}{A}\cdot(\underset{\sim}{\nabla}\times\underset{\sim}{B})$$

$$\underset{\sim}{\nabla}\cdot(\underset{\sim}{A}\underset{\sim}{B}) = \underset{\sim}{B}(\underset{\sim}{\nabla}\cdot\underset{\sim}{A}) + \underset{\sim}{A}\cdot\underset{\sim}{\nabla}\underset{\sim}{B}$$

$$\underset{\sim}{\nabla}\cdot(\pi\cdot\underset{\sim}{A}) = \nabla\cdot\pi\cdot\underset{\sim}{A} + \pi : \underset{\sim}{\nabla}\underset{\sim}{A}$$

$$\underset{\sim}{\nabla}\times(\psi\underset{\sim}{A}) = \psi\underset{\sim}{\nabla}\times\underset{\sim}{A} - \underset{\sim}{A}\times\underset{\sim}{\nabla}\psi$$

$$\underset{\sim}{\nabla}\times(\underset{\sim}{A}\times\underset{\sim}{B}) = \underset{\sim}{A}(\underset{\sim}{\nabla}\cdot\underset{\sim}{B}) - \underset{\sim}{B}(\underset{\sim}{\nabla}\cdot\underset{\sim}{A}) + \underset{\sim}{B}\cdot\underset{\sim}{\nabla}\underset{\sim}{A} - \underset{\sim}{A}\cdot\underset{\sim}{\nabla}\underset{\sim}{B} = \nabla\cdot(\underset{\sim}{B}\underset{\sim}{A}) - \underset{\sim}{\nabla}\cdot(\underset{\sim}{A}\underset{\sim}{B})$$

$$\underset{\sim}{\nabla}\times(\underset{\sim}{\nabla}\times\underset{\sim}{A}) = \underset{\sim}{\nabla}(\underset{\sim}{\nabla}\cdot\underset{\sim}{A}) - \nabla^2\underset{\sim}{A}$$

$$\underset{\sim}{A}\times(\underset{\sim}{\nabla}\times\underset{\sim}{B}) = \underset{\sim}{\nabla}\underset{\sim}{B}\cdot\underset{\sim}{A} - \underset{\sim}{A}\cdot\underset{\sim}{\nabla}\underset{\sim}{B}$$

APPENDIX B

Selected Physical Constants and Properties of Helium

$h = 6.6256 \times 10^{-27}$ erg s

$\hbar = 1.05450 \times 10^{-27}$ erg s

$k = 1.38054 \times 10^{-16}$ erg $(^{\circ}K)^{-1}$

$e = 4.80298 \times 10^{-10}$ cm$^{3/2}$ g$^{1/2}$ s^{-1} (esu)

$R = 8.3143 \times 10^{7}$ erg $(^{\circ}K)^{-1}$ mole^{-1}

$N_o = 6.02252 \times 10^{23}$ mole^{-1}

$M_{He} = 6.648 \times 10^{-24}$ g

Atomic mass 4.0038 (O^{16})
4.0026 (C^{12})

NBP 4.215° K, 760 mm

λ-point 2.172° K, 37.94 mm

Critical point 5.20° K, 2.26 atm., 0.0693 g cm^{-3}

Zero-point energy 47 cal mole^{-1}

$$\frac{\text{Volume of gas (STP)}}{\text{Volume of liquid (NBP)}} = 700.3$$

Parameters for Lennard-Jones Potential

$\epsilon = 14.11 \times 10^{16}$ erg $\qquad \sigma = 2.56$ Å

Landau parameters

$$\mu_o(p) = 0.16\,(1.0 - 0.0217\,p)M_{He}$$

$$\frac{p_o(p)}{\hbar} = 1.91\,(1.0 + 0.0029\,p)\ \text{Å}^{-1}$$

$$\Delta(T, p) = 8.68\,(1.0 - 0.0084\,T^{7})\,(1.0 - 0.0075\,p)\ ^{\circ}K$$

p in atm., T in °K

APPENDIX C

TABLE 1 - 1958 T Scale

Temperatures, °K, for values of vapor pressure of helium 4 (^{4}He) in mm Hg at 20° C and standard gravity, 980·665 cm sec^{-2}

P	0	0.001	0.002	0.003	0.004	0.005	0.006	0.007	0.008	0.009
0.01	0.7904 66	7970 61	8031 56	8087 53	8140 50	8190 47	8237 45	8282 43	8325 41	8366 38
0.02	0.8404 38	8442 36	8478 34	8512 33	8545 33	8578 31	8609 30	8639 29	8668 28	8696 28
0.03	0.8724 27	8751 26	8777 25	8802 25	8827 24	8851 23	8874 24	8898 22	8920 22	8942 22
0.04	0.8964 21	8985 20	9005 21	9026 20	9046 19	9065 19	9084 19	9103 19	9122 18	9140 18
0.05	0.9158 17	9175 18	9193 17	9210 17	9227 16	9243 16	9259 16	9275 16	9291 16	9307 15
0.06	0.9322 15	9337 15	9352 15	9367 14	9381 15	9396 14	9410 14	9424 14	9438 13	9451 14
0.07	0.9465 13	9478 14	9492 13	9505 12	9517 13	9530 13	9543 12	9555 13	9568 12	9580 12
0.08	0.9592 12	9604 12	9616 11	9627 12	9639 12	9651 11	9662 11	9673 11	9684 11	9695 11
0.09	0.9706 11	9717 11	9728 11	9739 10	9749 11	9760 10	9770 10	9780 11	9791 10	9801 10
0.10	0.9811 10	9821 10	9831 9	9840 10	9850 10	9860 9	9869 10	9879 9	9888 10	9898 9
0.11	0.9907 9	9916 9	9925 9	9934 9	9943 9	9952 9	9961 9	9970 9	9979 9	9988 8
0.12	0.9996 9	0005 8	0013 9	0022 8	0030 9	0039 8	0047 8	0055 8	0063 8	0071 9
0.13	1.0080 8	0088 8	0096 8	0104 7	0111 8	0119 8	0127 8	0135 8	0143 7	0150 8
0.14	1.0158 7	0165 8	0173 7	0180 8	0188 7	0195 8	0203 7	0210 7	0217 7	0224 8
0.15	1.0232 7	0239 7	0246 7	0253 7	0260 7	0267 6	0273 8	0281 7	0288 7	0295 7
0.16	1.0302 6	0308 7	0315 7	0322 6	0328 7	0335 7	0342 6	0348 7	0355 6	0361 7

TABLE 1

P	0	0.001	0.002	0.003	0.004	0.005	0.006	0.007	0.008	0.009
0.17	1.0368 7	0375 6	0381 6	0387 7	0394 6	0400 6	0406 7	0413 6	0419 6	0425 6
0.18	1.0431 6	0437 7	0444 6	0450 6	0456 6	0462 6	0468 6	0474 6	0480 6	0486 6
0.19	1.0492 6	0498 5	0503 6	0509 6	0515 6	0521 6	0527 6	0533 5	0538 6	0544 6
	0	0.01	0.02	0.03	0.04	0.05	0.06	0.07	0.08	0.09
0.2	1.0550 55	0605 54	0659 51	0710 50	0760 48	0808 47	0855 45	0900 44	0944 42	0986 42
0.3	1.1028 40	1068 39	1107 39	1146 37	1183 37	1220 35	1255 35	1290 34	1324 34	1358 32
0.4	1.1390 32	1422 32	1454 31	1485 30	1515 30	1545 29	1574 29	1603 28	1631 28	1659 27
0.5	1.1686 27	1713 26	1739 26	1765 26	1791 25	1816 25	1841 25	1866 24	1890 24	1914 23
0.6	1.1937 23	1960 23	1983 23	2006 22	2028 23	2051 21	2072 22	2094 21	2115 21	2136 21
0.7	1.2157 21	2178 20	2198 20	2218 20	2238 20	2258 19	2277 19	2296 20	2316 18	2334 19
0.8	1.2353 19	2372 18	2390 18	2408 18	2426 18	2444 18	2462 17	2479 17	2496 18	2514 17
0.9	1.2531 16	2547 17	2564 17	2581 16	2597 16	2613 17	2630 17	2646 16	2662 15	2677 16
1.0	1.2693 16	2709 15	2724 15	2739 15	2754 15	2769 15	2784 15	2799 15	2814 14	2828 15
1.1	1.2843 14	2857 15	2872 14	2886 14	2900 14	2914 14	2928 14	2942 13	2955 14	2969 14
1.2	1.2983 13	2996 13	3009 14	3023 13	3036 13	3049 13	3062 13	3075 13	3088 13	3101 12
1.3	1.3113 13	3126 13	3139 12	3151 12	3163 13	3176 12	3188 12	3200 12	3212 12	3224 12
1.4	1.3236 12	3248 12	3260 12	3272 12	3284 11	3295 12	3307 11	3318 12	3330 11	3341 12
1.5	1.3353 11	3364 11	3375 11	3386 12	3398 11	3409 11	3420 11	3431 10	3441 11	3452 11
1.6	1.3463 11	3474 11	3485 10	3495 11	3506 10	3516 11	3527 10	3537 11	3548 10	3558 10

TABLE 1

P	0	0.1	0.2	0.3	0.4	0.5	0.6	0.7	0.8	0.9
1.7	1.3568 10	3578 11	3589 10	3599 10	3609 10	3619 10	3629 10	3639 10	3649 10	3659 10
1.8	1.3669 9	3678 10	3688 10	3698 10	3708 9	3717 10	3727 9	3736 10	3746 9	3755 10
1.9	1.3765 9	3774 9	3783 10	3793 9	3802 9	3811 9	3820 10	3830 9	3839 9	3848 9
2	1.3857 89	3946 85	4031 83	4114 79	4193 78	4271 74	4345 73	4418 71	4489 68	4557 67
3	1.4624 65	4689 64	4753 62	4815 61	4876 59	4935 58	4993 57	5050 55	5105 55	5160 53
4	1.5213 53	5266 51	5317 51	5368 49	5417 49	5466 48	5514 47	5561 47	5608 46	5654 45
5	1.5699 44	5743 43	5786 44	5830 42	5872 42	5914 41	5955 41	5996 40	6036 40	6076 39
6	1.6115 38	6153 38	6191 38	6229 37	6266 37	6303 37	6340 36	6376 35	6411 35	6446 35
7	1.6481 35	6516 34	6550 34	6584 33	6617 33	6650 33	6683 32	6715 32	6747 32	6779 32
8	1.6811 31	6842 31	6873 30	6903 31	6934 30	6964 30	6994 29	7023 30	7053 29	7082 28
9	1.7110 29	7139 28	7167 29	7196 27	7223 28	7251 28	7279 27	7306 27	7333 27	7360 27
10	1.7387 26	7413 26	7439 26	7465 26	7491 26	7517 26	7543 25	7568 25	7593 25	7618 25
11	1.7643 25	7668 24	7692 25	7717 24	7741 24	7765 24	7789 23	7812 24	7836 24	7860 23
12	1.7883 23	7906 23	7929 23	7952 23	7975 22	7997 23	8020 22	8042 23	8065 22	8087 22
13	1.8109 21	8130 22	8152 22	8174 21	8195 22	8217 21	8238 21	8259 21	8280 21	8301 21
14	1.8322 21	8343 20	8363 21	8384 20	8404 21	8425 20	8445 20	8465 20	8485 20	8505 20
15	1.8525 20	8545 19	8564 20	8584 19	8603 20	8623 19	8642 19	8661 19	8680 19	8699 19
16	1.8718 19	8737 19	8756 18	8774 19	8793 19	8812 18	8831 18	8848 19	8867 18	8885 18

TABLE 1

P	0	0.1	0.2	0.3	0.4	0.5	0.6	0.7	0.8	0.9
17	1.8903 18	8921 18	8939 18	8957 18	8975 18	8993 17	9010 18	9028 17	9045 18	9063 17
18	1.9080 18	9098 17	9115 17	9132 17	9149 17	9166 17	9183 17	9200 17	9217 17	9234 17
19	1.9251 17	9268 16	9284 17	9301 16	9317 17	9334 16	9350 16	9366 17	9383 16	9399 16
20	1.9415 16	9431 16	9447 16	9463 16	9479 16	9495 16	9511 16	9527 16	9543 15	9558 16
21	1.9574 15	9589 16	9605 15	9620 16	9636 15	9651 16	9667 15	9682 15	9697 15	9712 15
22	1.9727 16	9743 15	9758 15	9773 15	9788 14	9802 15	9817 15	9832 15	9847 15	9862 14
23	1.9876 15	9881 15	9906 14	9920 15	9935 14	9949 15	9964 14	9978 14	9992 15	0007 14
24	2.0021 14	0035 14	0049 14	0063 15	0078 14	0092 14	0106 14	0120 14	0134 13	0147 14
25	2.0161 14	0175 14	0189 14	0203 14	0217 13	0230 14	0244 13	0257 14	0271 14	0285 13
26	2.0298 14	0312 13	0325 14	0339 13	0352 13	0365 14	0379 13	0392 13	0405 13	0418 14
27	2.0432 13	0445 13	0458 13	0471 13	0484 13	0497 13	0510 13	0523 13	0536 13	0549 13
28	2.0562 13	0575 12	0587 13	0600 13	0613 13	0626 12	0638 13	0651 13	0664 12	0676 13
29	2.0689 12	0701 13	0714 12	0726 13	0739 12	0751 13	0764 12	0776 13	0789 12	0801 12
30	2.0813 13	0826 12	0838 12	0850 12	0862 12	0874 13	0887 12	0899 12	0911 12	0923 12
31	2.0935 12	0947 12	0959 12	0971 12	0983 12	0995 12	1007 12	1019 12	1031 11	1042 12
32	2.1054 12	1066 12	1078 12	1090 11	1101 12	1113 12	1125 11	1136 12	1148 12	1160 11
33	2.1171 12	1183 11	1194 12	1206 11	1217 12	1229 11	1240 12	1252 11	1263 12	1275 11
34	2.1286 11	1297 12	1309 11	1320 11	1331 12	1343 11	1354 11	1365 11	1376 12	1388 11
35	2.1399 11	1410 11	1421 11	1432 11	1443 12	1455 11	1466 11	1477 11	1488 11	1499 11
36	2.1510 11	1521 11	1532 11	1543 11	1554 11	1565 11	1576 10	1586 11	1597 11	1608 11

TABLE 1

P	0	0.1	C.2	0.3	0.4	0.5	0.6	0.7	0.8	0.9
37	2.1619 11	1630 11	1641 10	1651 11	1662 11	1673 11	1684 10	1694 11	1705 11	1716 11
38	2.1727 10	1737 11	1748 11	1759 10	1769 11	1780 10	1790 11	1801 11	1812 10	1822 11
39	2.1833 10	1843 11	1854 10	1864 11	1875 10	1885 10	1895 11	1906 10	1916 11	1927 10
40	2.1937 10	1947 11	1958 10	1968 10	1978 10	1988 11	1999 10	2009 10	2019 10	2029 11
41	2.2040 10	2050 10	2060 10	2070 10	2080 10	2090 10	2100 10	2110 10	2120 10	2130 10
42	2.2140 10	2150 10	2160 10	2170 10	2180 10	2190 10	2200 10	2210 10	2220 10	2230 10
43	2.2240 10	2250 9	2259 10	2269 10	2279 10	2289 10	2299 9	2308 10	2318 10	2328 9
44	2.2337 10	2347 10	2357 10	2367 9	2376 10	2386 9	2395 10	2405 10	2415 9	2424 10
45	2.2434 9	2443 10	2453 9	2462 10	2472 9	2481 10	2491 9	2500 10	2510 9	2519 10
46	2.2529 9	2538 9	2547 10	2557 9	2566 9	2575 10	2585 9	2594 9	2603 10	2613 9
47	2.2622 9	2631 10	2641 9	2650 9	2659 9	2668 9	2677 10	2687 9	2696 9	2705 9
48	2.2714 9	2723 9	2732 9	2741 10	2751 9	2760 9	2769 9	2778 9	2787 9	2796 9
49	2.2805 9	2814 9	2823 9	2832 9	2841 9	2850 9	2859 9	2868 9	2877 8	2885 9
	0	1	2	3	4	5	6	7	8	9
50	2.2894 89	2983 87	3070 86	3156 85	3241 83	3324 83	3407 82	3489 81	3570 79	3649 79
60	2.3728 78	3806 77	3883 77	3960 75	4035 75	4110 73	4183 74	4257 72	4329 71	4400 71
70	2.4471 70	4541 70	4611 69	4680 68	4748 68	4816 67	4883 67	4950 65	5015 65	5080 65
80	2.5145 64	5209 63	5272 63	5335 63	5398 61	5459 62	5521 61	5582 60	5642 60	5702 60
90	2.5762 59	5821 59	5880 58	5938 58	5996 57	6053 57	6110 57	6167 56	6223 55	6278 56

TABLE 1

P	0	1	2	3	4	5	6	7	8	9
100	2.6334 55	6389 54	6443 55	6498 54	6552 53	6605 53	6658 53	6711 53	6764 52	6816 52
110	2.6868 51	6919 51	6970 51	7021 51	7072 50	7122 50	7172 50	7222 49	7271 49	7320 49
120	2.7369 49	7418 48	7466 48	7514 48	7562 47	7609 47	7656 47	7703 47	7750 47	7797 46
130	2.7843 46	7889 46	7935 45	7980 46	8026 45	8071 44	8115 45	8160 44	8204 45	8249 43
140	2.8292 44	8336 44	8380 43	8423 43	8466 43	8509 43	8552 42	8594 43	8637 42	8679 42
150	2.8721 42	8763 41	8804 42	8846 41	8887 41	8928 41	8969 40	9009 41	9050 40	9090 40
160	2.9130 40	9170 40	9210 39	9249 40	9289 39	9328 39	9367 39	9406 39	9445 39	9484 38
170	2.9522 39	9561 38	9599 38	9637 38	9675 38	9713 37	9750 38	9788 37	9825 37	9862 37
180	2.9899 37	9936 37	9973 37	0010 36	0046 36	0082 37	0119 36	0155 36	0191 36	0227 35
190	3.0262 36	0298 35	0333 36	0369 35	0404 35	0439 35	0474 35	0509 34	0543 35	0578 34
200	3.0612 35	0647 34	0681 34	0715 34	0749 34	0783 34	0817 34	0851 33	0884 34	0918 33
210	3.0951 33	0984 33	1017 33	1050 33	1083 33	1116 33	1149 32	1181 33	1241 32	1246 33
220	3.1279 32	1311 32	1343 32	1375 32	1407 32	1439 31	1470 32	1502 31	1533 32	1565 31
230	3.1596 31	1627 32	1659 31	1690 31	1721 31	1752 30	1782 31	1813 31	1844 30	1874 31
240	3.1905 30	1935 30	1965 31	1996 30	2026 30	2056 30	2086 29	2115 30	2145 30	2175 30
250	3.2205 29	2234 30	2264 29	2293 29	2322 29	2351 30	2381 29	2410 29	2439 29	2468 28
260	3.2496 29	2525 29	2554 28	2582 29	2611 28	2639 29	2668 28	2696 28	2724 29	2753 28
270	3.2781 28	2809 28	2837 28	2865 27	2892 28	2920 28	2948 27	2975 28	3003 28	3031 27
280	3.3058 27	3085 28	3113 27	3140 27	3167 27	3194 27	3221 27	3248 27	3275 27	3302 27
290	3.3329 26	3355 27	3382 27	3409 26	3435 27	3462 26	3488 26	3514 27	3541 26	3567 26

TABLE 1

P	0	1	2	3	4	5	6	7	8	9
300	3.3593 26	3619 26	3645 26	3671 26	3697 26	3723 26	3749 26	3775 25	3800 26	3826 26
310	3.3852 25	3877 26	3903 25	3928 25	3953 26	3979 25	4004 25	4029 25	4054 25	4079 26
320	3.4105 25	4130 24	4154 25	4179 25	4204 25	4229 25	4254 24	4278 25	4303 25	4328 24
330	3.4352 25	4377 24	4401 25	4426 24	4450 24	4474 24	4498 25	4523 24	4547 24	4571 24
340	3.4595 24	4619 24	4643 24	4667 24	4691 24	4715 23	4738 24	4762 24	4786 23	4809 24
350	3.4833 23	4856 24	4880 23	4903 24	4927 23	4950 23	4973 24	4997 23	5020 23	5043 23
360	3.5066 23	5089 23	5112 23	5135 23	5158 23	5181 23	5204 23	5227 23	5250 23	5273 22
370	3.5295 23	5318 23	5341 22	5363 23	5386 22	5408 23	5431 22	5453 23	5476 22	5498 22
380	3.5520 23	5543 22	5565 22	5587 22	5609 22	5631 22	5653 22	5675 22	5697 22	5719 22
390	3.5741 22	5763 22	5785 22	5807 22	5829 21	5850 22	5872 22	5894 21	5915 22	5937 21
400	3.5958 22	5980 22	6002 21	6023 21	6044 22	6066 21	6087 21	6108 22	6130 21	6151 21
410	3.6172 21	6193 21	6214 22	6236 21	6257 21	6278 21	6299 21	6320 20	6340 21	6361 21
420	3.6382 21	6403 21	6424 21	6445 20	6465 21	6486 21	6507 20	6527 21	6548 21	6569 20
430	3.6589 21	6610 20	6630 21	6651 20	6671 20	6691 21	6712 20	6732 20	6752 21	6773 20
440	3.6793 20	6813 20	6833 20	6853 20	6873 20	6893 20	6913 20	6933 20	6953 20	6973 20
450	3.6993 20	7013 20	7033 20	7053 20	7073 19	7092 20	7112 20	7132 20	7152 20	7172 19
460	3.7191 19	7210 20	7230 20	7250 19	7269 20	7289 19	7308 19	7327 20	7347 19	7366 20
470	3.7386 19	7405 19	7424 19	7443 20	7463 19	7482 19	7501 19	6520 19	7539 19	7558 19
480	3.7577 20	7597 19	7616 19	7635 19	7654 18	7672 19	7691 19	7710 19	7729 19	7748 19
490	3.7767 19	7786 18	7804 19	7823 19	7842 18	7860 19	7879 19	7898 18	7916 19	7935 18

TABLE 1

P	0	1	2	3	4	5	6	7	8	9
500	3.7953 19	7972 19	7991 18	8009 18	8027 19	8046 18	8064 19	8083 18	8101 19	8119 19
510	3.8138 18	8156 18	8174 19	8193 18	8211 18	8229 18	8247 18	8265 18	8283 18	8301 19
520	3.8320 18	8338 18	8356 18	8374 18	8392 18	8410 17	8427 18	8445 18	8463 18	8481 18
530	3.8499 18	8517 18	8535 17	8552 18	8570 18	8588 18	8606 17	8623 18	8641 18	8659 17
540	3.8676 18	8694 17	8711 18	8729 17	8746 18	8764 17	8781 18	8799 17	8816 18	8834 17
550	3.8851 18	8869 17	8886 17	8903 18	8921 17	8938 17	8955 17	8972 18	8900 17	9007 17
560	3.9024 17	9041 17	9058 18	9076 17	9093 17	9110 17	9127 17	9144 17	9161 17	9178 17
570	3.9195 17	9212 17	9229 17	9246 17	9263 16	9279 17	9296 17	9313 17	9330 17	9347 17
580	3.9364 16	9380 17	9397 17	9414 17	9431 16	9447 17	9464 17	9481 16	9497 17	9514 16
590	3.9530 17	9547 17	9564 16	9580 17	9597 16	9613 17	9630 16	9646 16	9662 17	9679 16
600	3.9695 17	9712 16	9728 16	9744 17	9761 16	9777 16	9793 17	9810 16	9826 16	9842 16
610	3.9858 17	9875 16	9891 16	9907 16	9923 16	9939 16	9955 16	9971 16	9987 16	0003 17
620	4.0020 16	0036 16	0052 16	0068 16	0084 15	0099 16	0115 16	0131 16	0147 16	0163 16
630	4.0179 16	0195 16	0211 16	0227 15	0242 16	0258 16	0274 16	0290 15	0305 16	0321 16
640	4.0337 15	0352 16	0368 16	0384 15	0399 16	0415 16	0431 15	0446 16	0462 15	0477 16
650	4.0493 15	0508 16	0524 15	0539 16	0555 15	0570 16	0586 15	0601 16	0617 15	0632 15
660	4.0647 16	0663 15	0678 15	0693 16	0709 15	0724 15	0739 16	0755 15	0770 15	0785 15
670	4.0800 15	0815 16	0831 15	0846 15	0861 15	0876 15	0891 15	0906 15	0921 16	0937 15
680	4.0952 15	0967 15	0982 15	0997 15	1012 15	1027 15	1042 15	1057 15	1072 15	1087 14
690	4.1101 15	1116 15	1131 15	1146 15	1161 15	1176 15	1191 14	1205 15	1220 15	1235 15

TABLE 1

P	0	1	2	3	4	5	6	7	8	9
700	4.1250 15	1265 14	1279 15	1294 15	1309 14	1323 15	1338 15	1353 14	1367 15	1382 15
710	4.1397 14	1411 15	1426 15	1441 14	1455 15	1470 14	1484 15	1499 14	1513 15	1528 14
720	4.1542 15	1557 14	1571 15	1586 14	1600 15	1615 14	1629 14	1643 15	1658 14	1672 15
730	4.1687 14	1701 14	1715 15	1730 14	1744 14	1758 14	1772 15	1787 14	1801 14	1815 14
740	4.1829 15	1844 14	1858 14	1872 14	1886 14	1900 15	1915 14	1929 14	1943 14	1957 14
750	4.1971 14	1985 14	1999 14	2013 14	2027 14	2041 14	2055 14	2069 14	2083 14	2097 14
760	4.2111 14	2125 14	2139 14	2153 14	2167 14	2181 14	2195 14	2209 14	2223 14	2237 13
770	4.2250 14	2264 14	2278 14	2292 14	2306 14	2320 13	2333 14	2347 14	2361 14	2375 13
780	4.2388 14	2402 14	2416 14	2430 13	2443 14	2457 14	2471 13	2484 14	2498 14	2512 13
790	4.2525 14	2539 13	2552 14	2566 14	2580 13	2593 14	2607 13	2620 14	2634 13	2647 14
	0	10	20	30	40	50	60	70	80	90
800	4.2661 134	2795 133	2928 133	3061 131	3192 130	3322 129	3451 127	3578 127	3705 126	3831 125
900	4.3956 124	4080 123	4203 122	4325 121	4446 121	4567 119	4686 119	4805 117	4922 117	5039 116
1000	4.5155 115	5370 115	5385 114	5499 112	5611 113	5724 111	5835 111	5946 110	6056 109	6165 108
1100	4.6273 108	6381 108	6489 106	6595 106	6701 105	6806 105	6911 104	7015 103	7118 103	7221 102
1200	4.7323 101	7424 101	7525 101	7626 99	7725 100	7825 98	7923 98	8021 98	8119 97	8216 96
1300	4.8312 96	8408 96	8504 95	8599 94	8693 94	8787 94	8881 93	8974 92	9066 92	9158 92
1400	4.9250 91	9341 90	9431 90	9521 90	9611 89	9700 89	9789 89	9878 88	9966 87	0053 87
1500	5.0140 87	0227 86	0313 86	0399 86	0485 85	0570 85	0655 84	0739 84	0823 83	0906 84
1600	5.0990 82	1072 83	1155 82	1237 82	1319 81	1400 81	1481 81	1562 80	1642 80	1722 80
1700	5.1802 79	1881 79	1960 79	2039 78	2117 78	2195 78				

TABLE 2 - ^3He Vapor Pressures on the 1962 ^3He Scale

T_{62}	0.00	0.01	0.02	0.03	0.04	0.05	0.06	0.07	0.08	0.09
0.20	0.012	0.024	0.046	0.084	0.144	0.239	0.382	0.592	0.891	1.308
0.30	1.877	2.636	3.633	4.921	6.561	8.619	11.173	14.304	18.105	22.673
0.40	28.115	34.546	42.086	50.864	61.017	72.686	86.022	101.179	118.319	137.610
0.50	159.224	183.339	210.139	239.811	272.546	308.540	347.992	391.106	438.087	489.145
0.60	544.490	604.337	668.902	738.402	813.059	893.094	978.729	1070.189	1167.698	1271.483
0.70	1381.771	1498.789	1622.766	1753.928	1892.506	2038.728	2192.821	2355.017	2525.542	2704.626
0.80	2892.496	3089.381	3295.508	3511.105	3736.398	3971.613	4216.976	4472.711	4739.044	5016.198
0.90	5304.397	5603.862	5914.815	6237.478	6572.071	6918.813	7277.923	7649.620	8034.120	8431.641
1.00	8.842	9.267	9.704	10.156	10.622	11.102	11.597	12.106	12.631	13.170
1.10	13.725	14.295	14.881	15.484	16.102	16.737	17.388	18.056	18.741	19.443
1.20	20.163	20.900	21.655	22.428	23.220	24.029	24.857	25.704	26.571	27.456
1.30	28.360	29.285	30.229	31.193	32.177	33.181	34.206	35.252	36.319	37.407
1.40	38.516	39.646	40.799	41.973	43.169	44.388	45.629	46.893	48.179	49.489
1.50	50.822	52.178	53.558	54.961	56.389	57.840	59.316	60.817	62.342	63.892
1.60	65.467	67.068	68.694	70.345	72.022	73.726	75.455	77.211	78.993	80.802
1.70	82.638	84.501	86.391	88.309	90.254	92.228	94.229	96.258	98.315	100.402
1.80	102.516	104.660	106.833	109.035	111.266	113.527	115.818	118.138	120.489	122.870
1.90	125.282	127.724	130.197	132.701	135.236	137.803	140.401	143.031	145.692	148.386
2.00	151.112	153.870	156.661	159.485	162.342	165.232	168.155	171.112	174.102	177.126
2.10	180.184	183.276	186.403	189.564	192.760	195.990	199.256	202.557	205.894	209.266
2.20	212.673	216.117	219.597	223.113	226.665	230.255	233.881	237.544	241.244	244.982
2.30	248.757	252.570	256.420	260.309	264.236	268.202	272.206	276.249	280.331	284.452
2.40	288.613	292.813	297.053	301.333	305.653	310.013	314.414	318.855	323.337	327.861
2.50	332.425	337.031	341.679	346.368	351.100	355.874	360.690	365.549	370.450	375.395
2.60	380.383	385.414	390.489	395.608	400.771	405.978	411.230	416.526	421.868	427.254
2.70	432.686	438.164	443.687	449.256	454.871	460.534	466.242	471.998	477.801	483.651

TABLE 2

T_{62}	0.00	0.01	0.02	0.03	0.04	0.05	0.06	0.07	0.08	0.09
2.80	489.549	495.495	501.488	507.531	513.622	519.762	525.951	532.189	538.477	544.815
2.90	551.203	557.642	564.131	570.672	577.264	583.907	590.602	597.349	604.149	611.002
3.00	617.907	624.866	631.879	638.945	646.066	653.241	660.472	667.757	675.098	682.496
3.10	689.949	697.459	705.026	712.650	720.332	728.072	735.871	743.728	751.644	759.620
3.20	767.656	775.753	783.910	792.128	800.408	808.750	817.155	825.622	834.153	842.747
3.30	851.406	860.130	868.918	877.773						

The units of pressure are microns (10^{-3} mm) of mercury below 1°K and millimeters of mercury at higher temperatures.

TABLE 3 - Molar volumes of ^4He

T(°K)	V_m cm³	T(°K)	Vm	T(°K)	V_m cm³
0.00	27.5793	1.85	27.5237	2.60	27.7341
0.05	27.5793	1.90	27.5106	2.65	27.7942
0.10	27.5793	1.95	27.4953	2.70	27.8581
0.15	27.5793	2.00	27.4787	2.75	27.9259
0.20	27.5793	2.05	27.4587	2.80	27.9978
0.25	27.5793	2.10	27.4352	2.85	28.0738
0.30	27.5794	2.15	27.4069	2.90	28.1538
0.35	27.5794	2.16	27.3993	2.95	28.2382
0.40	27.5795	2.162	27.3976	3.00	28.3266
0.45	27.5796	2.164	27.3958	3.05	28.4192
0.50	27.5798	2.166	27.3940	3.10	28.5156
0.55	27.5800	2.168	27.3920	3.15	28.6232
0.60	27.5803	2.170	27.3897	3.20	28.7312
0.65	27.5807	2.171	27.3886	3.25	28.8441
0.70	27.5811	2.1715	27.3879	3.30	28.9620
0.75	27.5816	2.1719	27.3872	3.35	29.0847
0.80	27.5822	2.1720	27.3870	3.40	29.2125
0.85	27.5829	2.1721	27.3869	3.45	29.3450
0.90	27.5836	2.1725	27.3867	3.50	29.4829
0.95	27.5843	2.173	27.3865	3.55	29.6252
1.00	27.5850	2.174	27.3862	3.60	29.7729
1.05	27.5856	2.176	27.3860	3.65	29.9257
1.10	27.5861	2.178	27.3859	3.70	30.0844
1.15	27.5863	2.180	27.3860	3.75	30.2467
1.20	27.5863	2.182	27.3862	3.80	30.4151
1.25	27.5859	2.184	27.3864	3.85	30.5889
1.30	27.5851	2.186	27.3868	3.90	30.7682
1.35	27.5838	2.188	27.3872	3.95	30.9533
1.40	27.5820	2.190	27.3876	4.00	31.1443
1.45	27.5795	2.20	27.3904	4.05	31.3413
1.50	27.5761	2.25	27.4136	4.10	31.5476
1.55	27.5719	2.30	27.4471	4.15	31.7542
1.60	27.5667	2.35	27.4867	4.20	31.9704
1.65	27.5603	2.40	27.5296	4.25	32.1932
1.70	27.5536	2.45	27.5757	4.30	32.4231
1.75	27.5450	2.50	27.6250	4.35	32.6402
1.80	27.5352	2.55	27.6777	4.40	32.9049

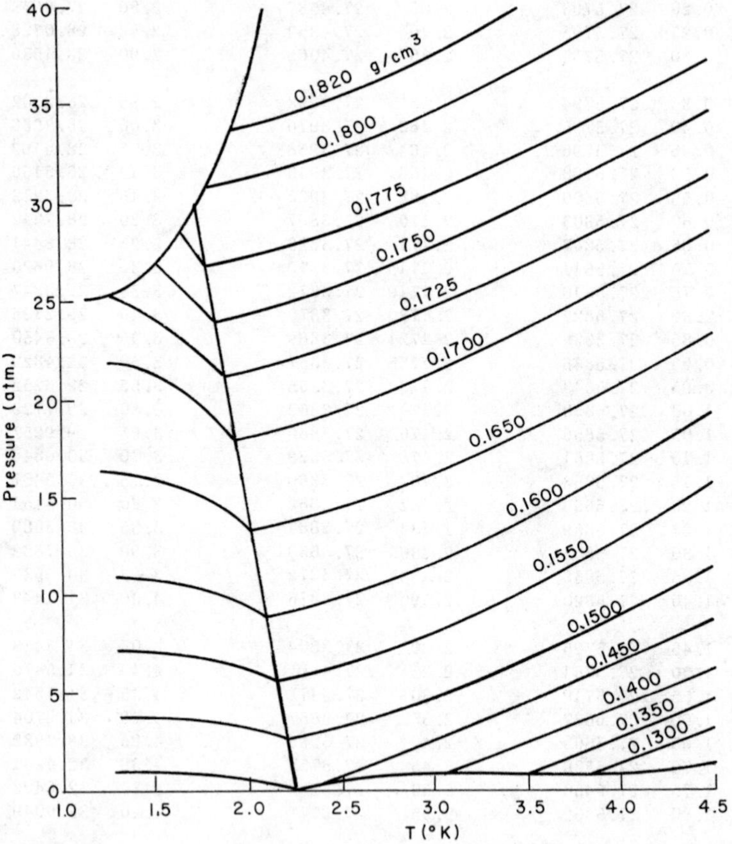

Fig. A. 1.

Isopycnals of ^{4}He

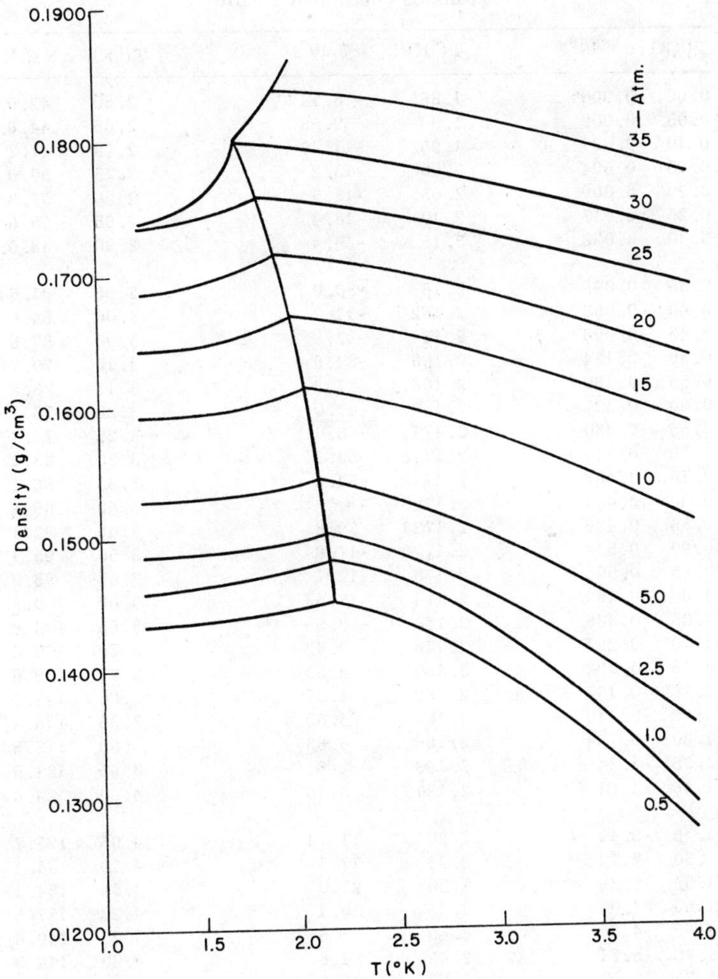

Fig. A.2.

Isobars of ^{4}He

TABLE 4

Expansion coefficient of ^4He

T(°K)	$\alpha \times 10^3$	T(°K)	$\alpha \times 10^3$	T(°K)	$\alpha \times 10^3$
0.00	0.000	1.85	- 8.71	2.60	42.0
0.05	0.000	1.90	- 9.98	2.65	44.6
0.10	0.001	1.95	-11.45	2.70	47.3
0.15	0.004	2.00	-13.2	2.75	50.0
0.20	0.009	2.05	-15.5	2.80	52.8
0.25	0.017	2.10	-18.4	2.85	55.6
0.30	0.028	2.15	-25.4	2.90	58.6
0.35	0.046	2.16	-30.0	2.95	61.6
0.40	0.068	2.162	-31.2	3.00	64.6
0.45	0.098	2.164	-32.8	3.05	67.6
0.50	0.134	2.166	-34.9	3.10	70.7
0.55	0.180	2.168	-37.9	3.15	73.8
0.60	0.227	2.170	-43.0	3.20	76.9
0.65	0.280	2.171	-48.1	3.25	79.7
0.70	0.343	2.1715	-53.1	3.30	83.1
0.75	0.408	2.1719	-64.9	3.35	86.1
0.80	0.461	2.1720	-∞	3.40	89.1
0.85	0.496	2.1721	-29.6	3.45	92.1
0.90	0.514	2.1725	-17.8	3.50	95.1
0.95	0.505	2.173	-12.7	3.55	98.0
1.00	0.465	2.174	- 7.63	3.60	100.9
1.05	0.386	2.176	- 2.55	3.65	103.8
1.10	0.261	2.178	0.42	3.70	106.8
1.15	0.094	2.180	2.53	3.75	109.6
1.20	-0.137	2.182	4.17	3.80	112.7
1.25	-0.416	2.184	5.50	3.85	115.4
1.30	-0.754	2.186	6.63	3.90	118.5
1.35	-1.14	2.188	7.61	3.95	121.5
1.40	-1.61	2.190	8.48	4.00	124.6
1.45	-2.13	2.20	11.71	4.05	127.7
1.50	-2.72	2.25	21.5	4.10	131.1
1.55	-3.38	2.30	27.0	4.15	134.1
1.60	-4.03	2.35	30.1	4.20	137.3
1.65	-4.80	2.40	32.3	4.25	140.6
1.70	-5.71	2.45	34.6	4.30	144.0
1.75	-6.57	2.50	36.9	4.35	147.6
1.80	-7.59	2.55	39.4	4.40	151.0

TABLE 5

T (deg K)	Thermal expansion coefficient α_p (10^{-3} deg^{-1})						
	v.p.	2.5 (atm)	5 (atm)	10 (atm)	15 (atm)	20 (atm)	25 (atm)
0.5	0.134	0.09	0.06	(0.04)	(0.02)	(0.01)	(0.01)
0.6	0.227	0.14	0.10	0.06	(0.03)	(0.01)	(-0.01)
0.7	0.343	0.19	0.12	(0.04)	(-0.02)	-0.06	-0.09
0.8	0.461	0.19	0.06	-0.10	-0.20	-0.28	-0.35
0.9	0.524	0.10	-0.12	-0.39	-0.58	-0.72	-0.84
1.0	0.485	-0.12	-0.45	-0.88	-1.18	-1.42	-1.62
1.1	0.301	-0.54	-1.02	-1.67	-2.14	-2.51	-2.83
1.2	-0.057	-1.22	-1.91	-2.85	-3.55	-4.11	-4.60
1.3	-0.624	-2.24	-3.22	-4.59	-5.6	-6.5	-7.2
1.4	-1.41	-3.70	-5.1	-7.1	-8.6	-9.9	-11.0
1.5	-2.44	-5.7	-7.9	-10.9	-13.3	-15.3	-17.0

Note: ( ) denote values where scatter in experimental determinations exceeds α_p.

TABLE 6

Specific heat of ^4He

T °K	c_{sat} joule / g deg	T °K	c_{sat} joule / g deg	T °K	c_{sat} joule / g deg
0.60	0.0051	1.20	0.322	1.80	2.80
0.65	0.0068	1.25	0.410	1.85	3.19
0.70	0.0098	1.30	0.516	1.90	3.63
0.75	0.0146	1.35	0.634	1.95	4.27
0.80	0.0222	1.40	0.780	2.00	4.95
0.85	0.0343	1.45	0.944	2.05	5.82
0.90	0.0510	1.50	1.127	2.10	6.92
0.95	0.0743	1.55	1.330	2.15	8.61
1.00	0.1042	1.60	1.572	2.18	11.6
1.05	0.142	1.65	1.83	2.186	14.3
1.10	0.191	1.70	2.11		
1.15	0.250	1.75	2.46		

TABLE 7

Specific entropy of ^4He

T °K	S joule/g deg	T °K	S joule/g deg	T °K	S joule/g deg
0.60	0.00169	1.20	0.0523	1.80	0.535
0.65	0.00215	1.25	0.0672	1.85	0.617
0.70	0.00276	1.30	0.0853	1.90	0.709
0.75	0.00358	1.35	0.1069	1.95	0.812
0.80	0.00475	1.40	0.132	2.00	0.929
0.85	0.00644	1.45	0.162	2.05	1.061
0.90	0.00885	1.50	0.197	2.10	1.215
0.95	0.0122	1.55	0.238	2.15	1.40
1.00	0.0168	1.60	0.284	2.18	1.53
1.05	0.0227	1.65	0.386	2.186	1.57
1.10	0.0304	1.70	0.395		
1.15	0.0402	1.75	0.461		

TABLE 8

Specific entropy of ^{4}He under pressure

P / T°K	saturated vapor pressure	2.5 atm	5 atm	10 atm	15 atm	20 atm	25 atm
1.150	0.039^5	0.041^0	0.043^0	0.049^0	0.057^5	0.068^0	0.080^0
1.200	0.051^5	0.053^5	0.056^0	0.063^5	0.074^0	0.086^0	0.100^0
1.250	0.066^5	0.068^5	0.072^0	0.080^5	0.093^0	0.108^0	0.125^5
1.300	0.085^5	0.088^0	0.091^5	0.102^0	0.116^0	0.134^5	0.157
1.350	0.107^5	0.110^5	0.114^5	0.127^0	0.144^0	0.167	0.194
1.400	0.132^5	0.136^5	0.142^0	0.157	0.178	0.205	0.238
1.450	0.162	0.166	0.173	0.192	0.216	0.248	0.291
1.500	0.196	0.202	0.210	0.232	0.261	0.300	0.350
1.550	0.237	0.244	0.253	0.278	0.313	0.360	0.421
1.600	0.284	0.292	0.303	0.332	0.374	0.430	0.502
1.650	0.337	0.347	0.360	0.394	0.444	0.510	0.597
1.700	0.398	0.409	0.424	0.464	0.524	0.602	0.709
1.750	0.466	0.479	0.497	0.545	0.615	0.709	0.838
1.800	0.545	0.560	0.581	0.637	0.721	0.836	
1.850	0.633	0.651	0.677	0.744	0.844		
1.900	0.732	0.752	0.782	0.863	0.982		
1.950	0.842	0.865	0.900	0.998			
2.000	0.963	0.994	1.035	1.164			
2.050	1.105	1.149	1.209				

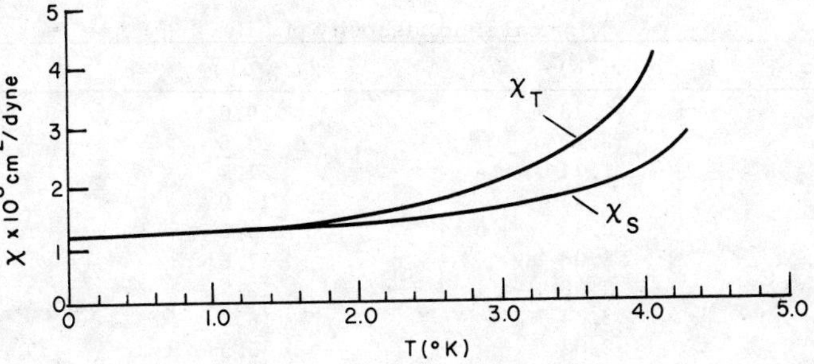

Fig. A.3. - Adiabatic (χ_S) and isothermal (χ_T) compressibility of ^{4}He

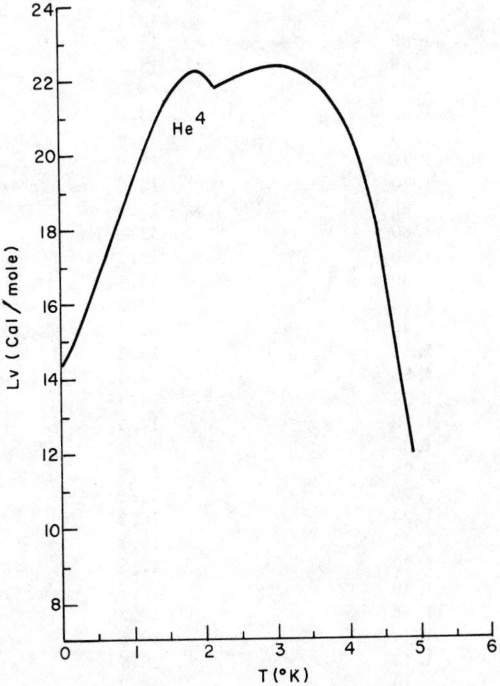

Fig. A.4.

Latent heat of vaporization of ^{4}He

TABLE 9

Normal fluid viscosity of ^{4}He

T(^{o}K)	$\eta(\mu P)$
2.18	26.0
2.16	23.6
2.14	21.7
2.12	19.9
2.10	18.6
2.08	17.6
2.06	16.8
2.04	16.1
2.02	15.5
2.00	14.9
1.98	14.5
1.96	14.2
1.94	13.8
1.92	13.6
1.90	13.4
1.88	13.2
1.86	13.1
1.84	13.0
1.82	13.0
1.80	13.0
1.75	13.0
1.70	13.0
1.65	13.1
1.60	13.2
1.55	13.3
1.50	13.5
1.45	13.8
1.40	14.1
1.38	14.3
1.36	14.5
1.34	14.7
1.32	14.9
1.30	15.2
1.28	15.4
1.26	15.9
1.24	16.3
1.22	16.9
1.20	17.5
1.18	18.3
1.16	19.3
1.14	20.6
1.12	22.7
1.10	26.8

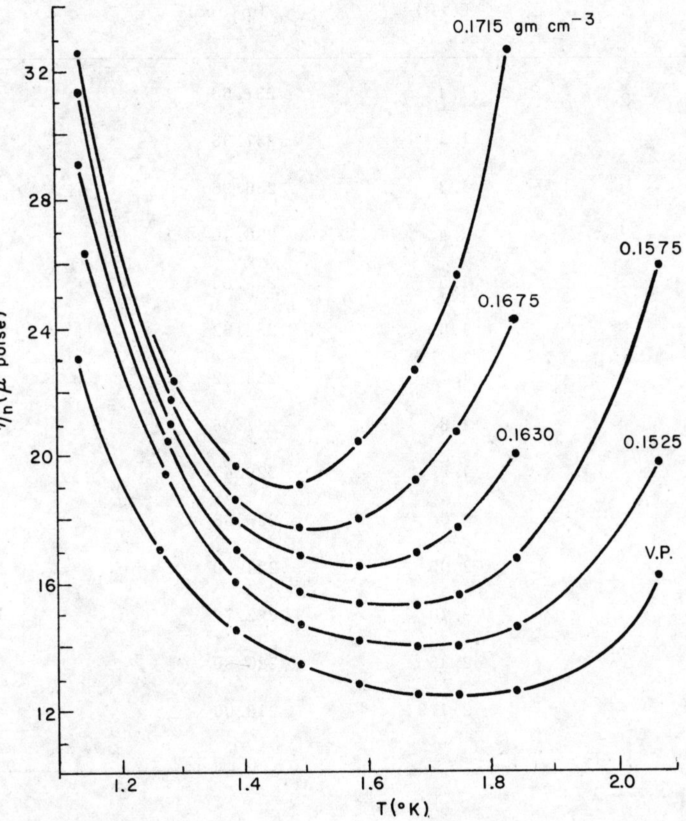

Fig. A. 5.

Normal fluid viscosity of ^{4}He at various densities

TABLE 10

Velocity of first sound in ^4He

T(°K)	u_1 (m/sec)
1.1	237.68
1.2	237.38
1.3	236.96
1.4	236.40
1.5	235.63
1.6	234.62
1.7	233.22
1.8	231.48
1.9	229.47
2.0	226.68
2.05	224.90
2.10	222.72
2.15	220.20
2.179	218.00

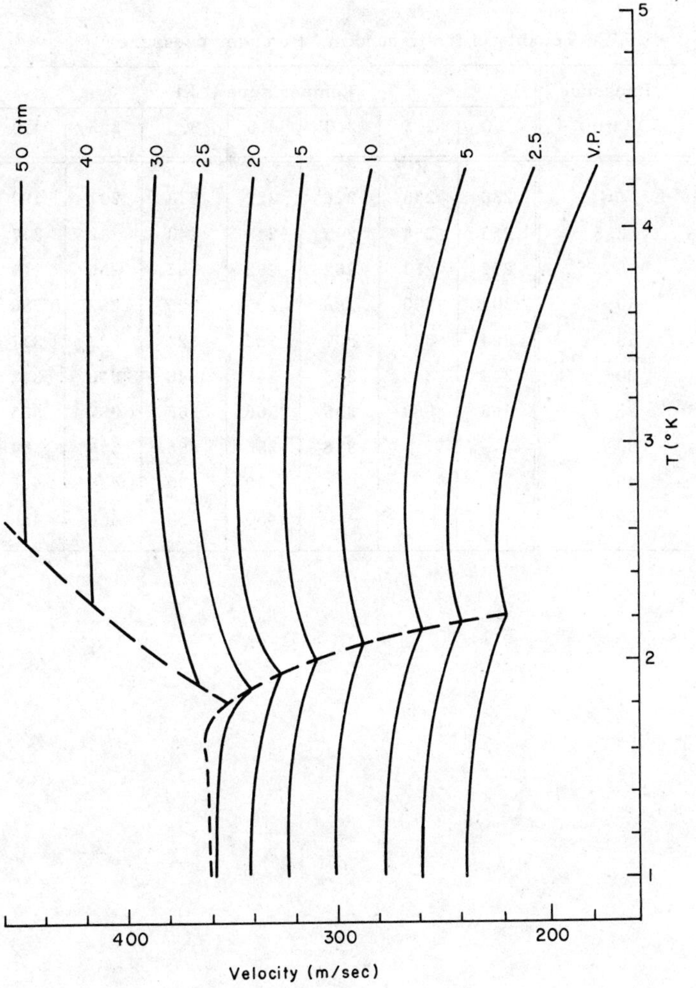

Fig. A. 6.

Velocity of first sound in ^{4}He at various pressures

TABLE 11

Velocity of first sound in ^{4}He under pressure

Pressure (atm)	Temperature (°K) 1.0	1.5	2.0	2.5	3.0	3.5	4.0
VP	236	235	226	222	218	207	190
2.5	255	254	245	243	240	232	217
5	272	271	262	262	261	255	245
10	301	300	288	295	295	292	286
15	324	323	307	322	323	321	317
20	344	343	333	346	346	346	343
25	363	360	355	366	368	367	365
30			376	385	386	386	384
40				419	420	420	419
50				450	450	450	450

TABLE 12

Velocity of second sound in ^4He

T ($^{\circ}$K)	u_2 (m/sec)
0.86	23.00
0.90	21.20
0.95	20.05
1.00	19.40
1.05	19.00
1.10	18.75
1.15	18.70
1.20	18.75
1.25	18.95
1.30	19.20
1.35	19.55
1.40	19.78
1.45	19.95
1.50	20.07
1.55	20.11
1.60	20.14
1.65	20.15
1.70	20.10
1.75	20.02
1.80	19.78
1.85	19.37
1.90	18.78
1.95	17.91
2.00	16.77
2.05	15.20
2.10	13.00
2.125	11.60
2.150	9.40
2.158	7.57
2.163	6.91
2.170	5.00
2.174	3.91
2.176	3.12

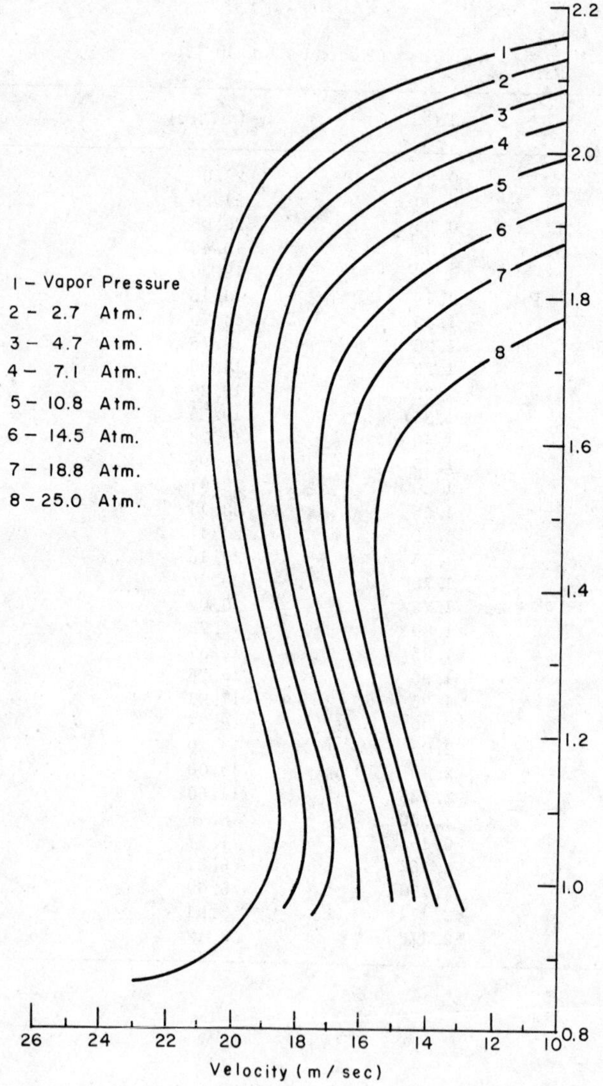

Fig. A.7.

Velocity of second sound in ^{4}He under pressure

TABLE 13

Normal fluid density in ^{4}He

$T(^\circ K)$	ρ_n (g/cc)
2.18	0.1450
2.16	0.1300
2.14	0.1200
2.12	0.1100
2.10	0.1055
2.08	0.0995
2.06	0.0945
2.04	0.0898
2.02	0.0855
2.00	0.0807
1.98	0.0778
1.96	0.0740
1.94	0.0702
1.92	0.0678
1.90	0.0624
1.88	0.0600
1.86	0.0568
1.84	0.0536
1.82	0.0504
1.80	0.0472
1.75	0.0400
1.70	0.0346
1.65	0.0289
1.60	0.02465
1.55	0.0205
1.50	0.0165
1.45	0.0136
1.40	0.01079
1.38	0.01000
1.36	0.00920
1.34	0.00840
1.32	0.00765
1.30	0.00686
1.28	0.00628
1.26	0.00568
1.24	0.00510
1.22	0.00458
1.20	0.00405
1.18	0.00360
1.16	0.00318
1.14	0.00280
1.12	0.00243
1.10	0.00212

TABLE 14

Ratio of normal fluid density to density of ^{4}He

T(°K)	ρ_n / ρ
1.10	0.0146
1.15	0.0205
1.20	0.0279
1.25	0.0371
1.30	0.0473
1.35	0.0608
1.40	0.0743
1.45	0.0937
1.50	0.114
1.55	0.141
1.60	0.170
1.65	0.199
1.70	0.238
1.75	0.275
1.80	0.325
1.85	0.380
1.90	0.429
1.95	0.494
2.00	0.554
2.05	0.631
2.10	0.7231
2.15	0.8558
2.18	0.9920

TABLE 15

Mobility of ions in ^{4}He

T(°K)	μ^+(cm^2/V sec)	μ^-(cm^2/V sec)
0.5	6600	288
0.6	1700	155
0.7	320	72.5
0.8	66	26.3
0.9	19	10.0
1.0	7.4	4.17
1.1	3.31	2.00
1.2	1.64	1.05
1.3	1.00	0.650
1.4	0.616	0.410
1.5	0.400	0.270
1.6	0.275	0.200
1.7	0.200	0.150
1.8	0.148	0.115
1.9	0.115	0.083
2.0	0.096	0.073

TABLE 16

Vortex Ring Radius, Energy, and Velocity

$$E = \frac{1}{2}\rho \kappa^2 R\left[\log\left(\frac{8R}{a}\right) - \frac{7}{4}\right]$$

$$v = \left(\frac{\kappa}{4\pi R}\right)\left[\log\left(\frac{8R}{a}\right) - \frac{1}{4}\right]$$

$\rho = 0.1451$ g/cc $\quad a = 1.28$ Å

R (Å)	Energy (eV)	Velocity (cm/sec)
100	0.2108	490.7
200	0.4840	272.8
300	0.7807	192.6
400	1.093	150.1
500	1.416	123.7
600	1.748	105.5
700	2.088	92.15
800	2.435	81.95
900	2.787	73.89
1,000	3.144	67.33
2,000	6.911	36.42
3,000	10.91	25.35
4,000	15.07	19.58
5,000	19.34	16.02
6,000	23.70	13.59
7,000	28.13	11.82
8,000	32.63	10.48
9,000	37.19	9.418
10,000	41.80	8,559
20,000	89.82	4.554
30,000	14.02	3.144
40,000	19.21	2.415
50,000	24.52	1.967
60,000	29.92	1.663
70,000	35.38	1.443
80,000	40.92	1.276
90,000	46.51	1.145
100,000	52.15	1.038

TABLE 17 - Phonon and roton number densities in ^4He - calculated from Landau model

T(°K)	P (atm)	N_{ph}	N_R	$\frac{N_R}{N_{ph}}$
0.10	0.	$.5070 \times 10^{19}$	$.3385 \times 10^{-15}$	$.6676 \times 10^{-34}$
0.10	2.5	$.3976 \times 10^{19}$	$.1715 \times 10^{-14}$	$.4313 \times 10^{-33}$
0.10	5.0	$.3317 \times 10^{19}$	$.8673 \times 10^{-14}$	$.2615 \times 10^{-32}$
0.10	10.0	$.2500 \times 10^{19}$	$.2205 \times 10^{-12}$	$.8822 \times 10^{-31}$
0.10	15.0	$.1948 \times 10^{19}$	$.5550 \times 10^{-11}$	$.2849 \times 10^{-29}$
0.10	20.0	$.1629 \times 10^{19}$	$.1378 \times 10^{-09}$	$.8457 \times 10^{-28}$
0.20	0.	$.4056 \times 10^{20}$	$.3376 \times 10^{04}$	$.8324 \times 10^{-16}$
0.20	2.5	$.3181 \times 10^{20}$	$.7548 \times 10^{04}$	$.2373 \times 10^{-15}$
0.20	5.0	$.2654 \times 10^{20}$	$.1685 \times 10^{05}$	$.6348 \times 10^{-15}$
0.20	10.0	$.2000 \times 10^{20}$	$.8340 \times 10^{05}$	$.4171 \times 10^{-14}$
0.20	15.0	$.1558 \times 10^{20}$	$.4087 \times 10^{06}$	$.2623 \times 10^{-13}$
0.20	20.0	$.1303 \times 10^{20}$	$.1976 \times 10^{07}$	$.1516 \times 10^{-12}$
0.30	0.	$.1369 \times 10^{21}$	$.7930 \times 10^{10}$	$.5793 \times 10^{-10}$
0.30	2.5	$.1074 \times 10^{21}$	$.1350 \times 10^{11}$	$.1257 \times 10^{-09}$
0.30	5.0	$.8956 \times 10^{20}$	$.2293 \times 10^{11}$	$.2561 \times 10^{-09}$
0.30	10.0	$.6749 \times 10^{20}$	$.6581 \times 10^{11}$	$.9751 \times 10^{-09}$
0.30	15.0	$.5260 \times 10^{20}$	$.1869 \times 10^{12}$	$.3554 \times 10^{-08}$
0.30	20.0	$.4399 \times 10^{20}$	$.5238 \times 10^{12}$	$.1191 \times 10^{-07}$
0.40	0.	$.3245 \times 10^{21}$	$.1268 \times 10^{14}$	$.3908 \times 10^{-07}$
0.40	2.5	$.2545 \times 10^{21}$	$.1883 \times 10^{14}$	$.7401 \times 10^{-07}$
0.40	5.0	$.2123 \times 10^{21}$	$.2792 \times 10^{14}$	$.1315 \times 10^{-06}$
0.40	10.0	$.1600 \times 10^{21}$	$.6099 \times 10^{14}$	$.3813 \times 10^{-06}$
0.40	15.0	$.1247 \times 10^{21}$	$.1319 \times 10^{15}$	$.1058 \times 10^{-05}$
0.40	20.0	$.1043 \times 10^{21}$	$.2814 \times 10^{15}$	$.2699 \times 10^{-05}$
0.50	0.	$.6337 \times 10^{21}$	$.1088 \times 10^{16}$	$.1716 \times 10^{-05}$
0.50	2.5	$.4970 \times 10^{21}$	$.1488 \times 10^{16}$	$.2995 \times 10^{-05}$
0.50	5.0	$.4146 \times 10^{21}$	$.2033 \times 10^{16}$	$.4904 \times 10^{-05}$
0.50	10.0	$.3125 \times 10^{21}$	$.3771 \times 10^{16}$	$.1207 \times 10^{-04}$

TABLE 17

T(°K)	P (atm)	N_{ph}	N_R	$\frac{N_R}{N_{ph}}$
0.50	15.0	$.2435 \times 10^{21}$	$.6925 \times 10^{16}$	$.2844 \times 10^{-04}$
0.50	20.0	$.2037 \times 10^{21}$	$.1254 \times 10^{17}$	$.6159 \times 10^{-04}$
0.60	0.	$.1095 \times 10^{22}$	$.2151 \times 10^{17}$	$.1965 \times 10^{-04}$
0.60	2.5	$.8588 \times 10^{21}$	$.2788 \times 10^{17}$	$.3246 \times 10^{-04}$
0.60	5.0	$.7165 \times 10^{21}$	$.3607 \times 10^{17}$	$.5034 \times 10^{-04}$
0.60	10.0	$.5399 \times 10^{21}$	$.5998 \times 10^{17}$	$.1111 \times 10^{-03}$
0.60	15.0	$.4208 \times 10^{21}$	$.9875 \times 10^{17}$	$.2347 \times 10^{-03}$
0.60	20.0	$.3519 \times 10^{21}$	$.1604 \times 10^{18}$	$.4557 \times 10^{-03}$
0.70	0.	$.1739 \times 10^{22}$	$.1837 \times 10^{18}$	$.1056 \times 10^{-03}$
0.70	2.5	$.1364 \times 10^{22}$	$.2289 \times 10^{18}$	$.1678 \times 10^{-03}$
0.70	5.0	$.1138 \times 10^{22}$	$.2848 \times 10^{18}$	$.2503 \times 10^{-03}$
0.70	10.0	$.8574 \times 10^{21}$	$.4381 \times 10^{18}$	$.5110 \times 10^{-03}$
0.70	15.0	$.6682 \times 10^{21}$	$.6672 \times 10^{18}$	$.9986 \times 10^{-03}$
0.70	20.0	$.5589 \times 10^{21}$	$.1002 \times 10^{19}$	$.1794 \times 10^{-02}$
0.80	0.	$.2596 \times 10^{22}$	$.9262 \times 10^{18}$	$.3568 \times 10^{-03}$
0.80	2.5	$.2036 \times 10^{22}$	$.1121 \times 10^{19}$	$.5507 \times 10^{-03}$
0.80	5.0	$.1698 \times 10^{22}$	$.1355 \times 10^{19}$	$.7976 \times 10^{-03}$
0.80	10.0	$.1280 \times 10^{22}$	$.1966 \times 10^{19}$	$.1536 \times 10^{-02}$
0.80	15.0	$.9974 \times 10^{21}$	$.2823 \times 10^{19}$	$.2831 \times 10^{-02}$
0.80	20.0	$.8342 \times 10^{21}$	$.4001 \times 10^{19}$	$.4796 \times 10^{-02}$
0.90	0.	$.3696 \times 10^{22}$	$.3287 \times 10^{19}$	$.8894 \times 10^{-03}$
0.90	2.5	$.2898 \times 10^{22}$	$.3889 \times 10^{19}$	$.1342 \times 10^{-02}$
0.90	5.0	$.2418 \times 10^{22}$	$.4594 \times 10^{19}$	$.1900 \times 10^{-02}$
0.90	10.0	$.1822 \times 10^{22}$	$.6369 \times 10^{19}$	$.3495 \times 10^{-02}$
0.90	15.0	$.1420 \times 10^{22}$	$.8741 \times 10^{19}$	$.6155 \times 10^{-02}$
0.90	20.0	$.1188 \times 10^{22}$	$.1184 \times 10^{20}$	$.9964 \times 10^{-02}$
1.00	0.	$.5070 \times 10^{22}$	$.9125 \times 10^{19}$	$.1800 \times 10^{-02}$
1.00	2.5	$.3976 \times 10^{22}$	$.1060 \times 10^{20}$	$.2666 \times 10^{-02}$

TABLE 17

T(°K)	P (atm)	N_{ph}	N_R	$\frac{N_R}{N_{ph}}$
1.00	5.0	$.3317 \times 10^{22}$	$.1230 \times 10^{20}$	$.3707 \times 10^{-02}$
1.00	10.0	$.2500 \times 10^{22}$	$.1644 \times 10^{20}$	$.6575 \times 10^{-02}$
1.00	15.0	$.1948 \times 10^{22}$	$.2175 \times 10^{20}$	$.1116 \times 10^{-01}$
1.00	20.0	$.1629 \times 10^{22}$	$.2839 \times 10^{20}$	$.1743 \times 10^{-01}$
1.10	0.	$.6748 \times 10^{22}$	$.2121 \times 10^{20}$	$.3143 \times 10^{-02}$
1.10	2.5	$.5292 \times 10^{22}$	$.2427 \times 10^{20}$	$.4586 \times 10^{-02}$
1.10	5.0	$.4415 \times 10^{22}$	$.2773 \times 10^{20}$	$.6280 \times 10^{-02}$
1.10	10.0	$.3327 \times 10^{22}$	$.3597 \times 10^{20}$	$.1081 \times 10^{-01}$
1.10	15.0	$.2593 \times 10^{22}$	$.4619 \times 10^{20}$	$.1782 \times 10^{-01}$
1.10	20.0	$.2169 \times 10^{22}$	$.5852 \times 10^{20}$	$.2698 \times 10^{-01}$
1.20	0.	$.8761 \times 10^{22}$	$.4319 \times 10^{20}$	$.4930 \times 10^{-02}$
1.20	2.5	$.6870 \times 10^{22}$	$.4881 \times 10^{20}$	$.7104 \times 10^{-02}$
1.20	5.0	$.5732 \times 10^{22}$	$.5507 \times 10^{20}$	$.9607 \times 10^{-02}$
1.20	10.0	$.4319 \times 10^{22}$	$.6966 \times 10^{20}$	$.1613 \times 10^{-01}$
1.20	15.0	$.3366 \times 10^{22}$	$.8723 \times 10^{20}$	$.2591 \times 10^{-01}$
1.20	20.0	$.2816 \times 10^{22}$	$.1078 \times 10^{21}$	$.3828 \times 10^{-01}$
1.30	0.	$.1114 \times 10^{23}$	$.7964 \times 10^{20}$	$.7150 \times 10^{-02}$
1.30	2.5	$.8735 \times 10^{22}$	$.8904 \times 10^{20}$	$.1019 \times 10^{-01}$
1.30	5.0	$.7288 \times 10^{22}$	$.9937 \times 10^{20}$	$.1364 \times 10^{-01}$
1.30	10.0	$.5492 \times 10^{22}$	$.1230 \times 10^{21}$	$.2240 \times 10^{-01}$
1.30	15.0	$.4280 \times 10^{22}$	$.1508 \times 10^{21}$	$.3523 \times 10^{-01}$
1.30	20.0	$.3580 \times 10^{22}$	$.1823 \times 10^{21}$	$.5092 \times 10^{-01}$
1.40	0.	$.1427 \times 10^{23}$	$.1362 \times 10^{21}$	$.9545 \times 10^{-02}$
1.40	2.5	$.1104 \times 10^{23}$	$.1509 \times 10^{21}$	$.1367 \times 10^{-01}$
1.40	5.0	$.9203 \times 10^{22}$	$.1668 \times 10^{21}$	$.1812 \times 10^{-01}$
1.40	10.0	$.6928 \times 10^{22}$	$.2026 \times 10^{21}$	$.2925 \times 10^{-01}$
1.40	15.0	$.5395 \times 10^{22}$	$.2437 \times 10^{21}$	$.4517 \times 10^{-01}$
1.40	20.0	$.4510 \times 10^{22}$	$.2891 \times 10^{21}$	$.6411 \times 10^{-01}$

TABLE 17

$T(^{o}K)$	P (atm)	N_{ph}	N_R	$\frac{N_R}{N_{ph}}$
1.50	0.	$.1755 \times 10^{23}$	$.2202 \times 10^{21}$	$.1254 \times 10^{-01}$
1.50	2.5	$.1358 \times 10^{23}$	$.2418 \times 10^{21}$	$.1781 \times 10^{-01}$
1.50	5.0	$.1132 \times 10^{23}$	$.2651 \times 10^{21}$	$.2342 \times 10^{-01}$
1.50	10.0	$.8521 \times 10^{22}$	$.3167 \times 10^{21}$	$.3717 \times 10^{-01}$
1.50	15.0	$.6635 \times 10^{22}$	$.3746 \times 10^{21}$	$.5645 \times 10^{-01}$
1.50	20.0	$.5547 \times 10^{22}$	$.4370 \times 10^{21}$	$.7878 \times 10^{-01}$
1.60	0.	$.2130 \times 10^{23}$	$.3416 \times 10^{21}$	$.1604 \times 10^{-01}$
1.60	2.5	$.1648 \times 10^{23}$	$.3723 \times 10^{21}$	$.2259 \times 10^{-01}$
1.60	5.0	$.1374 \times 10^{23}$	$.4051 \times 10^{21}$	$.2949 \times 10^{-01}$
1.60	10.0	$.1034 \times 10^{23}$	$.4765 \times 10^{21}$	$.4608 \times 10^{-01}$
1.60	15.0	$.8053 \times 10^{22}$	$.5550 \times 10^{21}$	$.6892 \times 10^{-01}$
1.60	20.0	$.6732 \times 10^{22}$	$.6377 \times 10^{21}$	$.9472 \times 10^{-01}$
1.70	0.	$.2621 \times 10^{23}$	$.5154 \times 10^{21}$	$.1966 \times 10^{-01}$
1.70	2.5	$.2072 \times 10^{23}$	$.5577 \times 10^{21}$	$.2691 \times 10^{-01}$
1.70	5.0	$.1685 \times 10^{23}$	$.6024 \times 10^{21}$	$.3576 \times 10^{-01}$
1.70	10.0	$.1253 \times 10^{23}$	$.6986 \times 10^{21}$	$.5576 \times 10^{-01}$
1.70	15.0	$.9840 \times 10^{22}$	$.8020 \times 10^{21}$	$.8151 \times 10^{-01}$
1.70	20.0	$.8289 \times 10^{22}$	$.9083 \times 10^{21}$	$.1096 \times 10^{-00}$
1.80	0.	$.3152 \times 10^{23}$	$.7651 \times 10^{21}$	$.2427 \times 10^{-01}$
1.80	2.5	$.2489 \times 10^{23}$	$.8222 \times 10^{21}$	$.3303 \times 10^{-01}$
1.80	5.0	$.2022 \times 10^{23}$	$.8821 \times 10^{21}$	$.4362 \times 10^{-01}$
1.80	10.0	$.1502 \times 10^{23}$	$.1009 \times 10^{22}$	$.6715 \times 10^{-01}$
1.80	15.0	$.1190 \times 10^{23}$	$.1142 \times 10^{22}$	$.9600 \times 10^{-01}$
1.80	20.0	$.1010 \times 10^{23}$	$.1276 \times 10^{22}$	$.1263 \times 10^{-00}$
1.90	0.	$.3855 \times 10^{23}$	$.1130 \times 10^{22}$	$.2933 \times 10^{-01}$
1.90	2.5	$.2998 \times 10^{23}$	$.1207 \times 10^{22}$	$.4024 \times 10^{-01}$
1.90	5.0	$.2432 \times 10^{23}$	$.1286 \times 10^{22}$	$.5286 \times 10^{-01}$
1.90	10.0	$.1803 \times 10^{23}$	$.1450 \times 10^{22}$	$.8043 \times 10^{-01}$

TABLE 17

$T(^\circ K)$	P (atm)	N_{ph}	N_R	$\frac{N_R}{N_{ph}}$
1.90	15.0	$.1440 \times 10^{23}$	$.1620 \times 10^{22}$	$.1125 \times 10^{-00}$
1.90	20.0	$.1254 \times 10^{23}$	$.1785 \times 10^{22}$	$.1424 \times 10^{-00}$
2.00	0.	$.4616 \times 10^{23}$	$.1680 \times 10^{22}$	$.3641 \times 10^{-01}$
2.00	2.5	$.3583 \times 10^{23}$	$.1781 \times 10^{22}$	$.4971 \times 10^{-01}$
2.00	5.0	$.2901 \times 10^{23}$	$.1884 \times 10^{22}$	$.6495 \times 10^{-01}$
2.00	10.0	$.2169 \times 10^{23}$	$.2097 \times 10^{22}$	$.9668 \times 10^{-01}$
2.00	15.0	$.1778 \times 10^{23}$	$.2309 \times 10^{22}$	$.1299 \times 10^{-00}$
2.00	20.0	$.1423 \times 10^{23}$	$.2509 \times 10^{22}$	$.1763 \times 10^{-00}$

PUBLISHERS' ACKNOWLEDGMENTS

We are most grateful to the authors and publishers indicated below for permission to publish various figures and tables.

Chapter 1

Fig. 1.3 Fairbank, W. M. 1963, Proceedings of the International School of Physics, Course XXI, ed. G. Careri (New York: McGraw Hill).

1.4 London, F. 1964, Superfluids Vol. II (New York: Dover)

1.6 Reif, F. and Meyer, L. 1960, Phys. Rev. 119, 1164.

Chapter 2

Fig. 2.1 Hammel, E. F. and Keller, W. E. Unpublished material, 1966.

2.2 Hammel, E. F., Keller, W. E., and Craig, P. P. 1963, Proceedings of the International School of Physics, Course XXI, ed. G. Careri (New York: McGraw Hill).

2.3 Hammel, E. F. and Keller, W. E. Unpublished material, 1966.

2.4 &
2.5 Donnelly, R. J., 1959, Phys. Rev. Letters 3, 507.

2.7 Atkins, K. R. 1959, Liquid Helium (New York: Cambridge University Press).

2.8 Tough, J. T., McCornick, W. D., and Dash, J. G. 1963, Phys. Rev. 132, 2373.

2.9 Donnelly, R. J. and Penrose, O., 1956, Phys. Rev. 103, 1137.

2.10 Donnelly, R. J. and Hollis Hallet, A. C., 1958, Ann. Phys. 3, 320.

2.12 Daunt, J. G. Mendelssohn, K. 1939, Proc. Roy. Soc. (London) A170, 423 and 439.

2.14 Hammel, E. F. and Keller, W. E. 1961, Phys. Rev. 124, 1641.

2.20a Atkins, K. R. 1959, Liquid Helium (New York: Cambridge

University Press).

Fig. 2.20b Atkins, K. R. 1959, Liquid Helium (New York: Cambridge University Press).

2.21 Shapiro, K. A. and Rudnick, I. 1965, Phys. Rev. 137, A1383.

2.22 Shapiro, K. A. and Rudnick, I. 1965, Phys. Rev. 137, A1383.

2.25 Tanner, D. J., Springett, B. E., and Donnelly, R. J. 1965, Low Temperature Physics, LT-9, eds. G. Daunt, D. O. Edwards, F. J. Milford, and M. Yaqub (New York: Plenum Press).

2.26 Rayfield, G. W. and Reif, F. 1964, Phys. Rev. 136, A1194.

2.27 Rayfield, G. W. and Reif, F. 1964, Phys. Rev. 136, A1194.

Chapter 3

Fig. 3.3 Yarnell, J. L., Arnold, G. P., Bendt, P. J., and Kerr, E. C. 1959, Phys. Rev. 113, 1379.

3.4a Miller, A., Pines, D., and Nozieres, P. 1962, Phys. Rev. 127, 1452.

3.4b Miller, A., Pines, D., and Nozieres, P. 1962, Phys. Rev. 127, 1452.

3.5 Reif, F. and Meyer, L. 1960, Phys. Rev. 119, 1164.

3.6 Reif, F. and Meyer, L. 1960, Phys. Rev. 119, 1164.

3.7 Meyer, L. and Reif, F. 1961, Phys. Rev. 123, 727.

Chapter 4

4.1 Snyder, H. A. 1963, Physics of Fluids 6, 755.

4.2a Snyder, H. A. and Linekin, D. M. 1966, Phys. Rev. 147, 131.

4.2b Snyder, H. A. and Linekin, D. M. 1966, Phys. Rev. 147, 131.

Fig. 4.3 Snyder, H. A. and Linekin, D. M. 1966, Phys. Rev. 147, 131.

4.4 Hall, H. E. and Vinen, W. F. 1956, Proc. Roy. Soc. A238, 204.

Chapter 5

Fig. 5.2 Fetter, A. L. 1965, Phys. Rev. 138, A429.

Chapter 6

Fig. 6.1 Atkins, K. R. 1963, International School of Physics, Enrico Fermi Course 21 (New York: Academic Press, p. 406).

6.2 Clark, R. C. 1965, Physics Letters 16, 42.

6.3 Parks, P. E. and Donnelly, R. J. 1966, Phys. Rev. Letters 16, 45.

6.5 Douglass, R. L. 1964, Phys. Rev. Letters 13, 791.

6.6 Parks, P. E. and Donnelly, R. J. 1966, Phys. Rev. Letters 16, 45.

6.7 Parks, P. E. and Donnelly, R. J. 1966, Phys. Rev. Letters 16, 45.

6.8 Cade, A. G. 1965, Phys. Rev. Letters 15, 238.

6.9 Parks, P. E. and Donnelly, R. J. 1966, Phys. Rev. Letters 16, 45.

6.10 Parks, P. E. and Donnelly, R. J. 1966, Phys. Rev. Letters 16, 45.

6.11 Tanner, D. J. To be published.

6.12 Tanner, D. J. To be published.

6.13 Springett, B. E. and Donnelly, R. J. 1966, Phys. Rev. Letters 17, 364.

6.15 Careri, G., Cunsolo, S., Mazzoldi, P., and Santini, M. 1965, Low Temperature Physics LT9 (New York: Plenum Press, p. 335).

6.16 Careri, G., Cunsolo, S. and Mazzoldi, P. 1964, Phys.

Rev. 136, A303.

Appendix

Table 1 Clement, R., Jr. 1961, Experimental Cryophysics, eds. Hoare, Jackson, and Kurti (London: Butterworth, Inc.).

2 Roberts, T. R., Sherman, R. H., and Sydoriak, S. G. Progress in Low Temperature Physics IV (Amsterdam: North Holland).

3 Kerr, E. C. and Taylor, R. D. 1964, Ann. Physics 26, 292.

Fig. A.1 Mendelssohn, K. 1956, Encyclopedia of Physics, Vol. XV, ed. S. Flugge (Berlin: Springer Verlag).

A.2 Mendelssohn, K. 1956, Encyclopedia of Physics, Vol. XV, ed. S. Flugge (Berlin: Springer Verlag).

Table 4 Kerr, E. C. and Taylor, R. D. 1964, Ann. Physics 26, 292.

5 Mills, R. L. and Sydoriak, S. G. 1965, Ann. Physics 34, 276.

6 Kramers, H. C., Wasscher, J. D., and Gorter, C. J. 1952, Physica 18, 329.

7 Kramers, H. C., Wasscher, J. D., and Gorter, C. J. 1952, Physica 18, 329.

8 Van den Meijlinberg, C. J. N., Taconis, K. W., and Ouboter, R. DeBruyn. 1961, Physica 27, 197.

Fig. A.3 A.E.C. Research and Development Report, Kelly, D. P., and Hanback, W. J., Comparative Properties of He^3 and He^4, MLM, 1161.

A.4 A.E.C. Research and Development Report, Kelly, D. P., and Hanback, W. J., Comparative Properties of He^3 and He^4, MLM, 1161.

Table 9 Tough, J. T., McCormick, W. D., and Dash, J. G. 1963, Phys. Rev. 132, 2373.

Fig. A.5 Brewer, D. F., and Edwards, D. H. 1963, Proceedings of 8th International Conference on Low Temperature Physics, ed. R. O. Davis (Washington: Butterworth).

Table 10 Chase, C. E. 1958, Physics of Fluids 1, 193 and Private communication, 1966.

Fig. A.6 Vignos, J. H. and Fairbank, H. A. 1966, Phys. Rev. 147, 185.

Table 11 Vignos, J. H. and Fairbank, H. A. 1966, Phys. Rev. 147, 185.

12 Maurer, R. D. and Herlin, M. A. 1949, Phys. Rev. 76, 948; and Pellam, J. R. 1949, Phys. Rev. 75, 1183. (Smoothed).

Fig. A.7 Maurer, R. D. and Herlin, M. A. 1951, Phys. Rev. 81, 444.

Table 13 Tough, J. T., McCormick, W. D., and Dash, J. G. 1963, Phys. Rev. 132, 2373.

14 Calculated data from Tables 13 and 3.

15 Smoothed data from Reif, F. and Meyer, L. 1960, Phys. Rev. 119, 1164.

16 Calculated data.

17 Calculated data.

INDEX

Abrikosov, A.A., Gorkov, L.P., and Dzyaloshinski, J. E., 69

absorption of second sound, excess due to rotation, 139

adiabatic demagnetization, 7

Andronikashvili, E. L., 16

angular momentum:
of a vortex line, 52;
of a system of vortex lines, 170

aquadag, 46, 140

Atkins, K. R., 173

B, B', B'', 127, 130;
B versus temperature, 144;
B' versus temperature, 142;
B'' versus temperature, 142

Bekharevich, I. L., and Khalatnikov, I. M., hydrodynamic equations, 115

Beliaev, S. T., 59

Bendt, P. J., Cowan, R. D., and Yarnell, J. L., 82

binding energy of He_2^+ ion, 173

binding energy of ions to vortices, 177

Bogoliubov, N., 159

Bogoliubov's theory of the weakly interacting Bose gas, 151

Bohr-Sommerfeld criterion, 51

Bose-Einstein gas, ideal, 148, 163:
condensation, 148;
confined between walls, 163;
specific heat, 150

Bose-Einstein gas, weakly interacting, 151:
condensation, 151;
excitation spectrum, 162;
Hartree S.C.F. approach, 163

boundary conditions, hydrodynamic, 35

boundary layer thickness, 16

Brewer, D. F., and Edwards, D. O., 28

Brownian particle, ion as, 183

bubble model of negative ion, 175

bulk viscosity, 124

Burdick, B., 176

Cade, A. G., 183, 194

capillary waves, 48

capture of ions by vortex lines, 175, 196, 199;
under pressure, 204

carbon resistors as thermometers, 8

Careri, G., Cunsolo, S., and Mazzoldi, P., 208

Careri, G., Cunsolo, S., Mazzoldi, P., and Santini, M., 207

Chandrasekhar, S., 146, 183;

Chandrasekhar, S. and Donnelly, R. J., 146

chemical potential, 59

Chester, G. V., 101

circulation in superfluid, 101;
from Hartree approximation, 167

Clark, R. C., 176

Cohen, M. H., and Feynman, R. P., 67

commutation relations for second quantized operators, 155

compressibility of He^4, 233

condition for superfluidity, Landau, 87, 163

conservation laws (hydrodynamic), 30, 101, 118

condensation, Bose-Einstein, 148, 151

continuity equations, Brownian particles, 184;
hydrodynamic, 30

core, vortex, 51, 101, 168

counterflow, 30, 35

Craig, P. P., Keller, W. E., and Hammel, E. F., 37, 39

critical transfer rate, 21

critical velocity: DeBroglie wavelength criterion, 60;
experimental, 11;
Landau criterion, 89, 149;
vortex generation, 58, 61

cryostat, 3

Curie's Law, 9

cylinders, concentric rotating, 14, 144

Daunt, J. G., and Mendelssohn, K., 21, 28

De Broglie wavelength, 52

De Broglie wavelength criterion for vortex generation, 60

density, helium (molar volumes), 225;
near point charge, 173;
normal fluid, 15, 82, 110, 112, 241;
of states, 75;
ratio of normal to total, 17, 242;
roton and phonon number, 79, 81, 93, 245;
superfluid, 15, 82, 86, 112;
weakly interacting Bose gas, 165

diffusion coefficient, 184

diffusion of He gas through glass, 5

discontinuity in drift velocity of ions, 208

dispersion relation, Landau, 65, 68, 82;

Bogoliubov, 162

dissipation function, 119, 125, 128

distribution function, Brownian particles, 183;
quasiparticles, 83

Domingo, J. J., 206

Donnelly, R. J., 60, 146

Donnelly, R. J., and Penrose, O., 18

Donnelly, R. J., and Roberts, P., 183, 190, 204

Douglass, R. L., 183, 191

drift velocity spectrometer, 56, 90

effective mass of ions in helium, 173;
positive ion, 174;
negative ion, 177

Einstein's relation, 190

energy, binding of He_2^+, 173;
binding of ions to vortices, 177

energy density: classical hydrodynamics, 103;
He II, 105;
He II with vorticity, 118

energy flux: classical, 103;
He II, 105;
He II with dissipation and vorticity, 118

energy gap, 65, 68;
temperature dependence, 69;
pressure and temperature dependence, 212

energy, internal: phonon, 80;
roton, 81

energy, ion near vortex, 180, 193, 196;
correction due to alteration of flow, 182

energy, negative ion in helium, 176

energy spectrum, 65, 68, 82;
Bogoliubov, weakly interacting Bose gas, 162

energy: vortex line, 52;
in Hartree S.C.F. approach, 168;
vortex ring, 55, 244;
set of vortex lines, 116

entropy: conservation 31, 101;
flux, classical, 103;
flux, He II, 111;
helium 4, 231;
helium 4 under pressure, 232;
helium II to second order in velocity, 113;
phonon, 80;
roton, 81;

escape: effect on capture, 196;
ion from vortices, 183;
negative ion probability, 192;
negative ion probability under pressure, 204;
positive ion probability, 195

Everitt, C. W. F., Atkins, K. R., and Denenstein, A., 50

excitation of sound, 44

excitation spectrum, 65, 68, 82;
Bogoliubov, 162

excited particles, ideal Bose
gas, 149

expansivity of helium 4, 3, 228;
under pressure, 229

Fairbank, W. M., 2

Fetter, A. L., 116, 166, 167,
169

Feynman, R. P., 58, 69

Feynamn, R. P., and Cohen,
M., 69, 74

film of helium II, 20;
capillary waves on, 49;
height dependence of flow, 21

first sound, 43, 74, 236;
at various pressures, 237,
238

flow of helium in films, 20, 21;
in narrow channels, 10

Fokker-Plank equation, 190

fountain effect, 23

fountain pressure, 22

fourth sound, 46

friction constant, 184

Frisch grid, 91

Ginsberg, V. L., and Pitaevski,
L. P., 168

Girardeau, M., 173

Glaberson, W. I., and
Donnelly, R. J., 61

Goldstein, H., 131

Gorter, C. J., and Mellink,
J. H., 38

Gross, E. P., 166, 176

ground state, 76, 148, 163

group velocity, 94

Hall, H. E., 129

Hall, H. E., and Vinen, W. F.,
129, 143

Hall, H. E., Ford, P. S., and
Thomson, K., 6

Hammel, E. F., and Keller,
W. E., 10, 22

Hartree self-consistent field
approach, 163;
equation, 164

helium film, 20;
capillary waves on, 49;
height dependence of flow, 21

helium 3 refrigerator, 5

healing length, 165

heat conductivity, 123;
effective, 29, 31, 37

heat leaks, 4

heat of vaporization, 233

Helmholtz free energy, 76;
phonon, 80;
roton, 81

Henshaw, D. G., and Woods, A. D. B., 74, 95

Hiroiki, K., Kestner, N. R., Rice, S. A., and Jortner, J., 176

Huang, K., and Olinto, A. C., 208

hydrodynamic equations, 101, 111;
including dissipation, 125;
including dissipation and vorticity, 128;
from variational principal, 129;
from kinetic theory, 129;
to second order in velocity, 114

hydrodynamic stability of He II, 144

identifites, vector and dyadic, 211

interaction between ions and vortices (see Ion), 177

internal convection, 28

internal energy: phonon contribution, 80;
roton contribution, 81

ion, 172:
as Brownian particles, 183;
capture cross section, 175, 196, 199;
capture cross section under pressure, 204;
critical velocity, 61;
critical velocity, de Broglie wavelength criterion, 61;
critical velocity, Landau criterion, 88;
effective mass, negative ion, 177;
effective mass, positive ion, 174;
mobility (see mobility), 90, 92, 175, 206, 207, 208, 243;
mobility under pressure, 95, 206;
production, 55, 172;
radius, negative ion, 175, 176, 177, 192;
radius, negative ion under pressure, 205;
radius, positive ion, 174, 195;
roton cross section, 93;
structure, bubble model, 175;
structure, negative ion, 177;
structure, positive ion, 173

irrotational flow of superfluid, 31, 50

isobars of helium 4, 227

isopycnals of helium 4, 226

Jortner, J., Kestner, N. R., Rice, S. A., and Cohen, M. H., 175

Kapitza resistance, 35

Kaufman, W., 116

Kerr, E. C., and Taylor, R.D., 3

Khalatnikov, J. M., 96, 125

lambda point, line, 1

Landau, L. D., 65, 66, 129;
and Lifshitz, E. M., electrodynamics, 173;
and Lifshitz, E. M., fluid mechanics, 31, 48, 103, 124, 145, 174, 182;
and Lifshitz, E. M., statistical mechanics, 79, 148

Landau: criterion for excitation generation, 89, 149, 207;
equations of motion, 34;
hydrodynamic equations, 101

latent heat at lambda transition, 1

latent heat of vaporization of helium 4, 233

lava stone, 140

Levine, J., and Sanders, T. M., 175

lifetime edge, 204

lifetime of ions in vortices, 183

lifetime of negative ions, 191

lifetime of positive ions, 194

Lifshitz, E. M., and Andronikashvili, E. L., 43, 96

Lin, C. C., 101, 130

London, H., 24;
fountain pressure derivation, 24

low temperature measurement, 7;
production, 3

Lucas, P., 136

m, kinetic contribution to momentum flux, 108

macroscopic quantum effect, 50

manometers, 8

mass: effective of ion in helium, 173;
positive ion, 174;
negative ion, 177

mass flow, 30. See also momentum density

measurement of temperature, 7

mechanical equilibrium, 24

mechano-caloric effect, 28

Meservey, R., 51

microscopic theory of helium II, 148

Miller, J. C. P., 187

Miller, A., Pines, D., and Nozieres, P., 74

Milne-Thomson, L. M., 116

mixture refrigerator, 6

mobility of ions, 90, 175, 207, 243;
jumps, 208;
low-field data, 92;
pressure dependence data, 95;
trapped in vortex lines, 206

mode degeneracy in rotating
sound resonator, classical
fluid, 136;
second sound, 139

molar volumes of helium 4, 225

momentum density: classical,
103;
He II, 30, 82, 84, 112

momentum flux: classical, 31;
kinetic contribution to, 110;
He II, 30, 111, 112;
including dissipation and
vorticity, 118;
kinetic contribution to,
definition, 109;
viscous contribution, 123

mutual friction force (see B,
B', B''), 38, 128

Navier-Stokes equation, 144

negative ion, 174. See also
ion

neutron scattering, 67, 74

normal fluid, 14, 87, 149;
density, 15, 82, 110, 112,
241;
density divided by total
density, 242;
viscosity, 17, 96, 125, 234;
viscosity at various densities,
235

normal mode splitting in resonant
cavity: classical, 136;
He II, 139

number density for phonons,
rotons, 79, 81, 93, 245

oscillations: torsional of single
discs, 15;
torsional of sphere, 19;
torsional of stack of discs, 16;
U-tube, 18;
vortex line, 129

Osborne, D. V., 51

pair correlation function, 73

Panofsky, W. K. H., and
Phillips, M., 173

Parks, P. E., and Donnelly,
R. J., 177

partition function, 76

Pauling, L., 173

Penrose, O., and Onsager, L.,
151

persistent current, 12

Peshkov, V. P., 66

Phase diagram, 1

phase transition: B. E. gas,
149;
helium, 1;
interacting Bose gas, 151

phase slip, 59

Phelps, A. V., and Brown, S.
C., 173

phonon, 66. See also specific
topic

physical constants, 213

Pitaevski, L. P., 168

Po^{210} as source of ions, 91, 172, 191

polarization of fluid near ion, 173

potential: chemical, 59;
interparticle in Hartree S.C.F. approach, 163;
thermodynamic, 26, 33, 105, 114;
velocity, 105, 110

pressure: contribution from superfluid vorticity, 126;
definition in Bekharevich-Khalatnikov theory, 107;
dependence. See specific topic;
fountain, 22

probability of escape of ion from vortex. See escape probability

propagation of sound in helium, 39

Q-factor of second sound cavity, 46, 143

quantum effects on flow, 50, 168

R, dissipation function, 119

radius of ion. See ion radius

Rayfield, G. W., 207

Rayfield, G. W., and Reif, F., 56

Rayleigh's criterion, 146

refrigerator, dilution, 6

He^3, 5

Reif, F., and Meyer, L., 5, 61, 90

Reppy, J. D., and Depatie, P. A., 12

resonator, second sound, 140

ρ, ρ_s, ρ_n. See density

Richards, P. L., and Anderson, P. W., 59

Roman, P., 155

rotating second sound resonator, 130

rotating viscometer, 14

roton, 66. See also specific topic

second quantization, 151

second sound, 43, 44, 66, 239;
resonant cavity, 46, 140;
under pressure, 240;
under rotation, 130, 136

second viscosity, 124;
of He II, 125

Shapiro, K. A., and Rudnick, I., 47

shear viscosity, 124;
of normal fluid, 17, 96, 125, 234, 235

Smoluchowski's equation, 184, 190, 200, 204

Snyder, H. A., 46, 140

Snyder, H. A., and Linkin, D. M., 140, 142

Sommer, W. T., 176

sound, 39, 130:
first, 43, 74, 236, 237, 238;
second, 43, 136, 239, 240;
third, 49;
fourth, 46

specific heat:
of He^4, 2, 230;
of ideal Bose gas, 150;
phonon contribution, 80;
roton contribution, 82

specific entropy: of He^4, 231, 232;
phonon contribution, 80;
roton contribution, 81

Springett, B. E., and Donnelly, R. J., 204, 206

strength of vortex, 52

structure factor, 73

superfluid: in ideal Bose Einstein gas, 149;
in Landau model, 87;
in non-ideal Bose Einstein gas, 151;
in Tisza's two-fluid model, 14

surface configuration in rotating He II, 50

surface tension: in bubble model, 176;
waves, 48

symmetry in Bose system, 152

Tanner, D. J., 197

Tanner, D. J., Springett, B. E., and Donnelly, R. J., 55

temperature: measurement, 7;
1958 He^4 scale, 214;
1962 He^3 scale, 223

tension of vortex line, 127

thermal conductivity: effective, 29, 31, 37;
of He^4, 123

thermal equilibrium, 24

thermodynamic potential, 26, 33, 105, 114

thermodynamic properties of He II, 75

thermomechanical effect, 22, 34

third sound, 49

Tisza, L., 14

torque on rotating viscometer, 14

torsional oscillations: of pile of discs, 16;
of single disc, 17;
of sphere, 19

transformations: between moving coordinate systems, 83, 102;
between rotating coordinate systems, 130, 169

turbulence, 18, 20

two-fluid hydrodynamics. See hydrodynamics

two-fluid model, 14

U-tube oscillations, 18

Van Itterbeck, A., 68

vapor pressure: He^3, 5, 223;
He ^{4}, 5, 214;
thermometer, 7

variational calculation: of energy spectrum, 69, 74;
of hydrodynamic equations, 129

velocity: first sound, 43, 74, 236, 237, 238;
second sound, 43, 239, 240;
third sound, 49;
fourth sound, 48;
roton, 94;
vortex rings, 244;
spectrometer, 56

vector and dyadic identities, 211

Vinen, W. F., 38

viscometer, 14

viscosity: bulk, 124;
ideal Bose gas, 149;
kinetic theory, 96;
normal fluid, 15, 17, 148, 234, 235;
second, 125;
superfluid, 15

vortex lines, 51:
angular momentum, 52, 170;
density of lines, 53, 170;
energy, 52, 116, 168;
filament tension, 127;
fluid density near core, 51, 167, 179;
generation in slits, 59, 90;
interaction with ion, see ion;
pinned, 61;
quantization, 51, 166;
system of lines, 116, 169;
velocity of pair, 54

vortex rings, 53:
energy, 55, 244;
generation, 57, 90, 94. 208;
interaction with ions, see ion;
velocity, 54, 244

vorticity in superfluid, 101, 115, 125

wave function: electron in non-ideal Bose gas, 176;
ideal Bose gas, 163;
superfluid, 58, 164;
vortex line, 166

weakly interacting Bose systems, 151, 157, 163

Whittaker, E. T., and Watson, G. N., 187

Woolf, M. A., and Rayfield, G. W., 176

X-ray scattering, 74

Yarnell, J. L., Arnold, G. P., Bendt, P. J., and Kerr, E. C., 67

zero-point energy of helium, 148, 213

zero-point motion, 69